60 YEARS

With Men and Machines

---

by Fred H. Colvin

Lindsay Publications Inc.

60 YEARS WITH
Men and Machines

AN AUTOBIOGRAPHY

by

FRED H. COLVIN

In Collaboration with
D. J. DUFFIN

60 Years With Men & Machines

by Fred H. Colvin

Original copyright 1947
by the McGraw-Hill Publishing
Company, New York and London

Reprinted by
Lindsay Publications Inc
Bradley IL 60915

Paper: ISBN 0-917914-86-4
Cloth: ISBN 0-917914-87-2

1 2 3 4 5 6 7 8 9 0

1988

To
My wife and sons
who have borne with
and encouraged me
through the years

WARNING

Remember that the materials and methods described here are from another era. Workers were less safety conscious then, and some methods may be downright dangerous. Be careful! Use good solid judgement in your work, and think ahead. Lindsay Publications Inc. has not tested these methods and materials and does not endorse them. Our job is merely to pass along to you information from another era. Safety is your responsibility.

Write for a complete catalog of unusual books available from:

Lindsay Publications Inc
PO Box 12
Bradley IL 60915-0012

A Word about the Author

It was a happy thought on Fred Colvin's part to put in print a record of his long and active life. It has taken two world wars to educate the people of this country on the fundamental importance of the machine shop in modern life. The machinist and the machine tools which he operates constitute the solid industrial foundation of our industrial civilization, whether it faces years of peace or years of war. That fact became publicly apparent only in the feverish activity of the preparation for and conduct of the national efforts that resulted in our military victories.

Fred Colvin occupies a unique position in the machine-tool industry. He has seen in his lifetime the transformation of that industry from an accessory of industrial development to firm establishment as its foundation. He has watched the development of the machine tool from a simple means of getting useful things done to the point where it embodies in its design and operation the transfer of the skill of the exceptional mechanic and engineer, in usable form, into the hands of hundreds of thousands and millions of operatives. It is this function of the transfer of skill that has made our nation supreme among the nations of the world in industrial might.

In this process Fred Colvin has been more than a detached observer. He has been an intimate part of it. He has traveled the country over. His native ability and ingratiating personality have led to close friendships with the men who were active in the industrial process. He has made his own great contributions to our progress. His story is well worth reading.

RALPH K. FLANDERS.
United States Senator
State of Vermont

Contents

CHAPTER ONE

The Machine That Can Reproduce Itself

Man is a tool-using animal. Nowhere do you
find him without tools; without tools he is nothing,
with tools he is all.
THOMAS CARLYLE, "Sartor Resartus," 1836

"Why," many of my friends will ask, "did you choose to ruin a perfectly good reputation by writing a book like this at the very tail end of your career?"

It is a question I am fully prepared to answer.

I know that a man seventy-nine years old should be thinking of seeking out some restful green-clad hill dotted with cypress trees and tastefully designed headstones, rather than of embarking on some ninety thousand more words after a lifetime of writing. Some folks will even say that I should have sold my typewriter about twenty years ago and retired to a farm. An acquaintance of mine, who had nothing better to do, recently computed on a rough basis that I had written slightly under 7 million words for publication during the past sixty years, and his unspoken corollary seemed to be that this was a very appropriate figure to stop at. I fully agree with such honest critics, but there is one thing they do not appear to take into consideration. It is that the situation has simply got out of hand. I can no longer control the urge to write.

There is another and perhaps better reason for this book. There is such a wealth of memories of persons and events crowding upon my mind from the accumulated experience of the past threescore years that if I do not get them down on paper while there is still time they will surely be lost to posterity forever. Whether this would or would not be a great tragedy for civilization I must leave for the kind and patient reader to decide.

My original purpose some years ago when I first began collecting notes for the present book was to write a detailed, definitive history of machine tools and their relation to the development of modern mass production in industry. In the course of compiling it, the material seems to have got all mixed up with personal anecdotes, sketches of the many interesting people I have met, and a kind of running biography of myself. The definitive history of machine tools, therefore, remains to be written; but the present work, because of what I believe is a more popular approach, should at least bring the high lights of that history to a wider audience than that provided in the ordinary trade journals. I can only hope that I am right.

For those who quite pardonably may not understand why machine tools are so important that anyone should want to write a history of them for popular consumption, I should like to state a few important facts in this introductory chapter. Those others to whom these facts are already quite commonplace may very profitably skip the rest of the chapter and begin elsewhere.

Machine tools have been rightly called the basis of all modern production, the very foundation of our present industrial setup. They are necessary for the manufacture of every class of engine and kind of mechanism, for the production of every type of manufactured product—fabric, textiles, metal goods, soap, foodstuffs, furniture, building materials, scientific instruments, or any other material article you care to name.

In the course of the following pages I will talk, and perhaps repetitiously, about the lathe—great-grandparent of all machine tools—and its diversified offspring, the turning, drilling, planing, slotting, boring, milling, sawing, shaping, and grinding machines. But before coming directly to them, I should like to get out of the way the material that was to have become chapter one of the definitive history, as follows:

Students of man's cultural history tell us that as long ago as

250,000 B.C. (which is as far back as I intend to go into the beginning of things), Man, or Homo sapiens of the anthropologists, began to settle down as a respectable hunter and fisherman, and thereupon took up the manufacturing of tools as a practical necessity. His first attempt at toolmaking was certainly modest enough. Using the materials of nature, he created a kind of fist hatchet, about 6 inches long and 3 inches wide, which he chipped from a piece of flint. This uncomplicated yet important tool was held in the hand and used as a knife, a scraper, a hammer, an ax, *and as a tool to make other fist hatchets*. It was therefore not only the earliest tool, but also the earliest machine tool as well.

Bone tools appeared later, such as bone needles, spears, and barbed harpoon heads—all of which were made from the fist hatchet or a similar tool. With these limited contrivances our paleolithic ancestors made clothing for themselves, brought in the Sunday dinner on the hoof, enlarged the living room in their caves, made fire artificially, hacked crude boats out of tree trunks, designed more elaborate tools and weapons, and in general paved the way for neolithic culture and the Age of Metals.

Passing rapidly over the next several thousand years of man's painstaking development, we find that about 4000 B.C. or thereabouts copper weapons and tools became increasingly common in Egypt, with bronze coming slowly into use as a more durable material. Iron, the symbol of the age in which we now live, was probably first used for making tools about 1350 B.C. The Bible, it will be remembered, says that Tubal, one of Cain's sons, was an instructor of workers in iron and copper. The smiths of those distant days used anvils, hammers, and tongs much like those found in the village blacksmith's shop of Longfellow's day. Egyptian carpenters had awls, saws, planes, files, and hammers all made from iron. Some of the other devices invented and manufactured by the early Egyptian craftsmen were the potter's wheel, metallic currency, rotating mills to grind grain, various kinds of wheeled vehicles, and looms for weaving cloth; and there was pottery, statuary, and jewelry in great profusion. The Egyptian high priests, we are told, had even a secret mechanism—probably operated by steam—for mysteriously swinging wide the massive doors of the temple without visible human aid. This trick must have gone over big with the country boys.

The early Greeks, as we have been told so often, neglected the material and practical side of life in favor of speculation and philosophical abstraction. As a result, they invented little or nothing in the way of mechanical things, unless we include the famous screw pump of Archimedes and his ingenious catapults for hurling rocks at the enemy. The contributions of their successors, the Romans, to civil engineering in the form of road building, aqueducts, masonry bridges, and massive architecture are too well known to be recounted here. But with the fall of Rome and the onset of the Middle Ages, mechanical invention and civilization itself came to a standstill, and it was not until as late as the eighteenth century that experimentation and invention, based on a revived interest in science, were reborn and reapplied to industry.

It was at this critical stage in man's development— the so-called "Industrial Revolution" of the early 1700's—that machine tools as such made their first appearance on the scene. Casting and forging are in themselves old accomplishments; they date back to well before the Christian era. Little can be done, however, by purely casting or forging processes—there is always need to finish certain surfaces smoothly and accurately to size in order to permit true fitting, so that the various parts of a mechanism may work properly. To be sure, there were ancient methods of drilling with the primitive bow drill and of turning with the spring-pole lathe. Both of these methods are still in use in some parts of China and Japan, and in other countries of southeast Asia where civilization as we know it has not yet made its inroads. But the shaping of metal, except by molding or hammering, is a fairly recent art. When Newcomen in 1705 and Watt in 1769 first developed working models of steam engines, the production of large-scale replicas of these was greatly held back by the impossibility of securing even moderately accurate machining of the parts that had to be fitted together properly before the steam engine would function. The lack of machines to turn and bore and to produce flat surfaces prevented the dreams of many advanced thinkers from becoming realities.

With the recognition of the need for good mechanical fit, some of the inventive genius that had heretofore been expended mainly on dreaming up new and wonderful mechanical devices set itself to the task of creating the tools by which these mechanisms might actually be produced and manufactured. Machines for drilling, turning, boring, and planing metal began to receive attention. These, it must be remembered, were all derived from the primitive lathe, of which the potter's wheel of the Egyptians was an early offshoot.

So that the general reader unfamiliar with the specialized science of machine-tool work may better understand the principles involved,

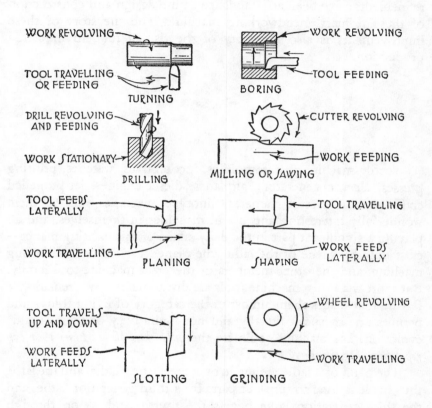

an illustration is given above showing the principal classes of metal cutting done by various kinds of machine tools.

Machines derived from the lathe include the boring, drilling, milling, sawing, and grinding machines; and when flat surfaces such as those encountered in steam-engine design were introduced in machinery, the planer was invented. The shaper was later developed for smaller articles that could remain fixed on a table while the cutting tool moved over it. The slotter is simply a vertical, reciprocating type of shaper, and the broaching machine makes its cut in one instead of many strokes. Much later in the development of machine tools came the gear-cutting machines, which provide uniform and accurate spacing or pitch between gear teeth so that the gears will mesh properly and run smoothly. Many improvements and refinements have been accomplished in the design and construction of these primary metalworking machines, and the story of these improvements is also the story of the rise of modern industrial production.

Textile machinery, automobiles, locomotives, watches, printing presses, electric generators, airplanes, diesel engines, jet-propelled craft, motion picture cameras, linotype machines—all of them wonderfully interesting and useful machines in themselves, and all playing a significant part in the daily affairs of this exciting planet— exist only by virtue of the lathe, the planer, the slotter, the boring machine, and the other members of the great machine-tool family. But more than this, machine tools are distinguished by a remarkable feature that places them almost in the category of living things and permits one to speak literally and not figuratively of their organic evolution. For machine tools are the *only class of machines that can reproduce themselves.*

The parts of a lathe are made on a preexisting lathe, and the lathe thus made is used to turn out parts for a third-generation lathe, and the third-generation lathe begets the fourth, and so on through succeeding generations ad infinitum. One can almost think of these machines as propagating their species in accordance with the Biblical injunction given to old man Adam and his children. If one is looking for the romance of machinery, it seems to me to lie in this intriguing fact. The power of reproduction, the biologists tell us, is one of the distinguishing characteristics of life. For myself as well as for many other workers in this field, the family of machine tools certainly possesses a kind of life. Automobiles and locomotives cannot, by any stretch of their transmission shafts or piston rods, reproduce themselves. Only the machine tools can do that.

Beginning with the demand of the builders of steam engines for machines that would bore cylinders more nearly round than the early crude machines, the range and adaptability of machine tools in the United States has increased to a remarkable extent in the past century. The early ideas were imported from England, where Henry Maudslay in 1797 invented the screw-cutting lathe in order to help Joseph Bramah manufacture a hydraulic press that he had devised. The screw-cutting lathe released a flood of inventions that brought into being the milling machine, the grinder, the boring mill, the shaper, and the turret lathe. Other English inventors such as Clement, Fox, and Naysmyth were motivated by their desire to help Watt and others build their steam engines. In New England, as early as 1838, fairly large planers were built and operated, using huge slabs of native granite or timbers from the virgin forests as beds for many of the early machines.

The growing importance of firearms in a frontier civilization led to the idea of making interchangeable parts for mass production— if only on a limited scale. The story is told that Eli Whitney of cotton-gin fame undertook to produce 10,000 muskets for the U.S. Army in two years. To convince the government officials of his capacity to produce at this rate, he is said to have laid before the experts ten barrels, ten stocks, ten triggers, and so on, in separate piles. Each of these parts had been made separately in his shop. He then asked one of the officials to select one piece from each pile at random, and to lay them together. When this had been done, Whitney astounded the experts by assembling a complete, working musket from the random pieces, and continued the process until all ten muskets had been assembled.

Samuel Colt, whose name is familiar to readers of wild West fiction, began in 1835 to manufacture his six-shooter on a mass-production scale. Colt made it a matter of policy to seek out and hire the best men available to design newer and more efficient machine tools for use in his Patent Firearms Company at Hartford, Connecticut. At about the same time, Joseph Brown of Providence, Rhode Island, realized the need for accurate measuring instruments and began the business that later became the well-known Brown & Sharpe Manufacturing Company, a name memorialized in the familiar "B & S gauge" standard.

The rise of such diverse inventions as the sewing machine and the bicycle turned the attention of machine-tool designers to newer and speedier combinations of mechanical movements that included screws, cams and levers. These significant additions introduced a new feature—automatic operation—into machine tools. The operator could now place the work in the machine and have it perform several finishing operations with no further human attention other than the usual oiling and tool sharpening. Later, even the necessity of placing each piece in the machine was eliminated with the development of automatic methods of feeding. Much of the development of machine tools in this country was fostered in the Naugatuck Valley of Connecticut, where inventive talent seemed to gravitate in the early days of the machine-tool industry.

How the industry has expanded to other centers of production during the past sixty years, how new improvements in the design of machines have produced increasing quantities of consumer goods, how this development affected the course of industry and society, and what the prospects for the future may be, would easily fill a volume several times larger and more profound than the present one.

The story of machine tools is inseparably bound up with the story of invention. There is hardly a mechanical invention in the entire history of human thought that could have been successfully developed without the aid of machine tools. This truth should by no means detract from the well-earned reputation of a Howe, an Arkwright, an Edison, a McCormick, a Tesla, a Hargreaves, or a Zworykin. It is mentioned only in order to place proper emphasis on the enormously important work accomplished in the past and continuing in the present by a relatively small group of artisans who are rarely mentioned in the history books and seldom make the newspaper headlines. It is perhaps understandable that the public should value the product more than the process and accept the automobile and jet-propelled plane without asking how either of these came into existence. For economists and social scientists interested in the growth of modern industrial production, the rest of this book may have some value. For those men and women directly or indirectly associated with the design and operation of machine tools, it may provide a different perspective of their trade and deeper appreciation of its importance. For the unfortunately diminishing band of pioneers and old-timers with whom I am happy to identify myself, this informal history may serve to renew old acquaintances and revive fading memories. And for the general reader who is gifted with a flair for mechanical things, or who has perhaps only a half-awakened interest in the romance of machinery, these pages may stimulate a desire to learn more about this indispensable industry.

It is certainly not for me to try to point out the social significance of machines, or to raise the question of whether our mechanical genius exceeds our capacity for social progress. I have always found it best to accept machines and the machine age as sturdy facts, to look upon man as a tool-using animal, and to try to learn how he has gone about improving the tools that he uses. The story of machine tools is therefore only an elaboration of a trend that began about 250,000 years ago with the invention of the fist hatchet.

Machinery, instead of taking the romance out of life as some contend, has served me in quite the opposite direction. Whether in the shop, where more or less intricate machines grow into being almost by magic, or in such engineering creations as the Panama Canal or Boulder Dam, the mechanically minded observer cannot fail to be impressed. And though I have been closely connected with machines and machinery for more than threescore years, I still find the greatest interest in visiting machine shops of all sizes and types. Perhaps it is a sort of harmless vice—like buying tickets on the sweepstakes or listening to fortunetellers—whereby I always hope to find something new and strange in the very next shop I visit. The knowledge that new machinery is constantly being invented and built provides a never-ending fascination even for one who has passed the allotted threescore and ten. Sometimes one finds history repeating itself in some phase or another of modern shop practice, just as it does in the styles of women's hats and dresses. Sometimes ideas and methods discarded years ago as impractical are resurrected and given a new opportunity to prove themselves. Talking motion pictures, for example, were a reality in both Europe and America well before 1900, but the public had to wait until 1927, when electronic recording and amplification made the projection of sound pictures practicable for large audiences. Similarly, a model power-driven airplane was successfully flown as early as the year 1848, but some fifty-five years had to elapse before machine tools and metallurgy made heaver-than-air aircraft engines a practical reality.

The kind of knowledge that we call pure science—astronomy, nuclear physics, theoretical mechanics, and the like—depends quite as much upon machine tools for proof as upon rigorous mathematical analysis. We have only to think of the reflecting telescope, the harmonic analyser, the mass spectroscope, the diffraction grating, the product integraph, the microscope, and other scientific instruments whose accuracy depends upon the accuracy of the machine tools that make them. In such machines the tolerances, or deviations from ideal size, must be limited to a few ten-thousandths of an inch if serious errors are to be avoided.

It is hardly possible to overemphasize the fact that the seeming miracles of modern science and industry are made possible by the work of a comparatively few men in an industry that is almost unknown to the general public. Add to this fact the almost certain knowledge that practically any worth-while project—from the making of a cheaper automobile to the peacetime harnessing of atomic energy—can be worked out by this group, and we can begin to understand the urge that keeps these men at their task even without the promise of any greater reward than the satisfaction of accomplishment.

In giving full credit to the scientist, the metallurgist, the chemist, the biologist, and the inventor, we should not forget an important fact: few of their discoveries could have been made available generally to mankind without the help of the operator at the lathe on which these discoveries were transformed into actualities. "No machine," John Donne might have said, "is an Island, complete in itself; every tool is a piece of the Continent, a part of the Main; and therefore never send to know for whom the drill turns; it turns for thee."

And having got this rather textbookish material out of the way mainly because it was bothering me, I should like now to make a fresh start.

CHAPTER TWO

In the Beginning Was the Belt Drive

The next thing to living one's life over again
seems to be a recollection of that life, and to make
that recollection as durable as possible by putting
it down in writing.
BENJAMIN FRANKLIN,
"Autobiography," 1798

It took an act of God in the form of the Great Blizzard of March 12 to 14, 1888, to shatter my five-year punctuality record at the Rue Manufacturing Company. The three-day snowstorm transformed most of Philadelphia into an alpine village and almost obliterated the small machine shop at No. 211 Race Street. It was a spectacular and even beautiful sight, but I was unimpressed. My putative grandchildren would never be able to say, "Grandpa never missed a day's work in his life."

Not that I hadn't tried for the record, though. Getting to work in those dim romantic days was often a minor achievement in itself. You must imagine a world without subways, trolley cars, busses, automobiles, or taxicabs. When I made my inauspicious debut as a machine-shop apprentice on July 5, 1883, the very last word in public conveyances was the horse-drawn omnibus, a poky sort of stagecoach that averaged 5 miles to the quart of oats. Due apparently to a shortage of Percherons on the Race and Vine Street route, the cars that served the Rue mechanics were drawn by lowly mules. These went much slower. To get to work on time in the winter meant rising in the middle of the night, waiting on a deserted street corner for the half-frozen mules to put in appearance, and then burrowing molelike into one corner in order to keep warm during the hour-long trip across the city.

For there was no heat in the cars for either passengers or crew.

A few years before, some of the more prosperous lines had gallantly installed potbellied stoves in the front end of each car to temper the wintry breeze, but this public-spirited gesture was short-lived indeed. It seems that a certain conclave of medical men ventured the opinion that heat was unhealthy in the horsecars, being a leading factor in the spread of pulmonary congestions and similar disorders. The potbellied stoves were forthwith removed, leaving the occupants once more exposed to the healthy arctic night. By the time I had become a regular customer on the Rue and Vine Street line, a concession had been made to the popular demand for warmer vehicles. The car-line operators caused several layers of bedding straw to be spread on the floor of each car, as a kind of thermal insulation. When it snowed or rained this straw became nice and soggy, and the steamy atmosphere inside the omnibus reminded me of an old-fashioned livery stable. But it was still cold.

This Toonerville Trolley of my younger days also provided me with a modicum of outdoor exercise such as I did not get working over the lathes in the Rue Manufacturing Company. Every so often, in fair weather or foul, the diligence I happened to be riding would casually leap its traces and founder in the soft earth alongside the tracks. When this happened, all able-bodied male passengers were expected as a matter of course to get out and push. The frequency with which this diversion occurred caused the route to be known as the "G.O.P. Line," which had nothing to do with party affiliations.

Transportation in those days was not limited to the horse car, however. Well-to-do businessmen rode to work in their own carriages, drawn by a spanking pair of trotters. For the less affluent workaday journeyman, there was the high-wheeled bicycle or "ordinary," which was a distinct improvement over the "boneshaker" velocipede of the 'sixties, but a daredevil contraption on cobblestone pavements. Without gears, the ordinary was strictly a tall man's vehicle in any contest of speed, but despite my 5-foot 5-inch stature I managed to get about fairly well on a high-wheeled Columbia on Sundays and holidays when traffic was at a standstill. I remember, though, that a number of pious townsfolk expressed strong convictions that Sunday was hardly the proper day of the week for young blades to be scorching up the public roads and that such behavior indicated an alarming tend toward paganism.

It is also quite possible that the fact that with our wheels we could pass their expensive horse-drawn rigs may have increased their dislike of the newfangled vehicle. Some towns in New England went so far as to pass laws that the Sunday bicyclists had to dismount at the edge of town and walk their wheels to the town line on the other side.

But whether I traveled by straw-littered jitney, by high wheeler, or on foot, I managed to get to my lathe each morning an instant or two before the whistle blew. The machine held a peculiar sort of fascination for me which not even our sixty-hour work week could diminish. Without knowing too much about the laws of genetics I would be inclined to believe that I inherited a flair for the mechanical from my father, Henry F. Colvin, who in turn derived his mechanical aptitude from Grandfather Colvin, the ante bellum gunsmith of Scranton, Pennsylvania. My father left his father's machine shop in the year 1857 for the more exciting career of fireman on a wood-burning locomotive that hauled troop trains and supplies for General Grant during the Civil War, rising to the position of engineer on the Lackawanna Railroad before hostilities ended. After the war, Father became an engineer in charge of locomotive erection for the Rhode Island Locomotive Works, continuing in this field during my non-age, and that is how it came about that tools and machinery were as familiar as the furniture in the Colvin family.

An apprentice in the machine shops of 1883 faced a situation not wholly unlike that of the craft guilds of the Middle Ages. In many cases the boy's parents had to reimburse the shop owner for teaching him the secrets of the trade. In the Rue Plant, however, a revolutionary new system was in effect—the shop owner actually paid the apprentice wages. He was careful, of course, not to turn the apprentice's head with money. In my own case, I began at the rate of 5 cents an hour for a sixty-hour week; or, to put it more impressively, I was paid $3 in cash every Saturday night. At the end of the first six month's apprenticeship, the wages were boosted by $16\frac{2}{3}$ per cent, which meant a half dollar a week extra in the pay envelope. What with promises of an additional 50-cent rise every six months thereafter, a young apprentice could see himself developing into a substantial citizen if he but lived long enough.

Going into the shop of the Rue Manufacturing Company at

fifteen was not exactly what I had hoped for and planned. It so happened that, in exchange for liberal concessions by the city, the University of Pennsylvania had made a number of scholarships available to students in what was then known as "Senior Classes," who passed examinations with sufficiently high marks. I was fortunate enough to have made the grade as to examination marks. But

The shop of E. Horton & Son, chuck makers, about 1851.

complications in the family, including Father's illness, made it seem best at least to start in the shop, with the possibility of going to the University later. The possibility never materialized and I was with the Rue Company for nearly ten years.

The instructor who was saddled with this responsibility was a bright young man named Charlie Westcott, who sported a walrus moustache in the best fashion of those bygone days, and whose striped shirts lent an air of distinction to the Rue Plant. On that momentous day of July 5, 1883, Charlie eyed me skeptically and asked, "Well, kid, do you know anything at all about machinery?"

"Not much, sir," I replied, "all I know is what I read in the *American Machinist* and what my father tells me. He's a locomotive man."

Charlie was a patient and understanding foreman. He smiled and said, "That's a start, anyway. But a lot of the machines we got around here just ain't ever been in the *American Machinist* or any other magazine. You have to work with these critters to get the feel of them. Hang your hat and coat on the wall over there and I'll show you around the place. Then maybe we'll let you fool with the bolt-cutter for a start when you know a little more about the machines."

I followed Charlie into the main room of the plant, which occupied the second floor of a three-story building. The Rue Company, I knew, manufactured a device called an "injector" that was used for feeding water into locomotive or stationary steam boilers. I could see about twenty-five or thirty men working at various kinds of lathes, and the noise and confusion was exciting. Charlie led me over to one of the machines.

"This here is an engine lathe," he explained. "Maybe you've seen a picture of one in the magazines. It's the most important machine in the whole shop. You got to have an engine lathe whenever you're doing any kind of turning work. And you can also use it for drilling, or grinding, or even lapping, too. This thing here that holds the work is called the 'chuck.' This other piece is the tailstock. . . . "

"I know," I interrupted. "It's just like in the picture. This wheel here is the hand traverse, and this little knob is the cross-feed clutch, and this flat part is called the 'carriage saddle,' I think."

Charlie looked at me and grinned, "You sure been eating up those magazines, young feller." He pointed to the machine next in line. "Do you know what this one here is?"

It looked familiar, but Charlie beat me to the answer.

"This here is what is known as a 'turret lathe,' named after the thing on top here that takes the place of the ordinary tailstock and center. The turret as you can see carries a couple of extra cutting tools of different kinds so that you can do drilling, boring, turning, facing, and tapping—all on this one machine. This particular job is a

Warner and Swasey and cost us over $300. Now let's take a look further on down the line."

Charlie led me through a labyrinth of whirring machinery, spinning line shafts, and busy mechanics.

"This one's a planer," he said, stopping at a long, flat, heavy-looking machine. "It's got a single cutting tool that gives you flat surfaces when you want 'em. It can do slotting too. Only for small parts, though." He ducked under a line shaft between two moving belts, and I followed.

"Watch out for those couplings on the shaft," Charlie shouted. "They'll tear your scalp off if you're not careful. Now here," he went on, pointing to a small, worn-looking contrivance, "is our one and only milling machine—the oldest thing in the place outside of old man Cathcart the night watchman. We use it mostly for curved surfaces but it don't work so well any more. And right next to it is the latest model drill press—a brand-new Pratt and Whitney. Maybe in a year or so we'll let you play with that baby."

I asked him where the power came from to run all these machines.

"From down in the basement," Charlie answered. "Down in the basement we got a big Corliss steam engine—you can go down later and look it over if you like—a big 25-horsepower job. You can feel it shake the building sometimes. It runs everything in the shop. There's one big belt attached to it that runs all the way up from the cellar to the main line shaft on this floor. Then these smaller shafts (countershafts, we call 'em) are run off the main shaft on each floor by means of these pulleys"—here he pointed to a maze of overhead belts and wheels—"that link up with the machines themselves. The 25-horsepower steam engine runs the whole shop."

It was truly amazing. When I look at some of our modern electrically driven machine tools that have up to four times as much horsepower on a single unit as had the entire thirty-four machines in the Rue Manufacturing Company, I am even more amazed. I have often wondered just what fraction of one horse's theoretical output reached each of these machines after its long journey from the basement.

Belt drives, of course, were standard for power transmission in those days. The electric motor was not entirely unknown in 1883, having been introduced commercially as early as 1866 by Siemens, Gramme, and others; electric street cars had already come into use by 1882. But because there were practically no generating stations or distribution systems (except to a very limited extent in New York City), electricity as a source of power remained largely an unknown quantity, and the average machine shop of the 'eighties had to be content to struggle along with line shafting, belting, and a network of countershafts and pulleys.

Dissipation of the steam engine's original horsepower output through friction and torsional losses was not the only drawback to belt drives. In the first place, fairly accurate shaft alignment was a constant problem, especially on long lines. Without a tolerably fair degree of alignment, the belts had a perverse way of creeping to one side of the pulley, causing one edge of the belting to develop a beautifully scalloped effect, after which it had to be thrown out. Then there was the matter of crossed belting for reverse drives—a perplexing arrangement at best, but positively treacherous when combined with faulty alignment. Trickiest of all, however, was the "quarter-turn" belt for driving a vertical shaft from a horizontal shaft, or vice versa. If the electric motor had accomplished nothing more than the elimination of this so-called "muley drive" from the machine shop, its inventors would still be deserving of plaques in any hall of fame.

Those who have never had to wrestle with the quarter-turn belt have no idea how such a simple device could prove so unruly. To understand the elements of the problem, at least in miniature, take two round lead pencils and a flat rubber band. Place the rubber band over the eraser ends of both pencils, keeping the pencils parallel. Now roll one pencil between the fingers, leaving the other free to turn. If the rubber band is stretched slightly to keep it from slipping, the rolling motion given to one pencil will cause the other to rotate in the same direction. If the pencils are held perfectly parallel, the rubber band will remain on the ends of both pencils. This setup represents the simple direct belt drive, which under ideal conditions gives no trouble at all for either direction of rotation. But if one of the pencils is tilted away from the parallel (representing faulty alignment of shaft), the rubber band, which is the belt, will promptly creep off the end of the other pencil, which is the driven pulley. This condition demonstrates what has been said above about the troubles of poor alignment, except that it may take a little time to obtain the scalloped effect on the rubber band.

Now if we continue to hold the pencils parallel, but move one of them a quarter turn so that it is vertical while the other is horizontal (at the same time keeping the rubber band on each pencil end), we will have a fair approximation of the quarter-turn belt

A typical engine lathe of the 1880's.

mentioned above. It looks simple, doesn't it? It is simple; yet when you come to install it in actual practice it becomes the trickiest thing imaginable unless you have the idea firmly fixed in mind. Depending on which pencil you made vertical—in other words, which way you placed the quarter turn in the belt—the pencils can now move in only one direction. As soon as you reverse the rotation, the rubber band flies off both pencil ends.

It would seem a simple problem to remember which way to put the belt on, but nine times out of ten the beginner in those days would put the quarter turn in the wrong direction, and as soon as he got it on (remember that the shaft pulley was always in motion), off it would fly immediately and wrap itself around the machinist and his lathe and perhaps knock down a few innocent bystanders. It was always an exciting adventure to watch a new man put on a quarter-turn belt. You could of course be fairly certain it would fly off instantly, but what made it interesting was trying to guess whether he would break a window or only hang himself on the rafters.

Besides the usual annoyances of hotboxes and accumulated dirt that plagued the early machinist, the old-fashioned belt drive was associated with the phenomenon of static electricity. Most of us in the shop knew nothing about electrical theory outside of Ben Franklin's experiments with the kite, but thanks to the belt drive, we were all constantly aware of this much-discussed but invisible force. The moving belts acted in a manner roughly analogous to the moving raindrops that make up a thundercloud, and when the right number of electrons had been knocked off, a difference of potential was built up between the moving belt and the unfortunate passer-by, who was often struck with a bolt from the blue as he thoughtlessly walked beneath it. Besides galvanizing a dreamy workman into sudden activity, this feature of the belt drive occasionally brought out latent inventive genius in some of the boys around the shop. I remember one machinist in particular who, fancying himself a second Helmholtz, occupied his spare time in charging a homemade Leyden jar from the static electricity on the belts. His outfit, from which he could then shoot long sparks to light our gas jets, consisted of an ordinary pickle jar filled with iron filings from the chip pan of his milling machine, with a small carbon rod sticking out at the top. If he had only had some kind of potentiometer around handy we could have measured just how many thousands—or millions—of volts our hard-working belts generated.

Then there was the matter of pulleys—the cylindrical drums mounted on the line shaft upon which the belts traveled. The present-day pulley comes in two halves that are easily slipped over a line shaft and fastened in place without disturbing the rest of the arrangement, but this was not so with the pulleys of the gay 'eighties. Our shop had never heard of such a thing as a split pulley. If a new pulley had to be installed for a machine added to the line, the entire shaft and every pulley on it had to be dismantled so that the new pulley could be strung on. It was very much like replacing the middle bead of a necklace—all the beads on one side of it have to come off first, and then have to be put back on again. But in the case of the pulleys, they had to go back on in a very definite sequence.

For the benefit of antiquarians and students of primitive behavior, I should like to describe the pulley-changing ritual in detail. First we removed the outer covering from the coupling (when it had one), and loosened the coupling bolts. Next, the end section of the shaft had to be slid sideways through the hangers, which supported the shafting. Then those pulleys near the hanger had to be loosened and shifted in order to permit the shaft to move far enough. Following this, the hanger boxes that were in the way had to be taken out, and one hanger bolt removed, so that the hanger could be swung out of the way of the pulleys. If this didn't provide enough leeway, the entire hanger had to come down. At this point—certainly if not before—a sling had to be rigged under the shaft to carry the weight while subsequent operations proceeded according to plan. When this had been done, somebody usually sent out for the beer and sandwiches, for there was a long night ahead for everybody.

Now the main job began. All the pulleys between the end of the shaft and the place where the new machine was to go were removed one after the other, together with all the numerous belts that had been connected to them. It was always considered advisable to try to remember the order in which these pulleys came off, and to make a mental note of exactly how many were removed, otherwise it might prove embarrassing later on. Next, the new pulley was slipped on the end of the shaft and jockeyed into its designated position. If it did not go on easily (and nobody paid too strict attention to tolerances and fits in those days), the pulley bore had to be eased out a little with a half-round file. As a slight complication, there were always a few burrs on the shaft caused by the setscrews that held each pulley in place, and these had to be smoothed down so that the pulleys could slip over them.

Finally, when the new pulley had been installed, all the preceding operations had to be done over again, this time in reverse, making sure that each pulley was put back in proper sequence, that all hangers and hanger bolts were replaced, and that each belt with its quarter turn or double quarter turn was back on its correct pulley. Woe unto the mechanic who, when this work was all finished, might pick up a pulley from the floor, saying "Here's one that seems to be left over!" It were better that the pulley be tied to his neck, and that he be cast into the sea.

It is easy to see how changing one little pulley in this kind of a setup could mean shutting down the whole shop, sometimes for an entire day and night. Sundays and holidays were therefore pulley-changing days par excellence. And all overtime was paid at the regular straight-time rate of 5 cents an hour for young apprentices like myself.

A word should perhaps be said about certain outstanding features of the line shafts. In those days the bars from which line shafts were made came from the rod mill with rough-finish diameters of $1\frac{1}{2}$, 2, or $2\frac{1}{2}$ inches. This meant that when the rod was "turned" or finished by turning off $\frac{1}{16}$ inch from the surface, the resulting diameters would be $1\frac{7}{16}$, $1\frac{15}{16}$, or $2\frac{11}{16}$ inches—a seemingly unnecessary complication in what should have been simple dimensions. Of course, this was before the days of standardization. One was always mildly surprised when a pulley or coupling happened to fit the shaft for which it was designed without requiring a little retouching with the file.

The hangers that held up the shafting were spaced according to either the number of machines, the power load taken off, or the general layout of the shop, with a span between hangers of 8 or 10 feet. In order to prevent undue bending of the line shaft due to belt pull, it was customary to employ a kind of military strategy by arraying the machines in opposing ranks so that the pull of the belts in one direction would be approximately offset by an equal amount of pull in the opposite direction. This kind of layout often resulted in strange bedfellows among the machine tools.

Sections of the line shaft were joined together by all sorts of coupling devices, some of which were downright dangerous. Plain, unguarded flanges, with their projecting coupling bolts and set-

A corner of the Rue Manufacturing Shop at 211 Race Street, Philadelphia, about 1888, showing primitive machine tools, belts, countershafts, and belt shifters

A quartet of Rue Manufacturing Company machinists in the late 'eighties—*l.* to *r.*, F. H. Colvin, Charlie Westcott, Harry Cathcart, and John Cullen

The author's birthplace at Sterling, Massachusetts

screws invisible even at moderate speeds, were still being used in many shops. They were as treacherous as buzz saws for the unwary workman. Even the ordinary straight couplings had projecting keys that could rip off a fellow's shirt sleeve if they didn't actually maim him for life. The Rue Plant was more fortunate than most shops in having Sellers compression couplings which had a wide-faced shell placed over the bolts that acted not only as a protective cover but also as an emergency pulley for light drives.

Inasmuch as belt transmission was all the rage in those days, it was only natural that the best brains in the field should concern themselves with belting theory. As I recall, there were two distinct

Rue's "Little Giant" Injector

THE CHEAPEST
BOILER FEEDER
Warranted to give Satisfaction.
Rue Manufacturing Co.,
523 Cherry Street,
PHILADELPHIA, Pa.
SEND FOR PRICE LIST AND CIRCULAR.

An early advertisement in the *American Machinist* (April, 1878) before the company moved to No. 211 Race Street.

schools of thought as to the nature of belt action, each of which had its champions who proved by the binomial theorem or a Fourier series that their particular theory was the only correct one. One group, whom we shall call the "friction" school, held that the belt operated entirely by the friction between it and the pulley face. The opposition group, or "aerodynamics" school, insisted that the driving force was clearly the result of the pressure of air against the belt during its contact with the pulley, and went so far as to calculate this force in terms of the usual 14.7 pounds per square inch of the belt surface. The air, they contended, lost power when it was trapped between belt and pulley; hence all you had to do was allow the air to escape.

The proponents of the air theory seemed to have the upper hand for a time; some manufacturers began making perforated belting, while others drilled their pulley rims so full of vent holes that the "trapped" air had no trouble whatever in working its way out.

Another moot point was the question of how smooth the pulley face should be for best results. Naturally, the friction advocates said they should not be too smooth, whereas the air-pressure crowd taught that pulleys should be as smooth as possible, arguing that this would permit the outer air pressure to make a better contact, or some such reasoning. Covering the pulley face with a tough paper was somehow claimed as proof by both parties, and the makers of wooden pulleys stepped quickly into the breach by advertising the fine gripping qualities of their pulleys, while pointing out their admirable smoothness in the same paragraph.

Although both the friction and the aerodynamics schools of belt drive have few alumni today, there is still a lively dispute going on about just how "sticky" the belt dressing of today should be for optimum power transmission where belt drive is still used. The question, it seems, amounts to a choice between the lesser of two evils: if the belt tends to cling to the pulley face there is excessive power loss through friction; on the other hand, if the belt does not tend to cling to the pulley, power is lost through slippage between them. For my part, I do not feel quite up to a rigorous analysis of the mechanics involved, but this should by no means deter the reader from a little independent research on the subject if he is so minded.

The machinist who runs a modern lathe cannot possibly experience the sense of high adventure that accompanied every operation on the old machines and that made even the threading of a small bolt as keenly exciting as a bout with rapiers. When you confronted one of these ancestral contrivances with a modest metalworking project in mind, you could never be quite sure which of you was going to come off second best in the encounter. For the machine tool of the 'eighties was a hazardous affair with exposed driving gears, open gas-flame illumination, and practically uncontrollable drive, to which must be added a complete unawareness on the part of the management of the need for safe working methods and conditions.

In these present days of fluorescent lighting and other high-intensity illumination for machine shops, it may be hard to imagine how the machinist of sixty years ago got any kind of tolerances with an open gas flame as his sole source of light. Yet that was all the light we had to work with on dark days or on the night shift. The gas jets, which were jointed behind the lathe and could be swung in a fairly wide arc, represented a twofold hazard—you might develop occupational blindness, and you might also burn down the shop. With this primitive flare, which rarely exceeded 2 candle-power, one had to rely mainly on instinct when boring a relatively small hole, since the only way to see what the borer was doing to the work was to swing the jet very near the hole and examine the work through the unoxidized or blue portion of the gas flame. It will be readily understood why eyestrain was usually a badge of service among pioneer machinists.

It always surprises me why no one ever thought of such a thing as safety goggles in those days. Eyeglasses had been in use for some three hundred years or more, but nobody seems to have looked on them as a possible device for keeping unwanted foreign particles out of the eye. In our shop at least it was a fairly routine occurrence for bits of emery and brass or steel chips to lodge themselves in a fellow's unprotected cornea on the average of one a day. Charlie Westcott, along with his other accomplishments, was quite an expert at removing all sorts of foreign matter from the eye. I remember one day when I was turning tool steel with my face rather close to the work; suddenly I felt a stab of pain as a steel chip flew up and sank into my right eyeball, blinding me in an instant.

"Charlie!" I yelled, clapping a hand over the injured organ, and executing a few impromptu dance steps in front of the lathe. Charlie dropped what he was doing and came running on the double.

"What the hell's the matter, Freddie?"

"My eye—I've just put my eye out! I'm blinded!" And I started yelling again.

This was old stuff for Charlie. He acted promptly. Backing me into a corner, he jammed my head tightly against the wall with his left arm and slipped out his pocket knife. Then, while I held back the eyelid with grimy fingers, Charlie dug his trusty knife blade into the cornea of my right eye. The steel sliver was in pretty deep, right over the iris where it couldn't be seen. While Charlie probed, I hollered.

"Go easy with that knife, Charlie—it's my eye you're fooling with!"

"Shut up and hold still. I almost had it that time."

"Leave me alone—I'll buy myself a glass eye in the morning."

"Got it!" cried Charlie triumphantly, holding up the knife blade so I could see the sliver with my one good eye. It was at least a foot long, I thought, but when Charlie later got out the micrometer it measured less than ⅛ inch.

I might add that, thanks to Charlie's operative technique, my right eye is still as sound as the left, although I suffer from a slight case of myopia brought on perhaps by too much scribbling in the past sixty years. But that was how we lived in the heroic days before safety goggles were introduced.

Another example of Charlie Westcott's surgical abilities occurred when I had my only accident on a planer. I was doing a small job with the work in the planer vise and carelessly put my left hand on the vise near the end of the stroke. The clapper block caught my hand and rolled the skin back about a half inch, exposing the sinews that operate the fingers. It didn't hurt particularly, and after stopping the planer and watching how the bared muscles worked, I washed out the wound and hunted up Charlie.

"That's a helluva way to stop a planer, Fred. You ought to know better than that. Come let me fix it up for you."

It was already washed out so he wrapped a few turns of clean bandage around it and grabbed the bottle of shellac, which we used for touching up patterns.

"Now hold still a minute, Fred. This won't feel so damn good, but it's good medicine for cuts"—and he poured shellac on the bandage. Of course the alcohol soaked through and wasn't exactly soothing. But this was standard treatment for cuts in those days. The alcohol disinfected the wound and the shellac made an airtight dressing to keep the germs out. This may not be according to modern medicine but it worked. I still have the small scar on the back of my hand—my only souvenir of the shop's shellac bottle.

The modern exhaust system for buffing and polishing rooms has eliminated another interesting aspect of early machine-tool work. Before exhaust systems were developed to carry away the fine particles of brass that fly from the polishing wheels, this metallic dust used to settle on the operator's hands, arms, face, and clothing. When combined with normal perspiration, the metal fused into the sort of verdigris or patina that is so much admired on bronze figures and other *objets-d'art*, and the hapless operator went home each night looking like a walking statue. This antique bronze finish

A "mechanical time-keeper," forerunner of the modern time clock. An employee checking in or out dropped a numbered brass disk in the cylinder, which fell into the "seven-o'clock" compartment (for example), and was later retrieved by the timekeeper, who checked the workman off in a book. The cylinder, operated by clockwork, remained an hour over each compartment, which certainly gave the workman enough leeway.

also caused skin eruptions resembling eczema or ordinary shingles and in general set the buffer operator apart from his fellow men.

Sanitary conveniences in the old shops probably came up to the legal standards of those days, but the standards were far from being fastidious. Each of us in the Rue Plant had his own galvanized iron bucket to wash up in at the end of the day's work. Sinks with hot and cold running water were a luxury of the idle rich, an affectation frowned upon by practical shop owners. When our hands were particularly grimy, we resorted to the use of waste rags dipped in light oil or kerosene, although the use of either was not sanctioned by the boss. The antique finish mentioned above was left to wear off in its own good time. The present-day circular washbasin that accommodates ten or a dozen men at one time is certainly a great step forward from the individual slop-bucket method, and plant owners have found there is a close relation between cleanliness and a low lost-time record.

Because central heating was still a newfangled and expensive proposition, our shop and others like it depended largely on the waste heat from the steam boiler in the basement to warm up the building in wintertime. Consequently, on frosty Monday mornings following the previous day's shutdown, the temperature in the shop often fell below freezing. This would have been fine if we had been handling frozen beef for a living, but we were supposed to be manufacturing injectors. On such days, hats, overcoats, and mittens were worn inside the shop for the first three hours, and if you have ever tried to work with a micrometer in such a getup, you can easily imagine how much work was accomplished of a crisp Monday morning. We looked like part of Admiral Peary's polar expedition and were as handicapped as a set of watchmakers wearing boxing gloves. The cold naturally affected the assembly of machined parts even when they were well within specified limits, for the metal would contract when moved from one part of the room to another part where the temperature might be 5 or 6° F. cooler. In our more enlightened practice today we take all machine-tool measurements at the standard temperature of 68° F. or 20° C., and an air-conditioned shop in which room temperature is kept near that figure will have less trouble with close fits and assemblies than it would have otherwise.

It is not certain that the design of the early lathes had anything to do with eliminating the male beard as an article of apparel, although the two were very intimately connected at one time. Young bucks of my day, as soon as their glands had sufficiently matured, followed the manly fashion of raising a set of whiskers. This held true for machinists as well as for men of other callings. Oldsters and young bloods alike in the Rue Plant sported a variety of current styles. Among the more popular numbers were the Vandyke, the full Grogan, the Imperial, the Dundreary, the plain goatee, the Hussar, the Gladstone, the Piccadilly weeper, the flowing Royal, the Edwardian, the Burnsides, and the bushy coverall or *surtout*. Influenced, no doubt, by the fine appearance of the men around me in the shop, I was thinking seriously of making some attempt at a modified Imperial myself, when the unfortunate case of Zeke Courtney dissuaded me from this move for quite some time.

Zeke was a young fellow in his early thirties who had been a first-class drill-press man before he came to the Rue Plant. He was about 6 feet 3 inches in his stocking feet, wore loose-fitting overalls, and was a trifle spindle-shanked in appearance. Zeke suffered from premature baldness and, as often happened in these cases, he tried to compensate for it by raising a whopper of a beard. At the time I am speaking of, it had attained a rich luxuriance, flowing in soft waves over his shirt front and making a collar and tie completely superfluous. It was rumored that Zeke had his beard washed and marcelled every Saturday night, but this may have been only malicious gossip.

One day when the boss was shorthanded he asked Zeke to cut a few screwthreads on the old engine lathe. This particular affair had been built about 1855 and even in my youth would have been considered a museum piece. Both the back gears and the screw-cutting gear were entirely exposed. This dangerous relic, moreover, had been so installed that the operator was obliged to squeeze himself in between the machine and a floor column, at the same time facing directly into the light from the near-by window. Zeke had to bend over double to see what kind of a thread he was getting. He poked his head close to the cutting tool and adjusted the cross-feed. That was as far as he got, for at this point Zeke also fed the end of his flowing beard into the screw-cutting gears.

The lanky machinist yelled long and loud, "Godamighty! Charlie! Help! Pull off the belt, somebody! Hey!" Half of the shop came running to the rescue.

What's all the rumpus about?"

"Zeke's caught himself by the whiskers! Look at him—he's halfway into the machine!"

"Well, pull off the belt, damn it. Don't stand there laughing at him."

"No, wait—give us those tinner's shears here."

"Somebody stop the line shaft, quick!"

"Hold his head up! Keep his pants out of the drive gears!"

By the time Charlie Westcott had finally got the countershaft belt off the pulley, Zeke was literally in up to his ears. His 6-foot 3-inch frame was wrapped solidly around the lathe in a fearful embrace. About 8 inches, more or less, of his beautiful beard was inextricably bound up in the gears. His left shirt sleeve was fouled on one of the back gears. He had become a part of his machine.

Zeke wasn't the only one who lost a beard to the machine in the old days, and he happened to be luckier than some other operators I knew. He sustained only a few minor scratches from his encounter, and even managed to salvage a fairly respectable-looking goatee. But he had to go back to wearing a collar and tie afterward.

The world of the 'eighties was reflected in our shop in other ways besides men's fashions. First, perhaps, I should orient this story a bit by stating that I was born just eighteen months after the assassination of Abraham Lincoln; was already in command of a few monosyllables when the last spikes of the Union Pacific Railroad were being driven; was all of four years old when William Marcy Tweed was indicted for systematic thievery; was doing my first sums when the banks closed for twenty days in 1873; and three years later was more interested in the newspaper accounts of Custer's Last Stand and the death of Wild Bill Hickok than in the new "improvement in telegraphy," which Professor Bell was then demonstrating in Boston. I remember Father telling me about a talented young man from New Jersey who had recently brought out a machine that reproduced the human voice from a tin-foil cylinder, a lamp that was lit by electricity, and a telegraph machine that could handle four separate messages at once. There was talk, too, of another Civil War following the disputed election of 1876, but I was too young to know what it was all about. Father also spoke about the nation-wide railroad strike, the hanging of the Molly Maguires, and the opening up of the Comstock lode in Nevada. When I reached the age of thirteen in 1880, the United States took its tenth census and included me in the total population of 50,155,783 souls living within the thirty-eight states of the Union.

We had hardly got over the shock of Garfield's assassination in 1881 when the papers were filled with all sorts of scandal about the Star Route frauds, in which the Assistant Postmaster General and a few other government officials were implicated. This was but the latest in a series of public scandals that I often heard Father and his friends discuss—the land grants and omnibus schemes of the early railroad days, the fast deals of Jay Gould and Jim Fisk in trying to get a corner on gold, and the plundering of New York City's treasury by Messrs. Hall, Sweeney, Connolly, and Tweed; together with the ill-famed Crédit mobilier that involved the President, the Vice-president, and several members of Congress; the Whisky Ring, and the trading-post deals of War Secretary Belknap and others. These and numerous other instances of graft and corruption seemed to indicate that a fair percentage of the population in those days was somewhat preoccupied with money-making, and felt that the ends justified whatever means were available. This attitude, it must be admitted, was reflected in the world of machinery as well as in other circles. '

I remember my first experience with this sort of thing after I had served my apprenticeship in the Rue Plant and had graduated to the position of trouble shooter. When a customer reported that he was having difficulty with one of our injectors, it was my job to find out why and to remedy the trouble if possible. One morning we received a letter from the master mechanic of a well-known railroad, stating that something had gone wrong with a batch of injectors we had recently sold him. I was surprised, for I had tested that particular batch of injectors myself and found them in good condition. Knowing that the usual cause of trouble lay not in the injectors themselves but frequently in an insufficient supply of water or leakage in the suction pipe, I asked our plant manager to let me go out and have a look at them.

"Let's wait a few days first, and see what happens," he answered, giving me a sort of sly grin. "We don't want to be too hasty, you know. They'll probably find the trouble themselves."

I waited as he had suggested, but at the end of the week I went to him again.

"Maybe I'd better take a run out to the railroad company and see if they have those injectors hooked up right. They tested O.K. here in the shop. How about it?"

The manager leaned back in his swivel chair and took a good look at me. "Listen, my boy," he said, giving me that sly grin again, "it's about time you knew the facts of life. In this business it isn't enough just to make a good injector—you gotta be a sort of a politician too."

I told him I didn't get the point.

"Look, Freddie lad," the manager said, "there are some pretty influential master mechanics and buyers in the companies we sell to, and they expect certain favors once in a while for throwing a little business our way. Otherwise they might take it into their heads to knock our product. You see what I mean?"

"But what about that letter we got—about the injectors not working right?"

"That, my boy, was just the old come-on—a polite way of telling us that a small favor is in order, if you know what I mean. Well," he added, getting up from his chair, "don't give it another thought. We won't have any trouble about that particular lot of injectors, and you don't have to run out and look at their water supply. Because I sent our friend a check for $50 this morning."

While this sort of thing may not have been the universal practice in the world of business, it helped to explain how some years later master mechanics who received no more than $1,800 a year in wages were able to afford fairly luxurious homes and brand-new automobiles. This was true particularly in the railroad industry, which was still under the influence of men who believed graft and bribery were part of the natural order of things. It was widely known that the railroads paid exorbitant prices for supplies of all kinds, and that many minor railroad officials were unaccountably prosperous and well-heeled. A friend of mine who worked for a supply house controlled by the redoubtable Diamond Jim Brady always held that the railway companies paid their bills to that gentleman without even looking at any of the figures except the total. He tested his theory one day by making a slight "mistake" in a bill so that an 80-cent gear was listed at $80 instead. The railroad paid the $80 without a whisper of complaint, and even refused a refund when the intentional error was pointed out to them. Those were great days, indeed, and nobody suffered from the system except the general public.

A year before I went to work as an apprentice in the Rue Plant, Ferdinand de Lesseps and his ill-advised engineers had begun their futile excavation of the first Panama Canal; another Frenchman, Pasteur, was experimenting with human rabies and inoculations; an American named Sprague was introducing New York commuters to their first trolley ride; and the breath-taking span of the Brooklyn Bridge was being made ready for traffic. Among other things that we read in the papers in 1884 was that a certain J. H. Darby of England had built a basic open-hearth furnace for the manufacture of steel at Brymbo, Wales; an American by the name of L. E. Waterman had brought out a wonderful new pen that carried its own ink reservoir; a young immigrant from Germany named Ottmar Mergenthaler had perfected a machine that cast and set a complete line of type; while in the same year William Jenney designed the world's first skeleton-steel building, William Baxter of Maryland demonstrated the first electric passenger elevator, and a Missouri writer of humorous works published a story called "The Adventures of Huckleberry Finn."

There was much to interest the mechanically inclined young man in the exciting decade of the 'eighties. The budding science of electricity was as fascinating and as full of promise then as our modern sciences of electronics and atomic energy are today. In addition to the *American Machinist*, which was even then a leading magazine in its field, new publications such as the *Electrical World*, the *Electrical Engineer*, and *Western Electricity* were eagerly devoured by interested students of the new science. My father took me to the monthly meetings of the Franklin Institute in Philadelphia before I was twelve years old, and although I was too young to understand very much about electricity, I recall that I listened attentively to the great Elihu Thomson (then but a twenty-seven-year-old professor at Central High School) when he lectured in 1880 at the Franklin Institute. Here, too, in 1887, I saw Emile Berliner make one of his first lateral-cut disk records, which were to supplant the earlier Edison cylinders and make mass production of phonograph records a practical reality. Frank Sprague, mentioned above in connection with the first trolley car, also lectured at the institute, predicting a tremendous future for electrical traction and speeds for electric locomotives that seemed fantastic in those days.

The Franklin Institute also introduced me in 1881 to the work of Frederic Eugene Ives, the inventor of the first half-tone process for reproducing illustrations photomechanically and also of the binocular microscope, of a rotogravure process, of natural-color still pictures, and of a three-color photographic process. I saw him demonstrate the latter invention at the Institute.

From the institute lectures and from the technical literature of the day we learned of William Stanley's invention of the electric transformer, which he demonstrated in 1886 at Great Barrington, Massachusetts, and of Nikola Tesla, the Croatian engineer who came to the United States in 1884 and 4 years later patented the alternating-current induction motor. We learned also that the successful application of electricity to welding was accomplished by Elihu Thomson in 1885, and that in the same year Charles Martin Hall of Ohio had obtained pure aluminum from its oxide by electrolytic action. In 1888 George Eastman presented the amateur photographers of the world with his mass-produced "Kodak," and William Burroughs of New York made life easier for accountants with his new adding machine. A twenty-nine-year-old Detroit mechanic named Henry Ford built his first gasoline motor car in 1892, possibly unaware that Maxim, Benz, Daimler, Panhard, Haynes, Winton, and the Duryea Brothers were doing exactly the same thing at the same time. On April 14, 1894, the first motion-picture "theater" was opened at 1155 Broadway, New York City, using Edison's patented kineto-scope, or peep-show device, that produced motion pictures lasting about 13 seconds for one person at a time. Samuel Pierpont Langley in 1896 successfully launched a steam-driven "aerodrome" or pilotless plane that stayed aloft for 90 seconds and covered a distance of about 2,600 feet. Charles G. Curtis, a Boston patent lawyer, invented the velocity-compounded steam turbine in 1896, a prime mover that became widely employed in electric power plants and in marine propulsion.

It is not, as one might think, such a far cry from our little injector-manufacturing plant at 211 Race Street, Philadelphia, to the momentous technological and scientific developments of the last two decades of the nineteenth century. Without going much below the surface, it might be pointed out that the injector which we and other companies made was a highly essential accessory to the operation of steam boilers; and since a steam turbine or steam engine cannot lead an independent existence without its boiler, the injector was therefore necessary to the operation of machine shops, electric power plants, steamships, and railway locomotives. Pursuing this line of reasoning a little further, we might add that the induction motor, the electric passenger elevator, the incandescent lamp, the electric transformer, electric welding, and electrolytic reduction of ores would have remained purely hypothetical theories without the electric power plant, which we have seen was somehow tied up with an injector or a similar device. Even the open-hearth process and its distant derivative, the steel skyscraper, had to depend upon steam from a boiler, and in turn upon an injector or other kind of water pump.

But the mechanics and the machine operators of the Rue Manufacturing Company, whether they realized it or not, were part of a much larger whole. They belonged to the great body of machinists, machine-tool operators, and designers in shops and factories scattered all over the world, who were making not only the parts which, when assembled, became the quadruplex telegraph, the telephone, the hydraulic dredge, the compound microscope, the linotype, the printing press, the phonograph, the trolley car, the electric motor, the adding machine, the automobile, and the steam turbine, but were making also the actual tools by which these parts could be endlessly duplicated, as well as other machines on which these same parts could be later assembled into a useful product. Looked at in this way, one can trace a thin but definite line from the machinist at his lathe to the captain at the wheel of a steamship, and even to the physical production of "The Adventures of Huckleberry Finn."

Thus it seems to me that the modest plant of the Rue Manufacturing Company, which we must now leave behind us, was, in spite of its belt drive, its gas-jet illumination, its exposed cutting gears, its subfreezing temperatures, its collection of personalized wash-buckets, and its small off-the-record gratuities, a kind of symbol of the Second Industrial Revolution that began in the late 'seventies of the nineteenth century and still goes on in this brave new world of atomic energy and microwave energy transmission. Our little shop, together with hundreds of others like it that have had their day, and with the anonymous army of workmen who ran the machines, formed the solid background of our modern industrial production and scientific progress. Without them, our machine-age civilization —whether for better or worse I must leave for the philosophers to decide—would remain a yet-unwritten chapter.

CHAPTER THREE

Giving the Machine a Voice

> *Positively we will neither publish anything in
> our reading columns for pay or in consideration of
> advertising patronage. Those who wish to recom-
> mend their wares to our readers can do so as fully
> as they choose in our advertising columns, but our
> editorial opinions are not for sale.*
> AMERICAN MACHINIST, Vol. I, No. 1, 1877

It is a curious fact that the printing press, which owes its present
existence to the development of machine tools, was itself responsible
for the tremendous growth of the machine-tool industry during the
past half century. Before the coming of trade publications and
technical magazines, machinists and tool designers in widely sepa-
rated shops all over the world had no means of knowing what progress was being made in their field except through occasional letters
between individuals, or through the reports of itinerant millwrights
or journeymen mechanics who had the opportunity to observe
methods and conditions in a number of different plants. Consequently when new tools or improved shop practices were developed
independently in a particular plant or locality, it might be months
or even years before the industry as a whole got wind of them, with
the result that progress in the machine-tool industry before the
'eighties was sporadic and localized. I mentioned earlier in connection with the primitive gas buggy that there were at least eight or ten
inventors working at the same thing at the same time in almost complete ignorance of each other's failures or successes. Something like
this was true of the machine-tool industry before the days of such
technical magazines as the *Northwest Mechanic*, the *Practical Mechanic*,

the *American Machinist, Machinery*, the *Locomotive Engineer*, and other trade papers that appeared during the last two decades of the past century.

With the publication and circulation of such periodicals, however, it became possible for the owners and operators of machine shops, the designers, engineers, shopworkers, apprentices, and buyers of machinery to get an over-all picture of the latest improvements, applications, and possibilities for development, as well as a share in the total experience of thousands of fellow workers in the field, plus a knowledge of their typical troubles and the remedies that they had found to be of practical use. Most important of all, the trade journal and technical publication made possible the concept of standardized practice and standardized measurement, without which it is safe to say our present machine-age civilization would be a great deal more chaotic than its severest critics can imagine. It has been through such mediums that the recommendations of the various engineering societies concerning the subject of standardization have been brought to the attention of everyone in the machine-tool industry.

The *American Machinist*, for which I have been writing for the past sixty years, played a not inconsiderable part in the dissemination of machine-tool knowledge and related information, and contributed, at least in a derivative fashion, to the late flowering of the industry. In saying this, I am thinking primarily of the work of hundreds of editors, contributors, and other workers who have been associated with the magazine during its nearly seventy years of existence.

The *American Machinist*, whose history is bound up with the history of machine tools, was founded in 1877 by Horace B. Miller and Jackson Bailey, who became its first business manager and first editor, respectively. It first saw the light of day in a three-story loft building at 96 Fulton Street in New York City. The aim of its founders was to establish a trade publication that would reflect the changing conditions in the machine-building industry, and, as specialization and coordination of techniques progressed, to concentrate its efforts on the problems that belonged to the shops. New methods of management and new ideas in machining practice were to be studied, expounded, and encouraged. New materials (the modern science of metallurgy was as yet unborn) were to be discussed with reference to their application to better cutting tools, to welding, to methods of test, problems of design, and to the over-all problem of simplifying and standardizing tolerances, limits, and gauges in the entire industry. It should be mentioned that this was three years before the founding of the American Society of Mechanical Engineers—an event which, fittingly enough, actually took place in the old offices of the *American Machinist* at 96 Fulton Street.

The *American Machinist* office at 96 Fulton Street, New York City, about 1880.

In 1888, when the paper was fairly well established, its editors decided to branch out into the field of locomotive operation with a more specialized magazine to be known as the *Locomotive Engineer*, and which was to serve the railroad mechanic in the same way that the *A.M.* was then serving the general machine-shop worker. Horace Miller, who along with Lycurgus B. Moore owned the *American Machinist* at that time, got in touch with my father, asking him on the basis of his long interest in locomotive engineering, and also as a pioneer subscriber to the earlier magazine, to suggest a likely candidate for the job of editor for the new paper.

Father was an omnivorous reader of all kinds of technical articles then appearing in print, particularly any reading matter dealing with railroad shop and roundhouse work. For some time he had been following with avidity the writings of a *Machinist* correspondent from Pueblo, Colorado, who signed himself John Alexander. Father admired Alexander's succinct style and phraseology, preferring his biweekly commentaries on tie plates, anticreepers, hump switching, M.C.B. couplings, and the like to the writings of such public figures as James Whitcomb Riley, the people's laureate. When Miller and Moore got Father's reply that the only possible editor worth considering for the new magazine was John Alexander, they set out posthaste for Pueblo, Colorado. Knowing from his letter that his full name was John Alexander Hill, they were able to locate him under his right name, made him an offer, and came home with a new editor under contract. It was thus that John Hill began a highly successful publishing career that was to lead to the founding of the McGraw-Hill Company, which at the present writing is the publisher of twenty-seven trade and technical magazines and an impressive list of books in nearly every field of human activity.

John Hill, who by 1896 was to make himself sole proprietor of the publication, was naturally curious to meet the man who was probably his most ardent reader and who had nominated him for the editorship. He came to our house in Philadelphia early in 1889, and both he and my father immediately recognized in each other a kindred fellowship founded on their mutual love for anything in the least way connected with a steam locomotive or a roundhouse yard. While I was still working on injectors at the Rue Plant, Hill came to visit me frequently at the shop and encouraged me in my chosen profession. I remember one week in early summer when, on my own time, of course, I made for him a model of the first steamship propeller, from patterns that Hill had obtained from its inventor, Isaac Driggs of Camden, New Jersey. This historic prototype, by the way, was later presented by Hill to the East Orange, (New Jersey), Public Library, where, I presume, it is now quietly gathering dust along with other artifacts of the past—unless some practical-minded curator during the recent war saw fit to contribute it to the scrap-metal drive.

In order to find out and report what was going on in representative machine shops throughout the country, the early trade journal employed traveling correspondents or roving editors on their staffs, whose duty it was to make extended trips into the hinterland and observe new methods and new materials in actual practice. This editorial policy had been begun as early as 1880 on the *American Machinist*, and several years later its scope was extended to include machine shops abroad as well as those in the United States. In 1897, Fred J. Miller, then editor of the *A.M.*, spent several months in European shops studying the ways in which American machine tools were being used in various factories, noting at the same time the differences between them and the tools native to the country visited. Ten years later an editor named J. Wallace Carrel, who subsequently became general manager of the Lodge and Shipley Company, made a similar survey for the *American Machinist*, which included Russia as well as Central Europe. Since then other editors have spent considerable time in England and on the continent, constantly adding to the world's knowledge of machine tools and methods. Editorial travel in recent years has run as high as 70,000 miles a year, and has included not only every industrial section of the United States, but also Alaska, Hawaii, the Philippine Islands, Canada, Cuba, Puerto Rico, Panama, China, and Japan. Through these editorial visits, shop proprietors, executives, and machine-tool operators have been brought into personal contact with the staff of the *American Machinist*, and through this medium have become part of an integrated body of craftsmen in an industry which, more than any other, requires a pooling of information and a constant effort towards standardization of methods.

Although there were fewer shops in the old days than there are now, the work of a roving editor was not any easier, because there was more territory for each man to cover, means of transportation were still quite rudimentary, and there were hundreds of different machine-shop methods for doing the same thing. In those days the roving editor lived the life of an itinerant drummer or bird of passage and had to combine the intrepidity of an explorer with the tenacity of a war correspondent. Machine shops were not always the easiest of architectural features to spot, even in a small town, being located on the outskirts of the city rather than on the main square. Merely getting to them was a feat in itself, particularly in winter when the horsecars were few and far between. When he got to the shop, the editor might find that it had been shut down for repairs (they might be replacing a pulley!), or if it were open, the plant operator or head foreman might not be in a particularly communicative mood that day. Some shop owners were of the rugged individualist or hidebound conservative schools and looked upon correspondents as little better than traveling salesmen, who could serve only to hold up normal operations while they asked a lot of silly questions or maybe advocated a new method of gauging.

I recall one instance of the way new methods were occasionally suspect among certain veterans of the old school. A friend of mine was demonstrating to the owner of an antiquated little machine shop, nestled somewhere in the foothills of the Alleghanies, the advantages of the master gauge blocks that were first manufactured by Carl Johansson in Sweden about 1904. These blocks, indispensable for all modern machine-tool work, are hard, flat, rectangular pieces of steel whose thicknesses have been accurately established within the almost unbelievable limits of 0.000002 to 0.000008 inch, and are intended, as they were then, as standards against which gauges and other measuring tools can be checked for accuracy. My friend, who was not trying to sell them but merely to show what was going on in the outside world, had interested the proprietor in these "Jo-blocks" to the point where he sent for his head toolmaker. This worthy gentleman was a grizzled old stager of the preadamite or hit-and-miss school of machinists.

"Some of those newfangled measuring blocks, eh?" he cackled, fingering the precision-smooth steel rectangles. "These young ship-jacks are always thinkin' up some span-new gimmick to complicate things with. Ain't nothing on the market today can take the place of a sharp eye and a steady hand, young feller. I been making tools for over forty-three years and I know what I'm talkin' about." He studied the shiny parallel surfaces skeptically for a while and then said, "Give us that ½-inch block here and I'll show this city feller something. Think these gimcracks here are accurate, eh? Wait till I show you."

From the pocket of his overalls he pulled out a battered micrometer caliper. "Always carry Betsy around with me," he grinned, "so's I can check things right on the spot." He blew a few hairs and pieces of lint from the spindle, whirled back the thimble, and slipped the caliper over the ½-inch Jo-block. Squinting in the poor light, he read the markings on the worn barrel.

"Four point nine—what did I tell you, young feller? Four point nine nine six—knew it all the time! Four point nine nine six and a wee bit! What did I tell you? This here gewgaw is off a good four-thousandths of an inch! Precision blocks! What kind of precision do you call that, eh? I coulda told you they were out to cheat the public with those doodads!"

My friend suggested that the discrepancy might possibly be due to the caliper.

"Look here, son," the old toolmaker said, "I've been using this mike since I was a journeyman apprentice back in '61, long before you were born, and I've never had any trouble with it from that day to this. Take your little toy blocks back to Mr. Johansson and tell him we don't need any knicknacks like them around in a first-class shop. We're doing all right as we are. Furthermore, you can tell that Swede from me that he better get himself a new pair of glasses! Tell him I said so!"

Not many of the early correspondents of the *American Machinist* ran into this sort of obstinacy more than three or four times in the course of a year's travels, but there were always a few craftsmen and shop owners who took a kind of personal pride in their art and looked upon it more as a secret, personal matter best reserved for the initiate, than as a part of a sweeping new technology that was even then revolutionizing every phase of industry. The general attitude among old-timers of sixty years ago was that machine-tool work was one of the fine arts, like the paintings of the early Renaissance, and that the inexperienced young fellows coming along then could never hope to equal, let alone surpass, the fine coordination of hand and eye that made the old toolmakers, with their primitive equipment, the marvels of their generation. As new and more accurate machines and gauges were introduced, making intuition and sixth sense a less important qualification for the first-class machinist, the old-timers complained, as only skilled handcraftsmen can, that their art was being debased by the machine.

Not that a few of the old mechanics were anything less than

genuine marvels in their own way. There are indeed few workmen today who can chip or file by hand to compare with the great masters of fifty or sixty years ago. The old toolmakers of that vanished day performed remarkably accurate work without the use of the fine instruments that are almost a commonplace in today's shops. These pioneer artisans had cultivated the "caliper touch" to an extraordi-

"Our Modern Machine Shop," humorous cartoon first reproduced in Sterling Elliott's *Catalogue* of the 'eighties.

nary degree of refinement, beyond which it is not possible for human senses to go. I knew of some old railroad machinists who could caliper the bore of a wheel, turn an axle to fit it, and even give a rather accurate estimate of the pressure necessary to force the wheel on the axle. But these estimable gentlemen, and others of their school, made the fundamental mistake of regarding machine-tool work wholly as an art. Art it is not. Though skill and judgment are necessary, machine-tool work is primarily a science, and it depends upon certain laws of physics, mathematics, and chemistry; like any other branch of engineering, it can be developed fully only by applying these laws in practice. So long as toolmakers and machinists depended largely upon their sense of touch for accuracy of measurement, standardization was not possible.

Some of the old mechanics, for example, had no use at all for the newfangled taps and dies that began to appear near the close of the past century. One skilled toolmaker in Greenfield, whom I knew slightly, believed they were nothing but a bother, and preferred a tap made from a piece of square steel with teeth cut out on the corners, which he claimed eliminated the need for fluting or squaring the shank. His favorite die was made by annealing an old, worn-out file, drilled and tapped in the center, with four small holes outside the thread drilled and filed into the tapped hole. This, he said, gave the necessary cutting edge and chip clearance, as well as the die-stock, all in the same piece. I often wonder what this old mechanic, had he lived to see them, would have thought of our modern methods in automobile work, where as many as fifty or more taps are driven simultaneously at drill speed.

Even the budding science of metallurgy was looked upon as a secret art by some of the early shop men, and indeed at one time every job of heat-treating, or of hardening and tempering, took on the nature of sorcery and black magic. Most of the heat-treating work was done in an open forge with a hand-operated rotary blower, and every operator had his own personal technique of "coking-up" the fire and applying the draft. There was much solemn hokum about the carbon composition of various steels, the proper ingredients to be used in the hardening bath, and even the kind of weather that should prevail during the ritual. Secret formulas consisting of all the specifics in the U.S. Pharmacopoeia, along with other odds and ends that smelled to high heaven, were fixtures in the old-fashioned machine shop, and none but the elect were permitted inside the shop while the incantations were going on.

There was one wizard I heard of, named McCandless, who guarded his secret for a quenching bath with infinite care. Once a week he would mix up a new batch of chemicals, keeping everyone at a prescribed distance during this solemn rite. To prevent possible rivals or secret agents of other shops from learning where he bought his ingredients and what his materia medica consisted of, McCandless worked out a system whereby on Saturday afternoons he would sneak off to a drugstore, buy one of his priceless ingredients, and then, to cover up his tracks, would saunter casually into the nearest saloon for a drink. When the coast was clear and the drink finished, he would slip out of the saloon by way of the back door and dash off to another pharmacy a few blocks away for the second ingredient. Just in case anyone was still on his trail, he would then drop into another tavern, polish off another three fingers of Old Crow, and like Operator *X* of the spy stories, only minus the traditional cloak and dagger, he would again vanish into the mysterious night in quest of the third, fourth, or ultimate ingredient.

Whether it was the thrill of adventure or the amount of Old Crow consumed in this manner, McCandless was always in such a state of heightened sensitivity on Monday mornings that he rarely got over the shakes before noon. On one such Monday morning he cracked two sets of cams in his secret hardening process, leaving them buried in the muck at the bottom of his cauldron while he dashed out to the nearest bar for a couple of quick ingredients. The manager thereupon called in a young machinist named Karl T. Herrmann who was groomed along more scientific lines. He first cleaned all the sludge out of the barrel and then hardened a new set of cams with clean water and a little salt, "drawing" them on hot sand. They came out with exactly the amount of file hardness required, and when McCandless of the mystic rites finally showed up he learned that science had suddenly displaced magic in heat-treating, and that he was minus a job.

Stories like these were gathered by the early correspondents along with details of an occasional new type of engine lathe or a new method of turning a flat reamer to a taper. The experienced editor who didn't mind traveling the length and breadth of the country in search of machine-shop news was aware that just as many interesting ideas and suggestions could be found in the small shops as in those that employed hundreds of men and machines. It must have been for just such a reason that James F. Hobart, special correspondent of the *American Machinist*, decided one day in 1885 to make the long trip from 96 Fulton Street in New York City to 211 Race Street in Philadelphia, so that he might see in what novel ways, if any, machine tools were being used to make injectors in the Rue Manufacturing Company.

Hobart, who must be held partly responsible for the reams and reams of printed matter that the present writer has perpetrated in the last sixty years, was not only a roving editor in the full sense of the word, but also a wandering millwright of considerable ability. From Massachusetts to Missouri, and from Minnesota to Florida, there were few locations in which he had not worked. He had an enviable familiarity with machine tools from the ground up and kept abreast of all new developments in the field. He was a kind of nineteenth-century minnesinger of the lathe, a member of that now vanished band of traveling mechanicians who wandered from one town to another across the country, not in search of employment— which they could have had at their back door—but in search of new experience, new problems, and new ideas. They helped considerably to spread new methods and new suggestions, and every shop they worked in profited to some degree from their wide experience.

Hobart was already a minor celebrity as far as I was concerned when he entered our shop in search of material. I had read every one of his articles that had appeared in the pages of the *American Machinist*, and though only eighteen at the time, felt I had learned a great deal from them. I had long envied his ability at putting words together in a clear, concise style, and his knack of making even the most complicated piece of machinery seem easy to understand. It was a wonderful thing to be able to visit other shops all over the United States, to see how different kinds of work was done, and then to tell about it in the columns of a paper that every shop owner and operator read and referred to. To be a member of the staff of the *American Machinist* was to me only a little less attractive than being President of the United States.

When Hobart came over to the lathe I was working at that day, I proudly showed him a few shop tools that I had made up in my spare time to simplify certain lathe and turning work. He examined them rather carefully and then asked me to demonstrate them on the machines. When I had finished, he said:

"Look, Colvin—I'll tell you what you do. You've got a couple of pretty good ideas there that I think a lot of other fellows could make use of if they knew about them. But if I write them up myself, you won't get any credit for them. So here's what you do. Make up a set of line drawings showing these gadgets in section and elevation, and number all the parts. Then write out a letter addressed to the editor of the *American Machinist*, explaining exactly how you use these things in the ordinary course of your shop practice. Make it short and to the point. Don't forget that the pictures will tell half of the story. And I can guarantee that we'll print your letter and drawings in the *Machinist* as soon as there's space available."

It was a red-letter day for me indeed. I was going to have something printed in the *American Machinist*—just like Hobart and John Alexander and Fred Miller and the rest! I rushed home that night, got out my drawing board and T-square, made six Patent Office type drawings of my "handy shop tools," and dashed off a 400-word "letter to the editor" describing my several brain children. And after waiting breathlessly all that winter and part of the next spring, I was rewarded when the *American Machinist* for April 3, 1886, on page 6, published my letter and drawings in its "Letters from Practical Men" column. I all but burst with pride. The editor had gone to the trouble of having my drawing made into a handsome wax-plate engraving (this was before the days of photogravure), and somebody had put fancy lettering on it as well, and the whole thing looked very official indeed. It was not, as might appear from the accompanying reproduction, the only communication on the page—there were three other letters from three other practical men—but mine was the only one with a two-column illustration, and the one that caught your eye.

I felt an overpowering impulse to rush out and buy up all the copies of that week's *Machinist* I could lay my hands on, so that I might casually pass them off on my friends with the offhand remark, "By the way, I've got a short piece in the *American Machinist* this week you might be interested in. Here's a copy I just happened to have around. Oh, you can keep it—I've no further use for it." I had visions of myself playing the role of Honest Fred, a hero out of Horatio Alger, who works himself up from grease monkey in an

LETTERS FROM PRACTICAL MEN.

Some Handy Shop Tools.
Editor American Machinist:

I send you herewith a few kinks which are in daily use by me in course of my ordinary shop practice. Fig. 1, I call my riveting block, which is merely a piece of round cast-iron, smaller at one end than at the other. I clamp it in the vise (it is six inches long) so that it projects far enough above the jaws to be convenient. I find that it makes a very useful tool for riveting. Sometimes I use one end and sometimes the other as the work requires.

a chuck; bored out to admit lathe center through it, and a little longer, say ¼-inch, than the distance from the shoulder of spindle to the point of center, with the slot across the center, as shown at *C*. The slots want to be deep enough to admit of movement of steel when turning taper reamers. I like it very well for such work, and hope I have made it clear.

Figs. 3, 4, 5 and 6 show a milling tool for use on turret lathes. It is a casting whose general shape can best be had from Figs. 3, 4 and 5, giving top, side and end views. A hole is bored in the center *B*, the shank

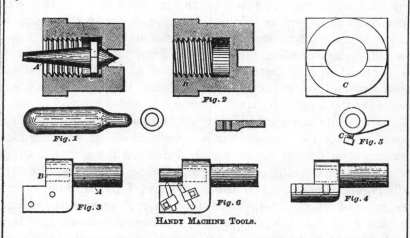

HANDY MACHINE TOOLS.

Fig. 2 represents my chuck, dog, or carrier—latter name, perhaps, is the best—for flat cutters, reamers, etc. I use it mostly for turning flat reamers to a taper. *A* is intended to show it in place over the lathe spindle with center in, although I have not succeeded as well as I could wish with it in that position.

You will readily see that with the flat steel center *A*, placed in the slot across the face of the carrier, it drives from both sides. *B* is the section of carrier; *C* is the end view. In plain words, it is a cast iron carrier; round, save a square at the rear end to take off of the lathe width. It is fitted to the lathe same as

having been turned to fit the turret. *B* is bored to receive the centering cutter, which keeps working through while the milling is being done; the cutter is held by set screw *C*, Fig. 5. Fig. 6 gives a general idea of the use of this tool, showing cutters in place. The milling cutters are merely flat pieces of steel held in place by clips, shown above, Fig. 6, offsetting the depth, or rather a little less than thickness of cutters. These clips are held by screws, as shown in Fig. 6. They are cheap and admit a large arrangement of adjustment. Center cutter can, of course, be made of any size. They are not patented.

FRED COLVIN.

First published work, from the *American Machinist*, April 3, 1886.

injector plant to the head of a vast empire of machine shops, or perhaps becomes owner and president of a chain of magazines encircling the globe and printed in all foreign languages, including the Scandinavian. But best of all, in terms of the here and now, was the check for $2.50 that came in the mail a few days later. Besides printing my letter in the magazine so that everybody could see it, they were even paying me for it! Not that I needed the money so much—I was already getting $4.50 a week from the Rue Company.

Before long I found myself writing a fair number of "letters to the editor" each year, and soon a few other trade publications were asking for letters and articles on the same subject. Not all the articles I wrote were accepted by any means, but those that were provided not merely an additional source of income but also an added stimulation to my youthful desire to be an editor. I had enough sense to realize, however, that if my writings were not to be confined to the "Letters from Practical Men" column, I would need a much broader shop background than I had at the time; and that advantage must be taken of every opportunity to visit other shops, to study new methods, and to absorb as much information as possible from the literature in all the periodicals and technical journals then current. Consequently I devoted the next five or six years to the broadening of my experience along these lines. Although still regularly employed at the Rue Plant, I found time to visit a number of other machine shops throughout Pennsylvania and parts of New York and New Jersey during vacation periods or on off days. And every now and then the *American Machinist* would print some new form of communication from its eager young correspondent.

By March 3, 1890, my immediate future looked hopeful enough to a young girl from Sterling, Massachusetts, so that she decided to risk her own future by consenting to marry me on that date. When my wife and I celebrated our golden anniversary on March 3, 1940, it appeared incredible to me that fifty years of married life had gone by so swiftly; it seemed as if it were only yesterday that I was deciding to leave the Rue Manufacturing Company to look for a job more in keeping with the needs of a married man and prospective head of a family. Time that went by so swiftly must have been pleasantly spent.

The opportunity for a new job came in December, 1892, when the general manager of the Wheelock Engine Company of South

Worcester, Massachusetts, who had seen some of my writings in the *American Machinist*, offered me a job as a kind of efficiency engineer at $15 a week. The money was certainly not a staggering sum, but the job offered a chance to get steam engine experience and perhaps to pursue the old hobby of mine and Father's of designing unusual valve motions; for the Wheelock engine of 1892 was a fairly close copy of the Corliss make except for the type of valves across the ends of the cylinders. Moreover, although I planned in advance to stay only about a year, the job of efficiency expert (the name had not yet been coined) in such a plant as the Wheelock Engine Company presented an endless variety of possibilities, for it was certainly the most poorly organized shop I had ever laid my eyes upon.

The nearest approach to a jig or fixture in the shop was a few manila-paper templets for making flange boltholes. Perhaps for the benefit of the uninitiated a word or two about jigs, templets, and fixtures may be appropriate. A jig (and I am not speaking about the Irish variety that requires a fiddle accompaniment) is a device for holding a piece of work and for guiding drills in their proper relation in a prescribed pattern, so that the operation of the tools is the same for each piece of work being cut. Duplicate or identical parts for mass production of machines can thus be made without resetting the lathe or drill for each new piece.

A fixture is a device for holding work, which is fastened to the machine, and secures a duplication of parts, the same as a jig does for holes. The usually accepted difference is that the jig is not fastened to the worktable. A templet, on the other hand, is a pattern (usually flat, made of metal or wood) that is adapted to the purpose of laying out or checking the shape of a machine part, or of spotting boltholes on flanges, or the like, so that all parts may be the same.

The Wheelock Plant made, to be sure, but few parts in sufficient quantity to warrant the use of jigs as a mass-production device; nevertheless, if the valve-gear parts we were making were to have any value at all as replacements on Wheelock engines already in operation, they had to be interchangeable. When I assumed the job of general fixer-upper, these valve rods were still being fitted by hand in accordance with the old intuition system previously mentioned. The result was that no two valve rods were near enough alike, except in general appearance, to be called "interchangeable" even as a figure of speech.

The superintendent of the Wheelock Shop was a likable chap who knew nothing whatever of shop methods, but who made up for this shortcoming, in a way, with an extensive knowledge of those foundries which had the various patterns for the different types of frames used on Wheelock engines. This may seem a trivial sort of qualification for a superintendent, but in those days, when shop records of any kind were considered so much unnecessary paper work, it was often a valuable asset. When we wanted a pattern for an *X* frame, for example, instead of going to the nonexistent files to see whether it was the Jones Foundry or the Amalgamated Iron Works that made this particular type for us, we would ask the superintendent, who would say, "Let's see, now—type *X* is the Nonpareil Casting Company, if I'm not mistaken—fellow name of Schwartz is the man you want."

The foreman who ran the shop harked back to the good old days of the Golden Age when a machinist was a practitioner of a secret art. Consequently he resented the introduction of any new ideas, especially when proposed by callow beardless youths more interested in writing articles than in actually running a lathe. The head draftsman was fortunately a young man who saw the necessity for accurate working drawings and dimensions that had to be followed to the letter by the lathe and drill operators if any degree of accuracy in assembly was to result. Between the two of us we managed to put over a few changes, although not without serious opposition from some of the operators of the old school, who refused, among other things, to face engine beds to drawing dimensions, thus upsetting our system of precut valve rods, so that in the end the shop reverted to cutting the valve rods to fit only after the complete engine had been assembled. Such a practice would be considered somewhat irregular today.

The Wheelock job was a great experience in many ways. Besides finding out how a fairly representative section of the machine-shop world felt towards new methods, I also learned quite a bit about steam engines by visiting power plants where our product was installed and trying to determine, by means of a Tabor indicator and steam-engine card, why some of the machines we sold were not giving their guaranteed economy. The trouble in most cases was traceable to faulty cam design, which prevented the valves from cutting off the steam at the proper point in the cycle. Helping to lay out the steam piping in the Wheelock Plant also provided a good deal of experience, involving not only the preliminary work with T-square, triangle, and ruling pen, but also the physical handling of the

"A Modern Blacksmith's Shop," satirical cartoon appearing in Sterling Elliott's *Catalogue* of the eighties.

pipes, globe valves, check valves, gate valves, steam traps, headers, bends, couplings, and other paraphernalia associated with steam piping. I even learned how to coat paper for blueprints and to reproduce my layout drawings by laying the coated paper and tracing in a kind of picture frame and then placing the apparatus on the sloping roof outside the drafting-room window, where it could soak up the sunlight. In cloudy weather we got mediocre blueprints that we couldn't read, and on rainy days we got no blueprints at all.

Two events of importance to me occurred in the year 1893. The first and more exciting of the two was the birth of our first child, Charles Herbert, on March 4. Charles, I might add parenthetically, now has four grown children of his own and retired not long ago as president of the Institute of Aeronautical Sciences. The second and less personal event was the Columbian Exposition, or World's Fair, that opened in Chicago on May 1. By the summer of 1893 I had sufficiently recovered from the excitement of my son's arrival to make the trip to Chicago to see the exposition, accompanied by my father.

This extensive display of the arts and sciences covered more than 600 acres of Chicago's Jackson Park and environs, and so did Father and I. Although I was only twenty-six at the time, I remember being near the point of physical exhaustion each evening when we returned to our little hotel near the fairgrounds, but the following morning would find me out again trying to keep up with Father as we went from one exhibit to another.

Among other things, we saw the Intramural Electric Railway, built on the fairgrounds with equipment supplied by the General Electric Company; the Transportation Building, glowing with colors and gold leaf, that had been erected on a steel frame designed by Louis Sullivan; the latest model Corliss steam engines, new types of micrometer calipers and cutting tools, Edison's new dynamos, alternating-current motors, horn-and-cylinder phonographs, model telephones and switchboards, typewriters, adding machines, printing presses, and even a few primitive automobiles with real pneumatic tires.

Staying at our hotel were Fred Hill, brother of John, and his wife. Fred was representing the new magazine, *Locomotive Engineering*, at the Fair, and in the course of our tours around the various exhibits, he introduced me to Fred J. Miller, who was then associate editor of the *American Machinist*. It seemed to me that the name of Fred was a good thing to have in publishing circles. I was greatly pleased to meet the man who had been instrumental in getting many of my articles published and with whom I had been corresponding for such a long time. Fred Miller acted as a guide to the Fair during the rest of our visit and pointed out many details that I might otherwise have passed up. He in turn introduced me to Peter Bullock, a fellow correspondent on the *American Machinist*, who was writing a series of

Court of Honor, Chicago World's Fair or Columbian Exposition, 1893

"Machinery Hall," Chicago World's Fair or Columbian Exposition, 1893

View of the old Robbins and Lawrence Shop at Windsor, Vermont, about 1874

Employees of the Jones and Lamson Machine Company of Windsor, Vermont, about 1874

Early use of flexible shaft to drive portable grinding wheel, about 1880

Turret-screw machine built by Robbins and Lawrence Machine Company, Windsor, Vermont, about 1874

James H. McGraw, Sr.

John A. Hill

Fred J. Miller

Frederick A. Halsey

articles on the subject of steam engines, for the magazine at that time was as much devoted to steam power plants as it was to machine shops, and its current editor in chief, Frank Hemenway, was considered an authority on steam-engine performance.

This emphasis on steam engines in a paper calling itself the *American Machinist* was of course perfectly natural in those days, for as the reader will recall nearly every machine shop in the country depended upon the steam engine to drive its lathes, planers, boring machines, gear cutters, and practically everything else in the shop except the time clock. Knowing my interest in steam engines, Bullock tore me away from the Fair for a day to visit the E. P. Allis Company in Milwaukee, where I could examine at first hand the most recent models of Corliss engines being built under the direction of chief engineer Edwin H. Reynolds, who had been Corliss's right-hand man in Providence. At the Allis Plant, which later became the Allis-Chalmers Manufacturing Company, we saw in various stages of manufacture and assembly the renowned Corliss steam engine that was then the world's most economical prime mover, having supplanted the old slide-valve engine by virtue of its great saving in fuel consumption.

There are not many readers of the present generation who realize the importance of the Corliss engine in its day. Neither the electric motor nor the internal-combustion engine, both of which are so common today, had yet made a place for themselves. Costing considerably more to build than the old slide-valve engine, the Corliss machine nevertheless won out in competition, largely because George Corliss personally guaranteed its economy by stipulating that the customer could pay for the machine out of the money saved by reduced fuel consumption during the first six months of operation. That Corliss was an original designer is proved by the radical new construction of the pumping engine that he built, under the same guarantee, for the Hope Street pumping station in Providence. The crankshaft was vertical, with the cylinders arranged radially around it, so that it may well be called the forerunner of the modern radial engine used so extensively in the airplane industry. He also equipped a locomotive on the Boston and Providence Railroad with the Corliss valve gear, in the hope of decreasing the fuel consumption of the locomotive, but an extended series of tests proved that this type of valve gear was not rugged enough to stand up under the extreme operating conditions met with in locomotive work.

The World's Fair of 1893, with its impressive array of art, architecture, science, and industry, led many of its 27 million visitors to believe that the United States was on the threshold of a wonderful new era of prosperity and economic development. But before Grover Cleveland was fairly started in his second administration, the disastrous panic of 1893, which had begun even while the Fair was opening with the failure of the Reading Railway and the collapse of the National Cordage Company, swept over the entire country, and any era of prosperity that was in the offing was postponed for at least 4½ years. The railroads were affected more than any other industry— partly because most of them had been built on shaky financial foundations—and by the winter of '93 about 20,000 miles of railways were in the hands of receivers, with all construction at a complete standstill. I well remember the nation-wide strikes that followed, and "General" Coxey's hobo army marching on Washington in 1894, and the burning of rolling stock in Chicago by uncontrolled mobs, and Cleveland calling out the Federal troops, and the imprisonment of Eugene V. Debs for conspiracy and contempt of court. Those were great and stirring times. It is no wonder that the Wheelock Engine Company, itself a product of overcapitalization and tied up with high finance, went down like chaff before the wind, leaving me high and dry in the midst of a depression without a job.

Times, as people said, were bad; by making drastic cutbacks in our family expenditures we managed to keep afloat, aided by the money for an occasional piece for one of the trade magazines and by odd jobs of drafting, consulting, and similar work. Then one day in 1894 came a letter from a certain Alexander Luchars of New York that was the most absorbing piece of literature I had read up to that time:

Dear Mr. Colvin [he wrote, quite laconically]:

Your name has been suggested to me by Mr. Frank Hemenway of the *American Machinist* to handle some special work I have in mind a few months from now.

Will you kindly call on me the next time you are in New York?

(*Signed*) Alexander Luchars

On arriving in the big city—about June 10, 1894, I saw Mr. Luchars immediately, and after a brief but interesting interview, I was offered the editorship of a new magazine that was to be called *Machinery* and was to appear for the very first time in September of that year. I promptly accepted, rushed home to Sterling to tell my

A woodcut of the author, made about 1892.

wife the good news, and returned to New York early in August to take up my new editorial duties.

This left, of course, only a scant two weeks in which to get material together for the first number, to set up type and page forms, to obtain a number of photographs for the half tones, and to look after all the other details involved in publishing a magazine; but Luchars had done quite a bit of preparatory work himself. Nevertheless it took about twelve 15-hour days to get everything ready for Volume I, Number 1, even though this first issue contained a mere sixteen pages.

Besides the thrill of thus realizing my childhood ambition to be editor of a magazine, even though it was but a newcomer to the field and placed me in a rival camp away from my favorite, the *American Machinist*, there was the added glamor of working in New York amid the selfsame scenes and surroundings from which the heroes of my Horatio Alger days had risen to fame and fortune. The tiny office of *Machinery* was located on Pearl Street in lower Manhattan, not far from that celebrated thoroughfare known as the Bowery, famous in song and story. The building we worked in was a landmark itself, having on its upper stories an immense painted sign in which a gargantuan fisherman was seen toting on his back a monstrous codfish so that anyone a mile off could plainly see where the essential oil of Scott's Emulsion came from. The New York *World* Building was then the tallest in the city, being all of sixteen stories high if you counted the gilded cupola that had a helical cast-iron staircase, which intrepid sight-seers climbed to obtain a breath-taking view of the metropolis.

At lunch time, I would often stroll through the fabulous neighborhood bounded by the Five Points, the Bowery, Baxter Street, Mulberry Street, and Pell Street, that had been the scene of so many thrilling exploits in the paper-backed novels of my younger days, half expecting to meet with Tattered Tom or Ragged Dick or Phil the Fiddler or one of the dozens of other characters which the Unitarian minister from Massachusetts created for the edification of his young readers. Here also was the engineering marvel of the day, the great suspension span of the Brooklyn Bridge—the only bridge across the river at the time—which its designer, John Roebling, did not live to see completed. And from the vantage point of the Battery one could see the outline of the great Statue of Liberty that had been unveiled only eight years before. New York, with its million-and-a-half population, was a crowded but exciting place to work in.

In order to fill up the sixteen pages of our first number of *Machinery*, I hurriedly solicited contributions from all the correspondents I knew or had heard of. Among the first writers whose articles appeared in the new publication were Arthur Herschmann, William Booth, Arthur Bollinckx, S. Ashton Hand, Hal Norris, Walter Cheney, and Charles Billings, all of whom were then fairly well known in machine-tool circles. The names of Cheney and Hand appeared on the masthead of *Machinery* as associate editors, although "contributing" would have been the more precise adjective. They were both of considerable assistance in the early days, and Hand later joined me as associate editor of the *American Machinist* in 1918, remaining with that paper for the rest of his life.

Charlie Billings, in addition to contributing several unique articles of antiquarian interest, told me of an old machine shop in North Chelmsford, Massachusetts, which sounded so intriguing that I had to rush out to see it myself at the first opportunity. This was the remarkable Silver and Gay Plant that was founded in 1820 and now occupies a very distinguished position in the history of American machine shops. Fascinating accounts of this old shop are to be found in Professor Roe's "English and American Machine Tool Builders," and in Guy Hubbard's "Development of Machine Tools in New England," both of which make absorbing reading for those interested in the development of machines in this country during the past hundred years. On my first visit I saw the famous old planing machine that Hubbard believes was built in 1831, supposedly the very first planer built in America. Using a plate camera and time exposures, I spent nearly all day photographing the old machines, which still remained on their original foundations. A few of these photographs are here reproduced. The planer, it will be noted, has a granite bed with cast-iron ways bolted to the stone. These were apparently chipped, filed, and scraped after they had been installed—a machining operation that has entirely disappeared from the repertory of the modern machinist. The table, which has a tool lifter mounted on it, was moved by a heavy link chain located beneath it, and may have had a tool-reversing mechanism as well, enabling it to cut on the return stroke.

The old milling machine was mounted on a heavy block of square timber and had many features that appeared only much later in the evolution of this particular type of machine tool. It is said that Frederick Howe, who learned his trade in this shop and later became manager of Brown and Sharpe, worked at this very machine and used it as a prototype for later milling machines built under his personal supervision. Hubbard, who is an excellent authority on such matters, dates this milling machine about 1820, but holds to the opinion that it was not the first of its kind, crediting Eli Whitney with building a comparable machine as early as 1818. So that the reader may have

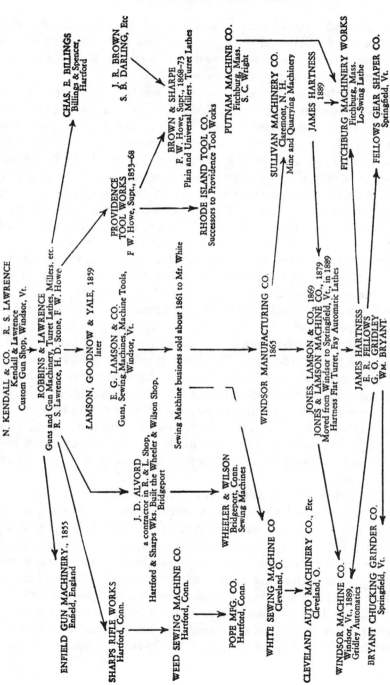

Genealogy of the Robbins & Lawrence machine tool family, showing the development of machine tools in New England. (*Guy Hubbard.*)

some notion of the way in which various genera and species of machine-tool makers branched out from their forebears, I have included what may be called a family tree of New England machine-tool shops, for which I am indebted to Guy Hubbard.

The new magazine *Machinery* somehow managed to survive the critical *post partum* period that often proves fatal to new publications, and by 1895 we seemed to be fairly well established and on the road to greater circulation. I was getting all of $30 a week, had a wife, child, and a home in East Orange, and in general was beginning to feel the increasing importance of my position. It was time, I felt, to move in larger circles. I would request membership in the American Society of Mechanical Engineers.

CHAPTER FOUR

A Society Sponsors the Machine

As flourishing societies of civil and mining engineers, master mechanics, and master car-builders exist, there is no good reason why a well-founded society of mechanical engineers will not do as well. That the time has come for the establishment of such a society is the expressed opinion of a large number of progressive engineers both East and West.
Editorial in the *American Machinist*,
February 28, 1880

The earliest printed document in the archives of the American Society of Mechanical Engineers is, of all things, a menu of a rather sumptuous dinner given at the old Astor House in New York on February 16, 1880. This repast, designed to satisfy both gourmets and gourmands, consisted of green turtle soup, boiled salmon with lobster sauce, filet of beef larded à la Financière, broiled turkey with oyster sauce, timbales à la Richelieu, chicken sauté à la Régence, mayonnaise of chicken, lobster salad, Roman punch, redhead duck, champagne jelly, charlottes russes, fruits, ice cream, coffee, and liberal servings of claret and champagne. It was the kind of dinner that made for social intercourse and conviviality, and somewhere during its six courses was born the American Society of Mechanical Engineers.

Earlier in the day on this historic February 16, 1880, a meeting of prominent engineers from eight states of the Union had taken place in the office of the *American Machinist* at 96 Fulton Street, in response to the following communication sent them by Prof. John E. Sweet of Cornell University, who had previously broached the idea to Jackson

Bailey, editor of the *Machinist*, Alexander Holley, and Prof. R. H. Thurston, of Stevens Institute of Technology:

January 18, 1880

Dear Sir,

It having been suggested by several prominent engineers that a national association of mechanical engineers would be desirable, and a meeting for the purpose of taking steps to organize such a society being in order, your presence is hereby requested at the office of the *American Machinist*, 96 Fulton Street, New York, the sixteenth day of February, 1880, at 1 o'clock sharp, at which time the necessary steps for organizing such an association will be made. Any inquiries in regard to the meeting will be cheerfully answered. Please avoid allowing this to be made public.

Very truly yours,

(*Signed*) John E. Sweet

Twenty-six mechanical engineers had accepted this discreetly worded invitation, with eighteen more represented by letter; those who put in an appearance at this first meeting were John E. Sweet, Charles T. Copeland, A. L. Holley, Charles T. Porter, W. P. Trowbridge, F. F. Hemenway, Samuel S. Webber, Henry R. Worthington, Frank C. Smith, M. N. Forney, A. B. Couch, John Fish, C. C. Newton, E. D. Leavitt, Jr., D. S. Hines, Stephen W. Baldwin, William Lee Church, Robert Grimshaw, W. H. Odell, Herman T. C. Kraus, George A. Barnard, T. R. Pickering, J. S. Coon, Egbert P. Watson, George M. Copeland, and Lewis F. Lyne.

It would be pleasant to report that everything went off smoothly at this first convocation of mechanical engineers, but such was not the case, and rarely is when a group of men get together on a matter where personalities and interests are involved. As a matter of fact, the first meeting almost ended in a general altercation, to put it mildly; and that is where the six-course dinner comes into the history of the American Society of Mechanical Engineers. Horace B. Miller, first publisher of the *American Machinist*, had wisely foreseen the possibility of a clash of personalities and the danger of protracted wrangling, and accordingly had arranged previously to invite the entire gathering to the famed Astor House for a kind of love feast so that the necessary reconciliations might be made over the timbales à la Richelieu and the flowing bowl. To what extent the claret, champagne, and redhead duck influenced the subsequent course of the American Society of Mechanical Engineers may never be fully known, but affect it they did, for the dinner ended with all the main points of contention settled to everyone's satisfaction, with much cordial shaking of hands and expressions of mutual good will between men who had considered each other rivals and potential enemies a few hours earlier in the day.

The new society accomplished a great deal at that first meeting. Besides deciding upon the name it should bear, it drew up a set of rules and bylaws setting forth the objects of the society and its proposed structure, outlined the various degrees of membership and the grades of qualifications for admissions, formulated a schedule for officers and elections, methods of voting, and a program of subsequent meetings, appointed a committee on nominations, and laid plans for the permanent organization of the society. The *American Machinist* for March 6, 1880, commenting on the results of the first meeting, spoke as follows:

In American mechanical annals, the sixteenth day of February, 1880, should be a red-letter day. Such an event as the birth of an American Society of Mechanical Engineers, under auspices so favorable, is one that does not occur every day or often.

Special notice should be given to the extent of the field that the new society may expect to cover. The address of the chairman of the preliminary organization, Alexander Holley, outlined this admirably. The mechanical appliances that are required to make all mining operations possible, not only in opening and working the mines, but in treating and utilizing the ores; the mechanism employed in building and operating railroads, bridges, aqueducts, ships, telegraphs, etc.; the vast and diverse array of mechanical appliances required by all branches of manufacture, as well as the great variety of tools and appliances employed in constructing all these, are all included in, and form part of, the field to be occupied by the new society. It should not be forgotten that the proceedings thus far have been entirely preliminary; the men who join the organization at the April meeting will be the charter members of the society.

Necessarily, the preliminary invitations to such a movement must be limited, not only by the personal acquaintance of its projectors, but by the necessity of representing the various localities. It was, by some, considered desirable that the prime movers in the organization should be, as far as possible, men who were not absolutely manufacturers. But the subsequent proceedings showed how readily trade rivalries could be overlooked or forgotten. The last drop of the curtain found one eminent engineer enthusiastically engaged in advocating the selection of his chief business rival for the presidency of the new society, upon the ground that his name would have a familiar sound in every shop in Europe, as well as every backwoods district of America.

Aside from the interchange of thought upon mechanical subjects, one great object of such a society is the better acquaintance of its members with each other. This idea was very happily expressed by one of the speakers. Alluding to a gentleman present as well-known to him through his reputation as the designer of one of the greatest pumping engines of the day, the speaker said that hitherto he had always thought of this particular engineer as having an immense walking-beam down the middle, with brass steps up the side. For the future, he should be able to mingle an accurate personal knowledge of the man with an abundant appreciation of his work.

It must have been a very wonderful dinner indeed.

The same magazine in its leading editorial for March 27 of that year adds:

The growing interest everywhere manifested in the new American Society of Mechanical Engineers is a gratifying sign of mechanical progress. The formation of the society takes place under the most favorable circumstances. Of the three grades, members, associates, and juniors, the former will include those properly entitled to write "M.E." after their names. Juniors will in time become eligible as members. Among associates will be included many prominent manufacturers and others whose business is directly dependent upon mechanical engineering, yet who have not given their attention to acquiring a knowledge of the details involved in its practice. It is worthy of note, however, that members and associates are to have equal privileges in the Society. The standard of qualifications for admission will, and should be, high.

The question of admission qualifications became a burning issue for a while, at least with Jackson Bailey, editor of the *Machinist*. It had been proposed that a candidate for membership should pass three of five qualifications involving experience as a designer of machinery, a supervisor of machinery operation, apprenticeship in an engineering business, holding an engineering degree or teaching in a school of engineering, and being either the author of a book on engineering or an inventor of a machine or process. Bailey, who was fundamentally a "practical" man, allowed himself to get quite incensed over these proposed qualifications in an editorial for April

3, 1880. Decrying the attempt to "fit the candidate for membership into narrow cast-iron molds," he went on to attack the proposals with crushing rhetoric:

> Tried by this measure, what a concourse of able engineers, who would be most desirable acquisitions to this Society, must thus be perpetually debarred from gaining admission! To our own personal knowledge, it would exclude a number of those most influential in bringing about the first meeting of the society, and who were present on that occasion, though every one of them is an experienced mechanical engineer of the first rank. . . . Now it is proposed by one of the organizing committee to modify the rules agreed upon at that meeting, so that they will, if passed, effectually crowd out some of those most instrumental in securing this important and desirable organization.
>
> A large body, probably the *greater* number of mechanical engineers of well recognized ability, would decline to apply for admission to the Society upon such terms, knowing that they can not *fill* the requirements laid down for membership. Most of them have too much professional pride to seek admission upon the ground of filling merely a *part* of the prescribed qualifications. The author of 'some book on mechanical engineering' is not very numerous, but it would often be better for the profession if there were even fewer of him. (!) Would an author be likely to give to the Society and to the public the results of his own private knowledge for free publication and distribution? . . . However this may be, no reader of the *American Machinist* needs to be told that there are engineers, contributors to the technical press, practical men in the shops, and others, who are writing their names in letters of steel upon the mechanical records of the time, the results of whose work will live when some of the book-writers and compilers are forgotten. One very serious result of requiring such a qualification for members would most likely be to cut off the practical men who are in position to reduce theories to practice.

Whether Bailey's stirring editorial was responsible or not, the "three-by-five rule" for membership qualification was not passed at the second meeting of the Society on April 7, 1880. The delicate subject of qualifications was nicely got around by simplifying the requirements but at the same time making it necessary that candidates must be proposed by at least three members or associates, to whom they must be personally known, and seconded by two others; the proposal had to be accompanied by a statement in writing of the grounds of their application for election, including an account of their professional service; on the basis of the facts there set forth the nomination was voted on by the entire society. In this way each case was judged largely on its particular merits, without reference to rigorous qualifications. The qualifications for admission as a junior, for example, were stated as follows:

To be eligible as a Junior, the candidate must have been in the practice of engineering for at least two years, or he must be a graduate of an engineering school. The term "Junior" applies to the professional experience, and not to the age of the candidate. Juniors may become eligible to Membership.

✺✺✺

It was as a junior, then, that I entered the society in December, 1895, being able to qualify for the first category of the above requirements, if not the second. In my case, however, the term "junior" applied to both age and experience, for I was still a callow youth of twenty-eight with a mere twelve years of contact with the world of machines, whereas my fellow members were for the most part learned gentlemen with a lifetime of experience behind them. Something had to be done, I thought, to put me on a more equitable footing with these savants, so I studiously applied my energies to raising a beard. This camouflage, I reasoned, would lead everyone to think I was an M.E. *summa cum laude*, and if called upon to speak, I would at least have something with which to occupy my right hand. But the device failed miserably when, after four months of earnest application, all I could produce was a kind of Vandyke instead of the full beard for which I had hoped.

In the preceding chapter I mentioned the names of Walter Cheney and S. Ashton Hand appearing on the masthead of the first number of *Machinery*. These worthy gentlemen, both of whom have passed on, were also my sponsors when I applied for membership in the American Society of Mechanical Engineers. I had first met Cheney about four years earlier through the medium of a short dissertation on end-cutting tools that had appeared over my name in one of the local Philadelphia gazettes. Cheney was at that time in business as a partner in the Meriden Machine Tool Company where he had designed a straight end-cutting and forming lathe for brass-work, with an underfeed principle that was then quite revolutionary, and is only now coming back into use. Whether it was to take exception to the article or to express interest in it, I forget which—I remember only that Walter called upon me the next day and we became fast friends from that time until his death. My other sponsor, S. Ashton Hand, had the more varied career of the two, having been

Sharpening a file by the sand-blast method, from the *American Machinist*, October 18, 1879.

in turn a sailor, a machinist, a draftsman, a photographer, a lathe builder, a plant superintendent, and a designer of printing presses before becoming associate editor of the *American Machinist* in 1917.

In the offices of that paper, Hand was known as "the Admiral," because the story had got out that one day during his gallant career of sailing before the mast, he had been standing on the forecastle deck keeping a sharp lookout for whales, or a landfall, and enjoying the beauty of the sea, when a high wave came and washed him overboard, causing him to spend the night alone on the broad deep with only a life preserver for companion, until he was picked up the following morning by the dinghy.

What the society lacked in numbers during the early years was more than made up for by the increased degree of intimacy and social contact that characterized every meeting. There was about them the air of the small-town college alumni gathering and the old-home-week reunion, in spite of the fact that a good deal of important business was transacted and many significant technical papers were read and discussed. As a new member eagerly looking forward to each monthly meeting of this fine group of men, I thought that no society could ever have a more genial secretary than Prof. Frederick Hutton, who never forgot a name or a face and who made all newcomers feel that they were already honorary members.

Through these A.S.M.E. meetings I made many interesting and valuable acquaintances, and although these men were for the most part much older and more experienced than myself, they went out of their way more than once to help the neophytes. Among them were Ambrose Swasey and Worcester R. Warner, who, starting as apprentices in Hartford about 1870, formed a partnership twenty-four years later that has become the great Warner and Swasey firm of today. There was also Prof. John E. Sweet of Cornell, mentioned earlier in this chapter as one of the original instigators of the society, who was a mentor for all young mechanics and budding engineers, as well as a designer with a very practical turn of mind, and who wrote many clear, sound articles on steam engines for the *American Machinist* of that period.

And there was "Uncle John" Brashear, an amateur astronomer of considerable note and one of the best lensmakers of his day, who had been decorated by many foreign governments for his work in both fields and who became the society's president in 1915. He often held us spellbound with his illuminating and almost poetic discourses on the sun, the moon, the planets, asteroids, comets, novae, double stars, the transits of Venus, the canals of Mars, the rings of Saturn, the orbit of Mercury, and on globular star clusters, spiral nebulae, galaxies and supergalaxies, until our imaginations knew no bounds and we had been transported beyond the limits of outer space.

One day in his observatory at Allegheny, Pennsylvania, when

the city lay under a heavy pall of smoke and fog that made celestial observations impossible, Uncle John entertained me for several hours by showing me how telescope lenses were made. He was working on a 12-inch objective lens for a refracting telescope at the time, and had nearly finished the tedious and painstaking work of grinding its surface to the correct mathematical curvature required for a distortion-free image.

"This sort of work is quite different from the type of grinding you machinists are familiar with in the machine shop," Uncle John told me. "Now and then you may have trouble with a fit when you have very close tolerances or if one part gets a little hotter than the other when you are assembling them. But let me show you how just the tiniest amount of heat—so small that you can hardly measure it—can almost ruin a lens, if you aren't careful." He placed the lens he had been working on in a specially prepared frame, and, at the required distance, its matching eyepiece, through which he directed me to look. I saw a clear image of a clump of trees that rose above the fog some distance away.

"I am now going to place just the tip of my little finger on the edge of the big lens," he said. "See what it does to the image."

As I looked, the image of the trees blurred, wavered, and danced before my eye, seeming to expand suddenly in one direction and contract in another. The trees appeared to be waving in the breeze. Then Uncle John took his finger from the lens and the breeze subsided.

"The heat from my finger expanded the surface of the lens where it was in contact," explained Brashear, "causing the rest of the surface to shrink, and of course throwing the whole lens out of focus. If that happened during the grinding operation, the grinding wheel would take off too much of the surface in one place and not enough in another, with the result that the lens would be ruined and would have to be remelted. So you can easily see how important temperature control is for lens grinding." I said I would certainly keep the point in mind.

The first headquarters of the society were, as we have pointed out, at 96 Fulton Street in New York City, for the society in its early days was considered by many as an offshoot of the *American Machinist* whose offices it shared; and the magazine's treasurer,

Lycurgus B. Moore, doubled as acting secretary of the new organization. But limitations of space together with the rapid growth of the society soon made new and larger headquarters necessary. With the appointment of Thomas W. Rae as first regular secretary at the meeting the A.S.M.E. moved to 239 Broadway, the offices of Henry R. Worthington, whose associate Rae was. Later, in 1890, the society again moved to the old Academy of Medicine Building on West Thirty-first Street, and in 1906 the gift of $1,500,000 from a retired Scottish manufacturer who had been successful in the steel business made possible the move to its present address, 29 West 39th Street, New York City, a fifteen-story building erected with Carnegie's bequest to house the four national engineering organizations—the American Society of Civil Engineers (1852), the American Institute of Mining and Metallurgical Engineers (1871), the American Society of Mechanical Engineers (1880), and the American Institute of Electrical Engineers (1884), together with the Engineers' Club and the Engineering Library. From 1883 up until the time of this last removal Professor Hutton had served continuously as part-time secretary, and in 1907 he was elected president of the society, at which time Calvin W. Rice was appointed full-time secretary and the membership had grown to 2,915.

On the occasion of the fiftieth anniversary of the A.S.M.E. in 1930, Mr. Rice wrote as follows in the society's publication, *Mechanical Engineering:*

The obligation of a national engineering organization today is twofold: it should operate for the benefit of its members, and it should be a channel whereby some portion of the professional activities of its members is constantly flowing out into the larger life of the age.

To understand the fifty-year development of the American Society of Mechanical Engineers toward the fulfillment of this twofold obligation, it is necessary to recall the status of mechanical engineering in 1880, the year of the Society's birth, and to realize the impossibility of meeting the second obligation adequately until, through years of existence mainly for the benefit of its members, it had helped to create a professional consciousness thereby to establish the profession (in its own estimation, at least) on a level with other professions of like worth and dignity.

Two groups of engineers had been organized previous to 1880, but in neither of these groups, the civil-engineering nor the mining-engineering, were the meetings or *Transactions* a suitable place for the power-plant, factory, or machine-shop man. True, the World's Centennial Exposition had roused such an interest in machines that in 1877 the *American Machinist* had been established, and the machine-minded man for the first time had a clearing-house for his ideas and a spot where he might find mental contact with men who were meeting problems like his. But he had no effective agency for bringing him into personal contact with other members of his profession, and no great stimulus to urge him to put the results of his work into written form for the dissemination of knowledge, the interchange of ideas, and the invaluable discussion which arises from such an interchange.

And that, I might add, is exactly what the American Society of Mechanical Engineers gave to the machine-minded man, over and above what such magazines as the *American Machinist* and *Machinery* gave him in another direction.

The annual meetings of the A.S.M.E., extending over a period of three or four days and held in New York City, afforded marvelous opportunities for getting acquainted with the most widely known men in the machine-tool industry and in related fields, although as the society's membership expanded and the number of specialized subgroups or committees dealing with separate subjects increased, one found one's contacts limited to a smaller and smaller proportion of the total membership. Serving on these committees, of course, brought one into even closer contact with the leading men in the various fields, but unless one was permitted to serve on more than a single committee, the interchange of ideas and dissemination of knowledge that was the aim of the society might be somewhat lacking in broadness and scope. Among the committees I was privileged to serve on were the first Screw Thread Committee, the Standard Tapers Committee, the Twist Drill Committee, the Committee for Small Tool Standardization, and the Committees on milling cutters and on tolerances and nomenclature. This work, extending over a period of many years, brought close contact with some of America's best engineers and was a valuable source of information on a great variety of subjects. Among the men I was happy to meet in this way were Prof. D. S. Jacobus, Dr. Durand, Prof. O. W. Boston, Frank O. Wells, Luther Burlingame, Herbert B. Lewis, Frank C. Spencer, and A. H. Carpenter.

It was through A. H. Carpenter that I first heard about one of the most interesting women I have ever known. I hasten to add that she was interesting to me purely in a business, or shall we say, a mechanical relationship, as will be presently brought out. This woman, a kind of Madame Curie of machine tools, was the renowned Kate Gleason, daughter of William Gleason, the founder of the Gleason Works of Rochester, New York, and at that time the only woman in the world connected with the machinery industry in a major sense.

Kate, whom I first met at an A.S.M.E. convention at Niagara Falls at the turn of the century, was an attractive young lady who had broken several of the Victorian concepts about woman's place being in the home, and having inherited a flair for the mechanical from her father, determined to follow her natural bent by pursuing a career that had hitherto been considered the exclusive bailiwick of men with long beards. Instead of sitting at home tatting or making samplers, Kate spent her youth learning her father's business from the ground up, both in the shop and in the field, so that when she branched out for herself about 1895 as a saleswoman for her father's gear-cutting machines, she knew as much as any man in the business.

Carpenter told me the story of how Kate came one day to the Acme Machinery Company, of which he was the manager, intent on selling them a batch of Gleason gear cutters. Carpenter was certain that this slim young girl knew little or nothing about the product she was selling and determined to prove this at least to his own satisfaction by calling in Thompson, his gear expert, to test her knowledge. The conversation, as Carpenter remembered it, went something like this:

"Well, young woman," Thompson began, "tell us what you can about your father's gear-cutting machines, in a general way at least, and why you think they are better than the ones we are using at the present time—although I should perhaps warn you in advance that I am considered something of an expert, you know, on gears and gear-cutting machinery."

"I am very glad to hear that, sir," said Kate demurely, "for it will make what I have to say that much easier."

"Let us get on, then," replied Thompson. "What are the special features, if any, about the Gleason gear cutter?"

"Our machines, as you undoubtedly are aware, sir, are intended for making bevel gears only, although like all other gear-cutting machines, they are merely specially designed milling or shaping machines, which, when used with a rotary cutter such as in our bevel-gear planer, fall into the milling-machine class—a feature that gives them greater speed of operation and a greater degree of accuracy than previously possible. As you know, the accuracy of the teeth depends upon the proper shaping of the teeth of the cutting tool, and the spacing on the accuracy of the indexing mechanism used, regardless of whether the gear teeth are being cut by a tool that follows a path established by a template, or by a cutter shaped to the space between the teeth, or by the relative motion of the cutter and gear. Now, on our spiral bevel gears . . . "

"Your what?" interrupted Thompson, somewhat bewildered by Kate's rapid-fire delivery.

"Spiral bevel. You're familiar with them, I'm sure?"

"Er . . . oh, certainly, Miss Gleason—I've seen them around. I mean I've heard of them—in fact we've got quite a few spiral gears here at Acme. They sort of run together at an angle, don't they?"

"Ah, but those are not really spiral gears, you see. They are really spur gears with helical teeth, whereas true spiral bevel gears have spiral or curved teeth that are cut with a trepanning machine. And these machines are made only by the Gleason Works. You see the difference, I presume."

"Sure—I was just thinking of the other type—I mean when you said spiral, well, a spiral is a spiral, you know."

"Not necessarily," said Kate, with a sweet smile, "but let us go back to the theory of gears. If it were possible to have a modification of the spiral bevel in which the pinion is located below or above the center of the mating gears, what kind of gear action would you expect from that sort of arrangement?"

"Why, er . . . what kind of gear action, you say? Well, now, let's see . . . the pinion is where, did you say?"

"The action of spiral bevel gears under this arrangement," continued Kate, ignoring Thompson's embarrassment, and sketching with her gloved finger tip a few mystifying circles in the air, "should more nearly approach that of a worm drive, the location of the pinion permitting its shaft to extend beyond the gear for support or other reasons. Such a gear arrangement exists in theory only of course, though a few designers are said to be working on the problem at the present time."

"Are they? That is to say, they are, aren't they?" Thompson fumbled, beginning to wish Miss Gleason were back in Rochester.

"Yes. But I really wanted to talk about our gear-cutting machines. Now first let us consider a pair of miter gears, where the angle of intersection is 45 degrees. If we . . . "

"Excuse me, Miss Gleason," interrupted Thompson, mopping his brow with his handkerchief, "but if you don't mind I would like to continue this interesting discussion at another time. I believe I have a slight touch of migraine coming on." And he left the office hurriedly without having given Kate an opportunity for placing an order for Gleason gear cutters.

It should be added that, besides Kate, there were also her brothers James and Andrew, who, along with their famous sister, took over the management of their father's business when he retired. James Gleason, or Jim, as I have come to know him, is head of the Gleason Works at this writing, and is about the same age as myself, which is very close to fourscore. About 1922, Jim, with the assistance of two of his engineers, F. E. McMullen and T. M. Durkan, developed the Gleason Straight Bevel Gear System, which provides a basis for designing straight bevel gears with the most desirable tooth forms for practical operating conditions, and the machines for making these and the spiral bevel and hypoid gears, which only the Gleason Works manufactures, are veritable masterpieces of design. I cannot leave Kate without adding that after her retirement from the firm, she found inactivity so uncongenial that she branched out into real estate, both in her home town of Rochester and also in several cities in the South, and before her death in 1933 she had become owner of several large hotels and other properties.

If I seem to dwell more on the personalities of the members of the A.S.M.E. rather than upon the society's accomplishments in the field of mechanical engineering, it is partly because the latter are recorded in much better form in the *Transactions* of that body, and partly because my memories of the individuals have a habit of crowding out the technical details whenever I take a backward glance. For instance, when I try to think of the early meetings of the A.S.M.E., the dashing figure of Oberlin Smith rises before my mind, and I see him, not as he delivered a profound paper on the subject of drawing presses, but as he tripped the light fantastic with a fair partner at one of the early A.S.M.E. dances. For Oberlin Smith loved to dance almost as much as he loved to tinker with machinery, and although when I first met him at the A.S.M.E. gatherings he was in his late seventies, he was more than a match for the youngest of us when it came to the two-step, the fox-trot, the maxixe, the tarantella, the waltz, the turkey trot, the shuffle, the strathspey, the schottische, the cakewalk, the breakdown, and similar feats of choreography current in the gay nineties.

My first contact with Oberlin Smith was through the same medium that had introduced me to Walter Cheney and to a number of other men of importance in the machine world. I had written an article that had appeared in the *American Machinist* while I was yet in my early twenties, in which I had made several trenchant remarks about the then current system of wire gauges, pointing out that the only sensible or logical gauge was that used in the electrical industry, where the numbers assigned to the different sizes of wires were based upon their actual diameters in thousandths of an inch, whereas all other gauge systems were merely artificial or arbitrary arrangements. The article caught Oberlin's eye and he sent me a very flattering letter of commendation, raising my ego to new heights and encouraging me to delve further into the general subject of standardization of measurements. Being an official of the Ferracute Machine Company of East Bridgeton, New Jersey, he cordially invited me to visit his plant, and gave me more than one personally conducted tour of the several shops, answering my endless questions with patience as well as clarity.

This genial and talented gentleman, who, I suspect, was named after the Alsatian pastor and philanthropist Jean Frédéric Oberlin, after whom Oberlin College was also named, had been president of the American Society of Mechanical Engineers five years prior to my joining it—that is to say, in 1890. The punch and coining presses made by the Ferracute Machine Company, after his designs, were very well known at the time, not only for their efficiency but also for their unusual size, as well as for the uses they were put to. On one occasion he invited me to his plant to see a new type of drawing press in operation, which he said was designed for making a highly essential product that every member of civilized society would sooner or later have to buy. Interested at once, I asked him what this highly essential product was. "Come down to the plant, Fred," he replied, "and see for yourself."

When I arrived, Oberlin pointed with pride to what was then the largest drawing press I had ever seen. "Isn't it a beauty?" he beamed, while I stared at the huge machine.

"It certainly is big enough," I replied. "What is this indispensable article of consumer goods you intend to turn out with it?"

"Coffins. One-piece steel coffins. Can you imagine the possibilities? Seamless-steel, corrosion-proof caskets, guaranteed to last a hundred years even in the worst type of subsoil. Can you imagine anybody wanting to be buried in an old-fashioned wooden casket once these things are on the market?"

I said I couldn't imagine.

It turned out later that the company which had expected to manufacture these durable sarcophagi had considerable difficulty in disposing of them to prospective purchasers, who may not have relished being thus encumbered on resurrection day, and went on favoring the old-fashioned method of interment. In any event, a considerable number of these steel caskets accumulated in their warehouse, and no one had any idea what to do with them, until it was discovered during the First World War that these caskets were ideal for storing and shipping loaded shells and other types of ammunition. Thus, with fitting irony, the caskets were eventually put to a specialized use in the field for which they had been originally designed.

Oberlin Smith was a man of many parts, for besides being the author of a standard text entitled "The Press Working of Metals," he was also an inventor of considerable talent and possessed keen foresight as to the possibilities of future mechanical developments. As early as 1891, in a lecture given before the Franklin Institute in

Philadelphia, he predicted the tremendous expansion of the automobile industry that was to take place forty years later, the widespread use of electricity for light and power, and prophesied many of the inventions and technological developments of our present era, such as electric refrigeration, air conditioning, long-distance telephony, and even network radio. For those who may not realize that these things were practically unthinkable in the 'nineties, I should like to point out that Oberlin turned out to be an exceptionally accurate prophet.

Oberlin Smith's flair for laborsaving gadgets together with his sound practical knowledge of what the machines of his day could be made to do was demonstrated to me quite dramatically one day, on one of my first visits to his home. He was driving me thither in one of the latest model horseless carriages of the day, and as we turned in to the driveway he stopped, reached out, and pressed a button in a corner post of the porch. I thought at first he was ringing a doorbell to announce our arrival, but instead I was surprised to see the garage doors opening by themselves as Oberlin serenely restarted the buggy and drove it into its stall. I am sure that if he had only the faintest glimmering of our modern science of electronics he would have rigged up a photoelectric eye to take the place of the button starter.

Quite recently I was informed by my late friend, P. Kennedy Reeves, who worked with Oberlin Smith in the Ferracute Shops for many years, that this practical gadgeteer had almost anticipated Edison's famous "talking machine." In 1878, the year after Edison patented the device now known as the phonograph, Oberlin had also built a talking machine, designed on a slightly different principle than that of the Wizard of Menlo Park, and apparently without prior knowledge of the earlier invention. Oberlin made no attempt to commercialize his recording machine, but was persuaded to describe it in a letter to Edison, which elicited a very commendatory reply from the latter, though leading to no further developments. It is true, of course, that Edison in 1877 thought of his talking machine as "no more than a toy," and it is highly probable that Oberlin regarded his own instrument likewise, for surely not even he could predict the rise of a Bing Crosby or a Frank Sinatra and phonograph-record sales of 2 million copies for a three-minute popular ballad.

Nevertheless, Oberlin Smith had in his living room in 1890 an instrument that might well be called the world's first juke box—an early Regina music box operated by sheet-metal disks or "records" with raised punchings on their surface, to which was added an automatic record-changing device, which most of us think is a very recent innovation. All that was lacking was the coin-in-the-slot mechanism and fluorescent side lights. But when it came to music, Oberlin preferred the "live" variety provided by the fiddlers and the cornetists at the dances given by the American Society of Mechanical Engineers.

Not long after becoming a junior member in the American Society of Mechanical Engineers, I was privileged to make the acquaintance of a man whom I consider to have been perhaps the most outstanding machine-tool builder of his day and certainly one of the most important designers in the entire history of machine-tool development—James Hartness, whose famous flat-turret lathe had already become a standard item of machine-shop equipment when I first met him in 1895. Although an excellent biography of Hartness by Prof. Joseph W. Roe was published shortly after his death in 1934 by the A.S.M.E., I am strongly convinced that far too few people know all they should about his significant accomplishments; I am accordingly attempting to remedy this situation in the remaining pages of this chapter.

Hartness put his first flat-turret lathe on the market while I was still an apprentice in the Rue Manufacturing Company. One of its revolutionary features was the method by which this lathe turned long rods; but before going into this, perhaps the reader should be reminded that the turret on a turret lathe is usually a round or six-sided block that rotates about its axis and has a hole in the middle of each side into which tools are inserted, which can then be brought successively into contact with the material being worked upon. The Hartness turret was practically a horizontal faceplate on which tools of a new design were bolted according to the needs of the particular work, and none of the tools overhung the base support, which was firmly clamped at the outer edge. In the turning operation referred to, Hartness started the cut (that is, began removing the surface of the rod) at the chuck, set a follow rest against the work, and fed toward the tailstock.

In order to avoid having a reverse on the carriage feed, the lathe was run backward when cutting from the headstock toward the tail, so that reversing the spindle caused the carriage to feed in the usual way. The carriage bearing on the bed was steel to cast iron, whereas that of all other lathes of the day was cast iron to cast iron. Old blueprints of the Hartness flat-turret lathe show steel shoes, one of them adjustable, in the lathe carriage, although these were later abandoned. All these features, together with the absence of overhang of the tools and the minimum overhang of the automatic chuck had beneficial and lasting effect on the design of all types of later machine tools.

Few persons familiar with the development of machinery realize that Hartness was probably the first person in this country to apply hydraulic feed to machine tools. In U.S. Patent No. 672,398, dated April 10, 1901, Hartness was allowed 113 claims, and a little over two years later (September 20, 1903) United States Patent No. 739,866 granted him 119 claims. The first of these patents is designated simply as "lathe," while the second refers to a "turret lathe." It is quite possible, of course, that Hartness became interested in the feasibility of hydraulic-feeding mechanisms as a result of his visit to the Paris Exposition of 1900, where a German machine builder named Pitler, whose products are now fairly well known in this country, exhibited a machine tool with a hydraulic feed. Pitler's device was, however, only very rudimentary and could have contributed only the germ of an idea on the subject to Hartness.

The patent claims for the hydraulic mechanism designed by Hartness provided for making the lathe either manually controlled, semiautomatic, or fully automatic, and combined the use of both air and liquid to secure the type of control desired. They also recognized the objections to air pockets and provided means for eliminating them. Furthermore, they included the use of a part of the air intended for control movements to be directed against the work or the tools for cooling purposes, which was a highly important feature in the days when tools could not be run at temperatures as high as our modern science of metallurgy now permits and still preserve their cutting edge against metal. Both patents include a total of 238 figures, which should give some idea of how thoroughly Hartness studied the problem. And yet, for some reason that may never be fully known, this great designer suddenly dropped the idea of hydraulic feeding for machine tools before it had become widely known or adopted in practice. It may be that he had run into some of the snags that later troubled Heald and other early designers in this field, or he may have felt that others would take up where he left off, and that there were other and possibly more interesting problems of design for him to work on.

One of the Hartness principles in the early days was that no shop should build more than one kind or size of a machine; he even ventured the opinion that the time was coming when pulley manufacturers would be building only one size of pulleys. This was standardization with a vengeance, surely. It was this fixed idea that for many years limited his production to the 2 by 24 flat-turret lathe, somewhat as Henry Ford limited himself to the Model T flivver, and it was only after much persuasion from friends and business associates that the Jones and Lamson Plant brought out, in due time, the 3- by 36-inch machine. Hartness was fundamentally correct, of course, in his assumption that a lathe manufacturer should concentrate his efforts on the type of machine that promised the greatest volume of production instead of trying to produce a large number of odd or special sizes which would have only limited use.

Membership in the Screw Threads Committee of the A.S.M.E. in all probability was the stimulus that led Hartness to develop the comparator, a device of his invention for checking the accuracy of screw threads, gear teeth, and similar machine parts. This and many inventions were perfected in his famous "underground laboratory," a small apartment which he had built below ground at some distance from his house, with subterranean passageways leading to the small astronomical observatory that he maintained as a hobby as well as to the house itself, so that he could work without fear of being disturbed either by extraneous noises, inclement weather, or inquisitive neighbors. I pass on his idea for whatever it may be worth to those who would escape, for a time at least, from the blare of the radio, the roar of traffic, and, as Hardy puts it, from the madding crowd.

A near-fatal accident in an early-vintage automobile he was driving proved such a shock to Hartness's nervous system that for a long time he was unable even to ride in one of these vehicles, let alone drive it. He remained highly sensitive about this acquired fear and desired most earnestly to overcome it. One day in 1916—Hartness was about fifty-six at the time—I met him in the lobby of the Kimball Hotel in Springfield, Massachusetts, and with ill-suppressed excitement he told me he had something very important to show me up in his room—something that had conquered his fear of automobiles and would permit him to drive again.

On the way up to the room I silently wondered what this something could be—surely it wasn't a case of Scotch, for James was not a drinking man; nor could it be a good-luck charm or a St. Christopher medal, for he was not that way inclined. Was it a radically new, foolproof, safety device of some kind, newly invented by himself to forestall automobile accidents? Or a hydraulic bumper, maybe, that cushioned the shock of head-on collisions?

Once in the room, Hartness dashed to his escritoire and pulled out what appeared to be a scroll or document of some kind. He brought it over to me and unrolled it with great display. I read:

> This is to certify that James Hartness has successfully completed the course of instruction prescribed by the State of New York Board of Aeronautics and is duly qualified as a licensed aviator. . . . Given at the training grounds of the Curtiss Aeroplane Company, Hammondsport, New York.

"I took her up alone for the first time this morning—'soloed,' they call it," he said eagerly. "Flying's a great sport and the easiest thing in the world once you get the hang of it. But the important thing is, now I'm not afraid to drive an automobile any more! Now I can buy that big Stevens-Duryea I've had my heart set on, and I can join the ranks of automobile drivers again!"

He always retained his interest in flying, and years later when he was elected governor of the state of Vermont (a quite unexpected demonstration of his amazing versatility), Hartness accomplished much toward the development of aviation in that state.

Hartness was an able president of the American Society of Mechanical Engineers in 1914, and his leadership of that body was an inspiration to everyone who knew him. He was one of its most broad-minded and farseeing members from the early 'nineties up to his death in 1934.

CHAPTER FIVE

High-wheelers and High Iron

*The time will come when people will travel in
stages moved by steam engines, from one city to
another, almost as fast as birds fly, fifteen or
twenty miles an hour.*
OLIVER EVANS,
"Patent Right Oppression Exposed," 1807

Fierce-throated beauty!
Roll through my chant with all thy lawless music,
thy swinging lamps at night,
Thy mad-whistled laughter, echoing, rumbling
like an earthquake, rousing all.
WALT WHITMAN,
"To a Locomotive in Winter," 1876

As to the precedence of the chicken over the egg, or vice versa,
I have no desire to speculate; I would merely point out that the same
question may be mooted, somewhat more profitably, with regard
to machine tools and transportation. The bicycle, the locomotive, the
automobile, and the airplane owe their development to machine
tools; but it is no less true that machine tools owe their development
to the bicycle, the locomotive, the automobile, and the airplane.
We are aware, of course, that the lathe and the drill press were in
existence long before these modern vehicles, and that even if we go
back to the primeval ancestor of transportation, the wheel, we must,
with due regard for logic, assume the prior existence of the tools
that made it. But there are certain modern types and designs of
machine tools, presently to be described, that would never have come
into existence without the stimulation of the transportation industry
and the mass production of the vehicles previously mentioned. A
good example to start with is the bicycle.

The modern bicycle was born only twelve months before the advent of Volume I, Number 1, of the magazine *Machinery*, which is to say, only one year before the present point in the chronological sequence of our story. While Alexander Luchars was casting about for an editor for his new paper, the "safety" bicycle of 1893, combined with the pneumatic rubber tire invented by the Belfast Irishman John Boyd Dunlop, was opening up a new era in the history of transportation, and the bicycle industry had embarked on a great period of development and prosperity both in this country and in England. This was the climax to a long career of improvement in design from the primitive "hobbyhorse" of 1816, which consisted of two wheels and a crossbar upon which the rider sat while he propelled himself with his feet against the ground—the brainchild of the pioneer French photographer, Niepce. The "boneshaker" velocipede of 1865 with its heavy wooden wheels, thick iron tires, and massive iron backbone gave way in 1874 to the high-wheeled "ordinary," equipped with ball bearings, and having light metal wheels supported by thin wire spokes. The reader will remember from Chapter Two how the high-wheeler vied with the horse car and the hansom cab as a means of locomotion. And in 1877 the bicycle-making industry in the United States was started when Col. Albert A. Pope of Boston, Massachusetts, organized the Pope Manufacturing Company, which turned out the "ordinary" in increasing numbers and the pneumatic-tired safety, which, except for changes in design, is closely similar to the modern bicycle of 1947. The great boom in bicycle manufacture that began when I was seeking a few sponsors for my application for junior membership in the A.S.M.E. resulted in bicycling becoming very fashionable among the wealthy classes, with rising prices and the development of a multiplicity of bicycle manufacturing firms; it was followed by the inevitable slump, heightened by the growing interest in automobiles, and it is only within comparatively recent years that the bicycle industry is once more coming into its own.

Next to the making of firearms and sewing machines, the advent of the bicycle gave the first real impetus to the designing and building of machine tools for mass production. These included principally the automatic screw machines and the turret lathe, although drilling machines were also used to an increasing extent. In the manufacture of the high-wheeler ordinary, with its front wheel 46 to 60 inches in diameter and its rear wheel from 14 to 20 inches, the principal machining problems were the bearings, the hubs, the axles, the crank mechanism, and the neck or steering head.

The front hubs on the ordinary were much larger than those of the modern bicycle, because they had a great deal more metal to support, and had heavy flanges with holes drilled and tapped in them for the nipples by which the spokes were held and adjusted for correct tension. These "direct" spokes were in turn flanged at the hub end and headed or peened over at the rim end; laced and tangent spokes, with tension-adjusting nipples at the rim, were developed considerably later. The axles went through the front hubs and had the cranks keyed or pinned to them. The hubs of the ordinary, and the head and crank hanger of the safety, required specialized machinery for their manufacture; one of the first machines of this type that I recall was the turret lathe of Bardons and Oliver, made especially for this type of work, which helped to introduce the use of broad-faced forming tools in machining wheel hubs in one continuous operation. The head and crank hangers of the safety were forgings that had to be machined to sheet-metal thinness—which meant cutting away about 80 per cent of the original metal! The cross slides of these turret lathes carried form tools to give the desired contour to the hubs, so that the spokes could be properly fastened; they also bored and formed the head at the upper end of the backbone so that the front wheel could be easily steered.

It was the bicycle also that stimulated the first attempts at commercial welding. At the Hartford Plant of the Pope Manufacturing Company an attempt was made as early as 1890 to weld the frame tubes of the bicycle into the heads and crank hangers, instead of brazing them as had been the accepted practice before that time. For some indeterminate reason, however—I suspect it was simply lack of experience—the welds proved to have the tensile strength of a good grade of chinaware, and the Pope Company, saddened but wiser, reverted to the old-fashioned method of brazing. The setback was only temporary, for hard on its heels came the great advances in sheet-metal work that permitted the heads and crank hangers to be blanked and formed from metal sheets, for which brazing was ideal as a method of joining; later, the tubing was made of sheets formed into a tube and welded continuously by passing the formed tube between rolling contacts, a technique that is still used by some of the leading manufacturers in the field.

Children of today get their first idea of what ball bearings are when Daddy presents them with their first pair of roller skates, and while they may not realize that rolling friction is less than sliding friction, they find that the ball bearings add considerably to their speed of locomotion. In my youth, ball bearings were a rarity, and it was not until I was in my twenties that I saw my first ball bearing— on an English high-wheeler that sold under the trade name of The British Challenger. The Columbia I got about on in the Rue Manufacturing days had a 48-inch front wheel equipped with "plain" or friction bearings, which had an interesting habit of freezing at the most unexpected times and added considerably to the thrills of cycling as an outdoor sport. I have seen and studied quite a lot of bearings in my time, as one might reasonably expect, but whenever I think of the subject I recall two painful and humiliating experiences between plain bearings and Fred Colvin, in which the former completely triumphed over the latter.

The first of these occurred during a contest of speed which I entered in a spirit of friendly rivalry with several contemporary young scorchers on a stretch of the Lancaster Pike near Ardmore, Pennsylvania, with a good proportion of the townfolk, including several members of the fair sex, lining the course on either side of the road. Although I had been a slow starter, and the Columbia was a trifle skittish that day, I was nevertheless considered a favorite among the money boys and a sure thing on a fast track. At the halfway mark the field spread out and I worked up into the lead, coaxing the Columbia gently as I pulled ahead a length, a length and a half, two lengths, two and a half—I was on the home stretch with the crowd cheering and the finish line only 50 feet ahead. And then it happened. The bearings on the front wheel suddenly seized the axle in a viselike grip. I took off over the handle bars in a kind of a jackknife dive, but with a twist like a half gainer. Landing on my back in the middle of the road, I was promptly run over by my own bicycle, which was thereupon disqualified as a riderless mount. The race was won by a rank outsider.

The second incident took place in my romantic phase when I was

Old type of turret lathe made by Pratt and Whitney, about 1870

J. B. Thomas and his giant micrometer caliper

Frank F. Hemenway

W. & H. Mitchell, Printers, Newcastle

This Indenture

made the *Seventeeth* Day of *April* in the
Year One Thousand Eight Hundred and Thirty *seven* between *Ralph Little Whyte* Son of
Alexander Whyte of Bithaum in the County of Northumberland and the said *Alexander Whyte*
of the one Part, and ROBERT STEPHENSON, of Newcastle upon Tyne, Engine Builder, of the other Part,
WITNESSETH, that the said *Ralph Little Whyte* of his own voluntary Accord, and by and with the Consent of
the said *Alexander Whyte* his Father, testified by the said *Alexander Whyte*
being a Party to and executing these Presents, doth put and bind himself Apprentice to and with the said ROBERT STEPHENSON, to learn the
Art, Trade, or Business of a *Draftsman* so far as the same relates to the said
Trade or Business of an Engine Builder, and to serve the said ROBERT STEPHENSON, and his present and future Partners, in the said Trade
or Business of an Engine Builder, and the Survivors and Survivor of them, and their and his Partners, from the Day of the Date hereof,
until the full End and Term of *Six* Years from thence next ensuing, and fully to be completed and ended; and the said
Ralph Little Whyte and *Alexander Whyte* do hereby, for
themselves jointly, their Heirs, Executors, and Administrators, and each of them, doth for himself severally, his Heirs, Executors, and
Administrators, covenant with the said ROBERT STEPHENSON, his Executors and Administrators, in Manner following, that is to say, that
during the Whole of the said Term the said *Ralph Little Whyte* shall and will faithfully serve
the said ROBERT STEPHENSON, and his present and future Partners, in the said Trade or Business of an Engine Builder, and the Survivors
and Survivor of them, and their and his Partners, as an Apprentice in the said Art, Trade, or Business of a *Draftsman*
so far as the same relates to the said Trade or Business of an Engine Builder; and shall and
will be true, just, and faithful to them and every of them, and the Agent and Agents of them and every of them; and their Secrets keep, and
their lawful Commands every where and in every Thing obey; and shall do no Damage to them or any of them, nor see it done by others, but
to the best of his Power prevent or forthwith give Notice of the same; and he, the said Apprentice, shall not embezzle, or waste, or lend the
Goods of his said Masters or any of them unlawfully to any; and Hurt to his said Masters or any of them he shall not do, or cause or procure
to be done; and he shall neither buy nor sell without his Master's Leave; at Cards, Dice, or other unlawful Games, he shall not play;
Taverns, Inns, or Alehouses he shall not haunt or frequent, unless it be about his Master's Business; nor from the Service of his said Masters
Day or Night shall absent himself; but in all Things, as an honest and faithful Apprentice, shall and will demean and behave himself towards
his said Masters and every of them, as well in Words as in Deeds, during all the said Term. And the said ROBERT STEPHENSON doth
hereby, for himself, his Heirs, Executors, and Administrators, covenant as well with the said *Ralph Little Whyte*
his Executors and Administrators, as with the said *Alexander Whyte* his Executors and Administrators, that
they, the said ROBERT STEPHENSON, and his present and future Partners, and the Survivors and Survivor of them, and their and his Partners,
or some or one of them, shall and will, during the Term of the said Apprenticeship, teach and instruct, or cause the said Apprentice to be
taught and instructed, in the Art, Trade, or Business of a *Draftsman* so far as the
same relates to the said Trade or Business of an Engine Builder, in the best Way and Manner that they or any of them can; and also shall
and will pay, or otherwise allow, the said Apprentice, during the said Term, the weekly Wages following, that is to say,—

Three Shillings and six pence Weekly during the first Year of the said Term, Four Shillings and six pence Weekly during the Second Year thereof Six Shillings Weekly during the Third Year thereof — Seven Shillings Weekly during the fourth Year thereof, Eight Shillings Weekly during the fifth Year thereof and Ten Shillings Weekly during the fifth and last Year of the said Term

And it is hereby mutually agreed by and between the said Parties hereto, that in Case the said Apprentice shall, at any Time or Times
during the said Term, be absent from his said Work by Reason of Sickness, Lameness, or from any other Cause, then and in such Case he, the
said Apprentice, shall not be entitled to receive any Wages for or in respect of such Day or Days during which he shall be so absent from his
said Work as aforesaid; and further, that he shall, after the Expiration of the said Term, serve such additional Time as he shall during the said
Term have been absent from his said Work as aforesaid, and shall only be entitled to receive therefore such Wages as he would have been
entitled to have received in respect of the Day or respective Days for which such additional Time shall be substituted; and further, that in Case
the said Apprentice shall be required at any Time during the said Term to work for his said Masters, or any of them, before the Hour of Six
o'Clock in the Morning, or after the Hour of Six o'Clock in the Afternoon, he, the said Apprentice, shall be paid for such Overtime at the Rate
of One-Quarter more than his weekly Wages for the Time being, provided always that the said Apprentice shall not be entitled to be paid for
any such Overtime unless he shall have worked his full Number of Hours during the preceding Weeks, it being the Intention of the said Parties
that any Deficiency in the regular and ordinary Times or Hours of Working may, if the said Masters think fit, be set off against such Overtime
as aforesaid until such Deficiency shall be made up; and further, that the said Apprentice shall be allowed, between the said Hours of Six
o'Clock in the Morning and Six o'Clock in the Afternoon, Half an Hour for Breakfast and One Hour for Dinner. In Witness whereof, the
said Parties to these Presents have hereunto set their Hands and Seals the Day and Year first above written.

Signed Sealed and delivered by the said Ralph Little Whyte Alexander Whyte and Robert Stephenson — in the presence of Edw Book

Ralph Little Whyte

Alexander Whyte

Robt Stephenson

Reduced facsimile of the apprenticeship indenture of R. L. Whyte, signed by Robert
Stephenson, son of George Stephenson, the inventor of the locomotive, on April 17, 1837

James Hartness

S. Ashton Hand

John E. Sweet

Frank Gilbreth

Winfield S. Rogers

J. R. Almond

L. E. Starrett

Ambrose Swasey

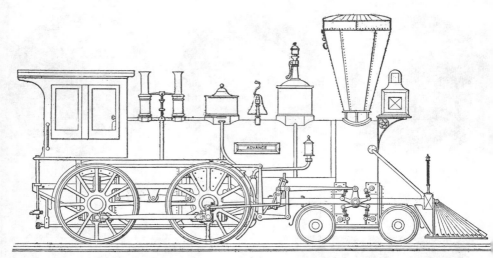

Locomotive "Advance," about 1880, equipped with Corliss valve gear; it was not rugged enough for regular railroad use

Shaw "balanced" locomotive with double crank on each side, about 1883

busily courting the young lady hereinafter referred to as my wife. Every Sunday, if the weather was fine, I would don my light-gray checked suit, with matching silk shirt, silk foulard, and broad-brimmed straw skimmer, mount my high wheeler, and pedal off along the country roads in the direction of my fiancée's house. This was known as "calling on one's young lady." On this particular Sunday I had got off to a late start, and, since both of us set a great store by punctuality, I was trying to make up for lost time.

Turning into the main road, I saw a horse-drawn sprinkling cart some distance ahead of me, wetting down the asphalt and traveling at a leisurely pace. Not wishing to trail behind this contraption for the rest of the journey, I bore down on the pedals with great energy, and prepared to whizz past the sprinkler before it got to the next bend in the road. I was doing about 20 miles an hour when I over-took it, and then it happened again. The front bearing froze, I went over the handle bars in the approved fashion, landed smack in the muddy wake of the cart, and skidded a few feet on my back until I was directly under the dripping spouts. Thereupon my bicycle ran over me as usual. The driver of the cart picked me up out of the muck, saying that he couldn't for the life of him understand the type of sport the younger generation was going in for these days; and when I arrived at my fiancée's house in my dilapidated finery, her father would have it that I had been drinking.

Although going over the handle bars was fortunately not an everyday occurrence, it was one more hazard added to the perilous sport of high-wheel bicycling, and manufacturers were forced to listen to the public's demand for safer designs. In the period between the demise of the high wheeler and the coming of the safety, there was an evolutionary stage that produced a few out-and-out freaks. One of these hybrids went by the name of Challenger Extraordinary. It had a much smaller front wheel than on the ordinary, and the front-wheel forks were slanted back at an angle of from 25 to 30 degrees, so that the rider, instead of sitting directly over the front wheel as heretofore, was saddled some distance behind it. The foot pedals were connected to the front axle by a series of levers and toggle joints that formed a sort of pantographic or accordion effect, and all in all the adjective applied to this contrivance was well chosen, for it was nothing if not extraordinary.

Then there was the "Star", designed by H. B. Smith of Smithville, New Jersey, and possibly the ordinary's greatest rival up until the development of the safety bicycle. The Star looked like the old high wheeler placed wrong end to, for it had the small wheel in front and the large one behind, with a straight tubular bone running up to the handle bars. This arrangement greatly cut down the number of flights over the handle bars, but the Star never became widely popular, since it was difficult to mount singlehanded. Moreover, it had independent levers on each side, instead of the crank motion of the original ordinary, that drove the front wheel by means of ratchet drums connected to the levers through straps outside the drums. While this stratagem permitted pedal strokes of almost any length, such versatility was often confusing to the novice. The low front wheel, combined with a freewheeling coaster brake, made the Star a good deal safer than the old high wheeler, but it was a heavy and unwieldy affair at best compared with the later safety bicycle.

The modern form of the bicycle, which began appearing about 1893 or 1894, is an excellent example of efficient engineering applied to mass-production methods. With chain-gear drive, ball bearings, and pneumatic tires, a tubular frame of great strength and lightness, wheels that support a load of more than ten times their own weight over all kinds of surfaces, it is easily the preeminent leader in the field of man-propelled vehicles. The greatest single contribution that the safety bicycle has made to mechanical progress was the ball bearing, the manufacture of which, though originally directed solely at the bicycle industry, has developed into a vast industry involving a large number of new tools, new machines, and new processes. The manufacture of bicycle hubs, moreover, made the forming tool and the oil-tube drill common appliances in the machine shop, for although not originated in connection with the making of bicycles, the possibilities of these machine tools had not hitherto been generally known. The turret lathe, both manual and automatic, also received tremendous impetus through the same influence, for while these machines were already in common use, they had been restricted in most shops to screw and stud making, with a limited application to larger work, and their position as a recognized part of the standard machine-shop outfit dates from their wide adoption in bicycle manufacture.

The safety bicycle was also largely responsible for the development of the flat-link chain, both of the block and silent types, which has since become one of the most dependable of our modern devices for transmitting power. It resulted in wider experience in the heat-treating of metals and in the manufacture and use of various steels for special purposes in industry. The need for strong, light wheels led wiremakers to investigate thoroughly the tensile properties of various kinds of steel wire for the spokes; the desire for a pneumatic tire that could be repaired on the road led to the development of the inner tube and to extensive research into the technology of rubber. And finally, the theory and practice of mass production was applied for the first time on a large, international scale in the bicycle industry, which had some 25 million customers at the turn of the century.

The bicycle impinged upon the locomotive through the medium of machine tools when the new turret lathes, which had been developed to form wheel hubs, were applied to the manufacture of locomotive crankpins; but the locomotive, being a self-contained power plant on wheels with over 600 separate mechanisms which in turn are composed of many thousands of machined parts, had a far more extensive effect upon the growth of machine tools than had the bicycle. It will be recalled that my initial effort as a machinist for the Rue Manufacturing Company was devoted to producing injectors for locomotives. This fact alone would tie machine tools in with railroading, yet the injector was only one of hundreds of other devices necessary to the locomotive that were made by the wheel lathe, the boring machine, the slotter, the miller, the planer, the drill press, and other specialized machine tools. Merely to list these parts would occupy about four of these pages, and I am not sure that I feel up to the task at the moment.

Richard Trevithick of England is generally credited with building the world's first locomotive in 1801, based partly upon the earlier work in the field of steam engines by Newton, Cugnot, and Murdock. His locomotive had four wheels, all drivers, 4 feet 6 inches in diameter; a 6-foot boiler with return flue, and one steam cylinder 8 inches in diameter and 54 inches long. After Trevithick came Hedley in 1813 with his "Puffing Billy," Stephenson in 1814 with his "Blucher," and later in 1829, the famous "Rocket" of Stephenson's Stockton and Darlington Railway. In the same year Stephenson's son Robert (whose signature appears on the indenture shown elsewhere) furnished to the United States his locomotive "America," which, although never placed in operation, may have influenced subsequent design in this country. The first locomotive built in the United States, the "Peter Cooper," attained a speed of between 5 and 18 miles per hour on the newly formed Baltimore and Ohio Railroad in the year 1830.

Two years earlier, in 1828, the Baltimore and Ohio Railroad was chartered by the state of Maryland, and became the first railroad built in the United States for the general transportation of passengers and freight; and between 1830 and 1842, eight additional railroads— The Mohawk and Hudson, the Utica and Schenectady, the Syracuse and Utica, the Auburn and Syracuse, the Auburn and Rochester, the Rochester and Syracuse, the Tonawanda, and the Attica and Buffalo—were under construction or in operation, together constituting the first railroad system connecting the Atlantic Ocean with the Great Lakes. It may be superfluous to add that these railroads later became the present New York Central System. By 1850, six more lines connecting Boston with New York, Albany, Ogdensburg, and the St. Lawrence River were completed; a year later the Erie Railroad was in operation between Weehawken, New Jersey, and Lake Erie, with several independent railways forming other lines between Lake Erie and the Eastern United States. By 1860, there were 30,000 miles of railroads in operation in New England, the Middle Atlantic States, the North Central States, and territories, and the territory southeast and southwest of the Mississippi River. Ten years later, the total mileage had increased to 54,000; in 1880, to 95,000; in 1890, to 163,000; and at the turn of the century, the figure stood close to 200,000 miles. We all remember that the year 1869 saw the completion of the Union Pacific Railroad, making possible a transcontinental journey by rail, and how this line, together with the Central Pacific, formed the outline of the subsequent development of our continental railway system.

It should be easy to understand how this tremendous development and expansion of the railroad in the United States between 1830 and 1900 affected not only the development of machine tools and shops but also the sphere of activity and the interests of the mechanics and toolbuilders themselves. To inject a personal note at this point, my father, Henry F. Colvin, who as we have seen left active railroad service soon after the Civil War, maintained a keen interest in railroading as long as he lived, so that as a boy I was brought up in intimate contact with railway men and with the insides and outsides of locomotives. From 1865 to 1878 Father cultivated his love for high iron in what he would have considered an avocational manner by "taking out" locomotives for the Rhode Island Locomotive Works—which means, in our modern terminology, that he was an erecting engineer who went out with new locomotives that were being delivered to various railroads and supervised their actual erection and commissioning or breaking in on their first official runs, somewhat in the manner of a naval captain in command of a shakedown cruise of a battleship. After thirteen years of this work he formally retired from the career of railroading, becoming thereafter a sort of an ex officio consulting engineer around the various shops and yards. When I was but eleven years of age he began taking me on extensive tours of the roundhouses and railroad shops in the East, so that I became familiar with locomotives and railway-shop work at a very early age. This, I should point out, was later to prove of great practical value to me when I became editor of *Machinery* in 1894, as has been already mentioned; but particularly useful when, as will be seen later in the present chapter, I joined the staff of Angus Sinclair's organ, *Locomotive Engineering*.

I should like to be able to say that, on all my editorial trips to railroad shops for *Machinery* or other magazines between 1894 and the present, the conditions I found indicated a rate and extent of progress in railway machine-shop work and tools equal to the progress in other machine fields, or at least to the progress in the railroad industry as a whole. Such is not, unfortunately, the case. I will mention one outstanding exception dating back to 1894 and then proceed to point out the opposite side of the picture.

One of my first editorial trips for *Machinery* was to the Juniata Shops of the Pennsylvania Railroad, which, as many of us will recall, celebrated its first centennial in 1946. These shops were located near Altoona, Pennsylvania, and were in 1894 the Pennsy's newest and most up to date. They had been built under the supervision of Henry Gordon, who had formerly been master mechanic at the Wilmington, Delaware, Shops of the Philadelphia, Wilmington, and Baltimore branch of the Pennsylvania, known to all in those days as the "P. W. & B. line," and were constructed with the idea that the majority of the new locomotives used by the railroad would be built in the new shops, while the repairing of old locomotives would continue to be done at the old shops in Altoona, near the center of the city across from the railroad station. Consequently, the machine-tool equipment of the Juniata Shops was new and well fitted for the work, as it most certainly should have been, and I remember that I was indeed delighted to observe this fact on my first official visit to the place.

In the average railroad repair shop, however, where maintenance was the only object, the machine-tool equipment was more often than not several years behind the times, or else totally unsuited to the type of work being done. I regret to add that this condition still prevails even in our twentieth-century shops of 1947, although there are encouraging signs of a renaissance here and there. There are nevertheless only a very small number of railroad repair shops today where the men and the work are not handicapped by out-of-date and inefficient equipment, and today as in the past it is too often the case that no new machine tools can be bought until the old one reaches the point where it can no longer be used. A few instances of what I mean may be helpful.

I used to visit periodically a certain railroad shop in the Southwest, which shall be nameless, and on each visit I would marvel and make many expressions of wonder at its antique boring mill, that appeared to have been built shortly before the Battle of Bull Run, though it was probably not more than thirty years old at the time of my first visit. It was undoubtedly a great work of art in its day, having numerous pleasing arabesques and curlicues worked into its cast-iron frame, and it was decorated with service marks in the form of a myriad of nicks and scars all over its surface. Being somewhat of a tease in my youth, I took delight in asking the shop superintendent, a forward-looking man, "When are you going to ship this thing off to the Smithsonian and get a new boring mill, chief?"

"You know darn well what the boss says—Old Ironsides is still in perfect working condition, we can't afford to be extravagant, and all that hocus-pocus. Don't you think that I'd like to junk that heirloom right now? How can we turn out any kind of accurate work on a thing like that? Suppose you talk to the boss about it and see what public opinion can do."

It went on for a year or more, with Old Ironsides getting older and the jokes growing more pointed, until one day I walked in on a routine visit and was stopped dead in my tracks by the sight of a brand-new, shining, latest model boring mill with all modern conveniences standing in the spot formerly occupied by the antique. When I recovered my breath, I asked what great upheaval in the laws of nature had brought about the sudden change.

"I owe that new machine," the superintendent said, "to a tramp machinist—and I didn't get a chance to thank him for it."

"A tramp machinist? Did he give you his life savings, or what?"

"This feller came in looking for a short-time job a couple of weeks ago—said he was passing through on his way to Minneapolis or some place and did we have a week's work that he could do. I put him on the night shift—gave him a few small boring jobs to do on Old Ironsides. That's how it happened."

"How what happened?"

"Well, you see, this old feller wasn't used to nightwork, I guess, or else he was all tuckered out from his travels, but anyway the very first night what does he do but fall asleep with the machine running. He had a cylinder in the chuck, the tool ate too far into the work, and when he woke up the whole damn feeding mechanism was pretty well shot to pieces. I guess he took one look at what he had done, grabbed his hat and his tool kit, and lit out for Minneapolis. He never showed up again—not even to collect whatever pay was coming to him—the poor cuss. And he didn't have to run away like that. I was all set to give him his full pay and a $10 bonus besides. He did me a favor I'll never forget, because the next morning the boss *had* to buy me a new boring mill!"

Such cases were by no means isolated to a few unusual shops. I remember another superintendent of a railroad shop in a different part of the country who had had one of those old Sellers car-axle lathes that resembled a glorified sewer pipe at first glance, with the bed of circular section and the ways on top. It was a very sturdy piece of machinery, built to outlast several generations of machinists. The superintendent, who had probably been reading up on current advertising literature, felt that a machine more than forty years old was somewhat passé in the best circles, and agitated constantly for a new model, but with the same results as our Southwestern man above. Taking the matter in his own hands, the superintendent caused to be circulated in the shop an offer of $15 reward to any machinist who could wreck the old Sellers lathe, provided that it was in the line of duty and during regular working hours. The last I heard of it was that he had upped his offer to $20 without achieving a serious break-down on the old war horse, which continued to display even more stamina than had been credited it.

A slightly different incident occurred on a visit to the South Tacoma Shops of the Milwaukee Railroad soon after they had spent several million dollars on the electrification of that part of the road that passes over the Cascade Range. Seeing a lathe of rather unusual appearance at work turning the commutator of a motor armature, I asked the superintendent if it was a very recent model, and what company made it, for I had never, I said, come across anything quite like it before.

"I don't imagine you have," he replied. "We made that baby ourselves—right here in the shop."

"Made it yourself! What, is the Milwaukee going into the machine-tool business, too?"

"I'll tell you how it was, Mr. Colvin. After they electrified this part of the road we naturally had quite a number of large motor armatures and commutators that had to be turned on a lathe. Only we didn't have any lathe. I kept asking and asking the front office to buy us a standard lathe so's we could keep the motors running. You know what they told me?"

I said I could probably guess.

"They told me that the company had already spent so much money in building the generating stations and laying out the power line along the track that there was no money left to spend on shop equipment. Can you figure that—no money to buy a little old standard lathe, when there wasn't a one in the whole machine shop? So what did we have to do to keep the motors running? We had to build our own lathe, by jeez, out of old spare parts and odds and ends—right here in the shop."

I asked him what he thought it had cost to build it.

"Plenty," he replied. "A helluva lot more than the best job we could have bought anywhere in the country. It was a crime, I tell you, to waste money that way—but they wrote off the cost of it as shop maintenance instead of new equipment, so everybody in the front office was happy, and the trains kept running on schedule."

It is a curious fact that many very capable railroad shopmen with whom I have talked in various parts of the country seem to consider their work so unique and specialized a field that the standard practices of the average or general machine shop are extraneous and inapplicable here. The technique of grinding, for example, which is certainly one of the basic methods of metalworking, was introduced only with general reluctance into railroad-shop practice, and progressed at a snail's pace for over fifty years. Why this should be is a subject for an interesting if lengthy monograph on railroad operation, which I will have the decency to spare the reader at this point. Nevertheless, it should be observed in passing that most of the seeming absurdities of railroad operation and shop practice, in the early days at least, arose from the simple fact that the men high up in the organization—the presidents, vice-presidents, chairmen of the board—were bankers, financial geniuses, stock exchange tycoons, manipulators, speculators, big operators—men who did not know a driving wheel from a truck wheel, or even a sleeper from a tie plate at forty paces, but who understood all about land grants, pooling, long- and short-haul economics, discriminatory rates, controlling stock, and other interesting details.

The first real progress in the use of grinding machines in railroad shops occurred, if my memory can be depended on, about the year 1907, when a planetary grinder of the Heald type was introduced in a few of the leading shops for the reconditioning of air-brake cylinder barrels. Later, the Bettendorf works, evidently encouraged by the new attitude, brought out a grinding machine designed solely for railroad-shop work, which among its other applications became very well adapted to grinding the ends of side rods for receiving the floating bushings that are now so widely used. These floating bushings, incidentally, were a radical departure from earlier notions of railroad machinery, in the days when rod brasses were made adjustable in order to keep the clearance between brass and pin at the correct amount for quiet running. But unless these brasses were properly adjusted, the center distance was sure to be too short or too long, and of course the result was very often a broken crankpin or side rod, slow schedules, and every now and then a railroad wreck of minor proportions. About 1890, some nameless but daring railroad designer introduced side rods with solid ends in which solid bushings were free to turn either on the pin or in the rod; this was intended to eliminate the need for adjusting the side-rod brasses at frequent intervals.

But old-time throttle jerkers went around resenting this innovation, saying they had devoted a good part of their training and experience to tightening up side-rod brasses, and here was one of those bailing-wire mechanics who was trying to tell them how to run a locomotive, and undermining their prestige as well. The old-timers said furthermore that the solid-end side rods were no earthly good because they made a hell of a racket when the engine was starting up, due to the initial wearing of the brasses and the subsequent slapping of the rods against the pins. If some stripling just out of college thought he knew more about locomotives than the old hands, let him just try highballing the express on the night run to Cedar Rapids and see how smart he was. But gradually the old-timers were won over to the new order when they began to realize that the floating bushings had virtually eliminated the possibility of broken crankpins and side rods, and other sources of trouble as well. These bushings, which stimulated the use of the grinding machine, are now in almost universal use in railroading, and are even installed on the main or connecting rods in order to eliminate further sources of trouble.

Another railroad-shop practice that is going into the discard all too slowly is that of rolling axles and crankpins on the bearing surface as a method of finishing. I am not sure where this started but for many years it was very widespread indeed. After turning the bearing part of the axle, or journal, a hardened steel roller mounted in a suitable holder was put in the tool post and forced against the axle. It was fed along the length of the bearing and, according to the advocates of this process, this roller hardened the surface of the axle by its peening action, producing the very best finish possible, the *ne plus ultra* or de luxe type of finish. No doubt it did. But there was one trivial detail overlooked. The smooth good-looking surface *was not round*. That is, the axle, or piston rod, or whatever, was not truly cylindrical—because in the rolling process the metal of the rod, not being of uniform density, was pushed or squeezed into the soft spots and piled up on the hard spots so that, under a medium-powered microscope, the surface looked like a cross section of the Blue Ridge Mountains of Kentucky. Consequently as the rod moved in and out of the packing in the cylinder-head stuffing box, it wore itself and the cylinder lining very rapidly in spots, and after a time broke down completely. Then too, the use of a single rolling tool forced against the axle imposed undue strains on the lathe centers. To avoid this, some shops made rolling tools which held the rollers in a frame that forced them against the axle on both sides. This saved the lathe centers but still produced bearings that were not truly round.

I preached against this fundamental error of rolling practice for many years, pointing out that the grinding machine was the only proper device for truing a rod or axle, but I am sorry to say that I was the voice of one crying in the wilderness. It was a long time before those in the front office mastered the elementary principles involved and came to the conclusion that maybe the grinding machine wasn't such a bad idea after all.

Bill Cunningham, who was superintendent of motive power on the Denver and Rio Grande Line (John Hill's old road, by the way), once sent me photographs of some crankpins that had been rolled in the manner outlined above and then ground with a light cut. These rolled pins were found to be so much "out of round" that several additional grindings were needed to render then truly cylindrical. To make matters worse, the Magnaflux outfit that the front office had given him showed that the pins had more cracks on their surfaces than an old set of glazed chinaware. Cunningham wrote that he had been much happier in his ignorance before the Magnaflux outfit came along, because now he was almost afraid to send a locomotive out on the road when he thought of all those cracks on the surface of the crankpins that he had never dreamed existed before. Yet Cunningham, being a very progressive railroad man, readily adjusted himself to the new technology and saw to it that the rolling practice was abandoned, in his shops at least.

Lest the reader should think I am completely down on all railroad machine shops and railroads in general, the result of having fallen out of an upper berth in my youth, or some such prejudicial incident, I hasten to state that such is not the case. I have seen in my time a fair number of railroad shops that were very well run and had the latest and most efficient types of machine tools. I have seen some innovations in machine-tool practice that originated in railroad shops and were highly commendable advances in technology.

The first application of magnetism for detecting cracks in axle journals and other parts that I ever saw or heard of was in the Coney Island Shops of the Brooklyn and Manhattan Transit Company in 1920. I immediately wrote up this discovery with great enthusiasm in the *American Machinist*. The magnaflux method of crack detection, which may have been an entirely separate invention, is very similar in technique and is in wide use today, although, to be sure, the old method of painting with a mixture of chalk and water is still seen in many shops.

And while there were far too many shops in need of efficient management in the recent past, there were also a good many well-run railroad shops that compared favorably with the best in the field. Nevertheless it is an inescapable fact that in no other line of machine-shop work are greater contrasts to be found than in the railroad shops in various parts of the country. Much of the difference is due, as has been hinted at earlier in the chapter—to the machinations of high finance and to the personalities of officials, both shop men and the higher-ups. I should like to present a few instances of what I mean by "contrasts."

Early in 1900 the New York Central Railroad opened its new

shops at Depew, New York, and I made it a point to visit them at the earliest opportunity. I was much impressed by the layout of the buildings, the saw-tooth roofs admitting much light and air, the modern arrangement of the various departments, the neat and spacious rooms, and the general air of efficiency about the entire plant. And then I made a close inspection of the machines themselves. They comprised the most extensive collection of secondhand equipment I had yet seen. They had been taken "as is" from a number of older shops along the line and each machine gave clear evidence of having already seen its best days. The only thing new about the machine shop was the building and the grounds.

On the other hand, I found another new railroad shop in Birmingham, Alabama, some years later, in which every one of the numerous machines was brand-new, having been bought especially for the occasion when the shop was erected. This, I thought, was really getting off to a new start and had a fine effect on the general morale of the place, even though it represented a considerable outlay of funds.

Then, of course, there was the old shop in Mobile, where the master mechanic bitterly complained to me that he had been with the shop for all of forty years and in that time had not seen a single new machine purchased or erected. The old Santa Fe Shops at Topeka had a curious mixture of fairly up-to-date machines and collector's items, and the shop executives appeared to be perfectly contented with the whole assortment. I should add that this was back in the 1930's.

Two well-equipped and well-run shops that stand out in my recollections are those of the Norfolk and Western Railroad at Roanoke, Virginia, and the Chesapeake and Ohio Shops at Huntington, West Virginia. I have known R. G. Henley at Roanoke and E. A. Murray at Huntington for many years, and besides being excellent executives in every respect, both men always went out of their way to provide material for *American Machinist* articles in their field. The Roanoke Shops have long pioneered in accurate machine work on steam locomotives, being particularly noted for the accurate machining required by their large locomotives with roller bearings in the driving wheels that are held in place by shrink fits, the necessary expansion being secured by a hot-water bath. This is a far cry from the old methods where a thirty-second "scant" was the commonly accepted and ultimate refinement in measuring.

Modern railroad mechanics must know where to use close fits and where a loose or "sloppy" fit is more appropriate. Tolerances and limits that apply very well to stationary steam, gas, or diesel engines may be entirely out of place when applied to a locomotive. For the locomotive is a steam power plant that has no stable foundation, whose base is never in perfect alignment with the superstructure, and whose bearings must be designed to allow for vertically moving axles, for jarring and jolting of wheels over "frogs" and switches, and for end play on curved portions of track. Locomotive designers and maintenance men, therefore, must possess a good deal of special knowledge known but to a few in other fields of mechanical engineering.

Yet it has often happened that locomotive designers, together with railway officials, have been responsible for huge and unnecessary expenditures of money and materials in connection with the operation of their repair shops. A striking example of this somewhat contradictory propensity was brought to my attention by the shop superintendent of one of the shops of the Big Four outside of Indianapolis several years ago.

Standing in the superintendent's second-floor office overlooking the main room of the shop, I gazed down upon one of the neatest and most impressive storage or stock piles I had ever seen. Tires, driving wheels, axles, cylinder castings, parallel rods, main frames, equalizers, reach rods, eccentric rods, arch tubes, spring hangers, cockshaft arms, guide yokes, pedestal tie bars, stiffening angles, expansion plates, drawbars, trunnion bearings, hopper doors, dome casings, headlights, brake cylinders, and hundreds of other locomotive odds and ends were stacked in orderly array but in frightening quantities. It seemed that at least ten dozen fully equipped locomotives could be assembled from the vast assortment of parts on hand, with enough parts left over to keep all of them running for a half century. I made a remark to this effect.

"That there stock pile," said the superintendent, "is my biggest headache in twenty years of railroading. And there's nothing I can do about it. We have over fifty different types of locomotives running on this road, and I have to carry spare parts for each type. Maybe there's only one or two engines of a certain make out of the thousand on the line, but I gotta carry a complete stock of spare parts for them just the same."

"I should imagine it's a pretty expensive proposition."

"Do you know what that stock pile cost just to set up, without any maintenance figured in? Over half a million dollars! Half a million dollars worth of spare parts just because we got fifty different kinds of locomotives running."

I've heard the same story many times. The alibi offered usually is, "We are always interested in trying out new designs of engines, so that we can improve our service; if we stuck to the one type of locomotive we would soon find ourselves behind the times." Now it is certainly desirable to experiment with new models in any line of machinery. That way progress lies. But it is clearly wasteful and extravagant for every railroad in the country to try out new designs of locomotives at the same time and independently of one another. It has been suggested on many occasions that research and experimental work be carried out by a coordinating or central organization, such as the American Railway Association, using the best facilities available on a single large railway system. Duplication is expensive and a waste of effort, and this applies to many other phases of railroading besides locomotives.

To end this section on a note of optimism, I should like to mention the technique employed by my old friend M. H. Westbrook, who was in charge of the Grand Trunk Shop in Battle Creek, Michigan, for many years. Before buying a machine, he first sold the idea to the man or men in his shop who were to run it. He'd take the man to some other shop where a similar machine was in use, have him watch it in operation, and afterward discuss its features with the operator. Then Westbrook would ask his man what he thought of the new machine, pointing out where it was superior to the present model and how it would save the operator a lot of extra work. This procedure always paved the way for a favorable reception of the new equipment when it arrived in the shop, where otherwise there might have been resentment or indifference. The Grand Trunk Shop was unusually efficient because of Westbrook's forward-looking management, up-to-date equipment, safe working conditions, and neat and attractive layout. The latter feature is often a physical impossibility in a railroad yard, although the Moncton, New Brunswick, and Needles, California, shops were equally attractive, as well as a few others whose names escape me at the moment.

The reader, I trust, will remember the account of John Alexander Hill and the *Locomotive Engineer* given in the third chapter, and how Hill had become the first editor of that magazine at the urgent insistence of its proprietors, Miller and Moore. This was of course before Hill had met James McGraw, and long before the imprint on the title page of this book had come into existence. John Hill's specialty was railroad-shop and roundhouse work, and after about four years as editor in chief of the railroad paper, he formed a partnership with the editor of the *Car Builder*, a gentleman named Angus Sinclair. Together they bought the *Locomotive Engineer* from Miller and Moore, subsequently changing its name to *Locomotive Engineering* as an indication of the change in ownership and a broadening of its field.

The new paper flourished under the energetic leadership of Hill, who began to display a natural genius for publishing as well as an extensive knowledge of mechanical subjects. So well did he promote the interests of *Locomotive Engineering* that by 1896 he was in a position to take advantage of a great opportunity that presented itself.

Illness on the part of Lycurgus B. Moore, together with sundry other complications, had brought a change of ownership and management in the *American Machinist* about this time. The new owners knew little and cared less about the fine points of machine-shop practice, being interested in the magazine only as a speculative enterprise and a quick cash turnover. Bluntly stated, they were trying to sell it again for something more than they had paid for it. Hill's partner Sinclair, a thrifty Scot who had made some shrewd investments in the Westinghouse Air Brake Company when it was starting up, had provided most of the capital for *Locomotive Engineering*, and Hill himself had been wisely accumulating a nest egg from the profits of that journal. Consequently these two men offered to purchase the *Ameri-*

can Machinist from its interim owners in 1896, the offer was immediately accepted, and Hill and Sinclair forthwith became the *Machinist's* new proprietors.

Hill was now part owner of two leading trade papers. With characteristic zeal, he set to work improving and expanding the scope of both, sending Fred Miller to Europe to study the machine-tool field there and hiring a considerable number of talented editors and assistant editors, while the combined circulation leaped from 25,000 to 40,000 a month in less than a year. Angus Sinclair, it must be admitted, was something less than a zealot about machinery, being more interested in the clipping of dividend coupons than in active business promotion, with the result that he would spend a good part of each year in a hunting lodge in Scotland while Hill carried on alone with the bulk of the work. Moreover, Angus did not get on well at all with Fred Miller, particularly after Fred had become editor in chief of the *Machinist*. These and other sources of friction soon led to a dissolution of the Hill-Sinclair partnership.

John made Angus a give-or-take sort of offer when they were about to split up. Each member of the original partnership would take either the *Machinist* or *Locomotive Engineering*, but not both, and would run it independently of the other from here out. Angus, who had been the *Locomotive's* angel, surprised everyone by choosing the *Machinist*, about which he knew decidedly very little; it was thought that he did so only because he wanted the satisfaction of sending a cable to Fred Miller, who was in Europe at the time, telling him that he was fired! He was finally persuaded that the railroad paper was his best bet, for it was the field in which he was best known and in which he had made his reputation. Sinclair must have realized that he could never have handled the *Machinist*, and would probably have run it into a fair-sized hole in a couple of years.

When Angus had been properly reestablished as sole proprietor of *Locomotive Engineering*, he approached me one day in 1897 and said,

"Colvin, how would you like to come and work for me on my railroad paper? As associate editor in chief and business manager, I mean?"

I was somewhat startled by the unexpected offer and did not reply immediately. After a moment I said, "Well, you know I'm still chief editor of Luchar's paper, *Machinery*. Ever since I got our Volume I, Number 1, three years ago, I have felt that I owe it to Luchars to stick with it as long as he wants me. I'll have to think it over, Mr. Sinclair."

"Think it over, by all means, Fred—but I might as well tell you that I've already spoken to Luchars about it. He says it's a great opportunity for you and he isn't going to stand in your way. Besides, you'll be doing the same work Mr. Hill was doing—building up the paper, you know—almost like a partnership. You'll be your own boss, too, Freddie lad, for the most part, anyway."

And after a little more persuasion and reflection on the matter, I transferred to *Locomotive Engineering* in 1897. Fortunately for me, Hill had laid an excellent foundation on which to build, and I was able to increase the circulation considerably, and even the advertising to some extent. For five years, in addition to supplying a good share of the editorial matter, I looked after the subscription work, which meant constant correspondence with a host of agents on all the railroads, the soliciting and preparation of advertisements, and rather extensive junkets into remote sections of the country in order to keep in touch with the latest developments in railway practice. It was all very interesting and all very strenuous.

My early railroad contacts through Father now came in very handy. From friends and acquaintances in the railroad industry I heard of many new and important developments and through them I was often in a position to get a sort of advance preview of the latest devices. One of these experiences still lingers in my memory after nearly fifty years. This was my hand-to-hand encounter with the famous Kincaid stoker, the first mechanical stoker to be used on a locomotive anywhere in the world, so far as I am aware.

I had heard about this ingenious mechanism early in 1898, and finding myself one day in the city of Cincinnati where John Kincaid, the inventor-engineer of the Chesapeake and Ohio Railroad, had his residence, I decided to pay him a business call to inquire after his brain child. His wife greeted me, saying that she was sorry John was not at home, but that I would find him at the yard in Hinton, West Virginia. Well, I thought, that is not exactly around the corner, but it is worth the trip if I can get a news article out of it. So I boarded a train and arrived at Hinton at 10 P.M.

Here I was met by the master mechanic who had been apprised of my coming (I had cleared through the C. & O. office in Cincinnati with my press pass). With great consideration and respect I was placed aboard the most rickety stagecoach I had ever seen, which somehow managed to hold together until we had reached Hinton's leading and only hotel. There I was ushered into the main suite, consisting of a single room that unaccountably had three doors leading into it, all of them without locks of any kind. I am not a suspicious man by nature, but I felt better when I had jammed three chairs under the doorknobs just before going to sleep. But these are mere details.

Arising early the next morning, I purchased a pair of overalls at the general store (they were, of course, several sizes too big) and proceeded to the roundhouse where the world's first mechanically fired locomotive was being made ready to pull out its train of coal cars. Kincaid, unfortunately, was nowhere to be found; he had got a sudden call from somebody someplace else, or something; I would have to find out about the operation of the stoker by riding in the cab with the engineer and fireman and observing as best I could.

The engine was a large freight locomotive with a long, narrow firebox that was accounted very difficult to fire by hand, so that the Kincaid stoker would be given a fairly severe test on its first official performance. The stoker consisted of a hopper into which the fireman shoveled the coal; below the hopper was a cylinder with a steam-operated piston that had three different lengths of stroke controlled by an automatic mechanism. The first of these strokes was a long, swift movement that shot the coal to the front end of the firebox. The next stroke deposited the coal in about the center, while the last dropped it just beyond the fire door. A convex casting ahead of the cylinder spread the coal quite evenly over the fire surface, and the number of piston strokes per minute could be regulated by the fireman to suit the engine's demand for steam.

Everything was in readiness for our momentous trip. I was eager and excited. I asked a lot of questions. The engineer turned to me and said:

"Look, mister. There's something I think I oughta tell you. This road we're going out on is a single-track line, that runs up over the mountain and drops down again at Clifton Forge, the next junction point from here. At the very top of the mountain there's a tunnel, about a mile long, more or less, and this tunnel's so narrow that "Big Liz" here will just about squeeze through. Do you get what I mean?"

"Sure. I won't put my head out going through the tunnel."

"That isn't what I mean, mister. It's a long, hard pull up that mountain with a string of coal flats behind you. Sometimes we just about make it and sometimes we don't. Once you pass the middle of the tunnel you're O.K., but with a heavy load you're liable to get stuck on the hump, and I mean that's right where this tunnel is. Only last week Bill Dietrich was out on the run and got stuck smack in the middle of the tunnel and couldn't get started. He lost his head and instead of getting down on the ground he tries to get up more steam and pull out of there. What happens of course is that he knocks himself out with the smoke, and if it wasn't for the fireman dragging him out he would have been a dead pigeon."

"That's right, mister," said our own fireman, handing me a piece of wet cloth about the size of a large bandanna. "Here—take this and hold it over your mouth and nose when we get into the tunnel. This'll keep you from getting asphyxiated, anyhow."

I began to wish I were not so doggone inquisitive about mechanical stokers. As we neared the top of the grade, I could see the narrow entrance to the tunnel, black and forbidding. The locomotive was straining mightily with its string of coal cars, giving out tremendous puffs of yellow and gray smoke that was already beginning to fill the cab. I had read all about carbon monoxide poisoning, and was beginning to wonder if it wouldn't be advisable to uncouple a few coal flats and come back for them later. At the entrance to the tunnel the locomotive gave a great gasp and staggered in. The black walls immediately closed around us, and at the same time a great belch of smoke and soot and gas rushed into the cab, blinding and choking me. I could hear the roar of the engine as we chugged slowly through the tunnel, but I could no longer see the engineer or the fireman or the gauge lamp, or the stoker which I had come along to observe.

The lamp had gone out. The thick, sulphury smoke filled the darkness and the locomotive struggled on. I was trying to think what to do if Big Liz suddenly gave up, when the engineer's voice boomed out:

"Hey, Mr. Colvin! If we stall now, climb down outta this cab to the ground right away, you hear? Get down on the ground as quick as the Lord will let you, get up ahead of the engine and out of this gas! Get out of the gas as quick as you can!"

I already had one foot on the gangway.

But we did not stall. Big Liz puffed and snorted her way over the hump and out of the tunnel like the amazon she was, and when we hit the sunlight and fresh air again everybody breathed easier.

When the smoke cleared and I could see again, I rushed to open the cab window on my side to gulp down a little oxygen. I must have been a shade too eager, for the window suddenly came loose and swung down on top of my head with a crash of splintered glass, and when the surprised engineer and fireman looked round at me, I was standing by the side of the cab with the window draped about my neck. I undoubtedly made a very favorable impression on them with this diverting byplay, for they seemed to enjoy the performance most heartily. But we reached Clifton Forge, the end of the division, on time and without further mishap; the Kincaid mechanical stoker had done a good job and I had material for a scoop in *Locomotive Engineering*. And a taste of sulphur in my mouth for about a month afterward.

I had a great many more interesting experiences as roving editor for Angus Sinclair's *Locomotive Engineering*, and got to know quite a bit about railroads in general. Some day I may get around to writing a book about railroads, although the time is getting short and I am afraid it wouldn't be glamorous enough. For the present, however, we will take leave of the subject.

While I was with Sinclair, he decided to branch out into another field of transportation that was showing signs of great potential development. Accordingly he purchased the *Automobile Magazine*, a journal that had only recently been started, and made me its new editor and advertising manager, with the understanding that when it had become a paying property I was to have a proprietary interest in it. It was through this medium that I made my first contacts with the infant automobile industry in the year 1900, but that is a story in itself and I see we have come to the end of this chapter.

CHAPTER SIX

Natural History of the Automobile

Carriages without horses shall go,
And accidents fill the world with woe.
The Prophecies of Mother Shipton, 1862

Whenever I find myself in a traffic jam on one of our numerous highways and lesser thoroughfares, I sometimes like to while away my time in a juridical discussion with myself on the pros and cons of the red-flag law. First I take one side of the case, and then the other. If the traffic delay lasts long enough, I usually have time for a peroration to the jury; most of the times, however, I am doing well if I can file my brief before the line starts moving again. The fact that the law has been off the statute books since 1896 doesn't bother me one whit; it is the principle of the thing that interests me.

On the off chance that you may not know what I am talking about, I should like to explain that away back in 1831 (three dozen years before I was born) the English Parliament met in plenary session and, after serious debate, reared back and passed a law familiarly known as the "red-flag law" which, in my con phase, I hold to have been entirely discriminatory and unjust, and in my pro phase, I hold to be one of the great landmarks of jurisprudence. This law had to do with horseless carriages, which were beginning to be seen in increasing numbers in those days, and required that the driver of such a vehicle (which we may loosely call an automobile) be at all times accompanied by a confederate on foot, who was to precede the carriage at a distance of twenty paces, carrying a red flag by day and a red lantern by night. For drivers of an uncertain turn of mind the law also specified that a second footman so equipped should bring up the rear. Drivers appearing in public solo were held in contempt of court and had their vehicle impounded or sold for junk. As though this were not humiliating enough, the owners of toll roads and toll bridges raised their prices for horseless carriages until only the very affluent could indulge in Sunday driving, and things looked black indeed for the future of the automobile industry, if anyone happened to be giving it a thought.

Yet the red-flag law had certain interesting possibilities. For one thing, it eliminated a great deal of unnecessary gadding about hither and yon without any definite purpose in mind but to wear out the machine quickly and get a new one. It also tended to curb the would-be speed demon, who was thereby limited to how fast his assistant could walk or run ahead of him. Moreover it lent a certain air of pomp and ceremony—dignity, if you will—to the business of driving, which only a motorcycle escort can provide in this day and age. And of course it entirely nipped in the bud any tendency toward hit-and-run driving, so that even a blind person could cross the road in complete safety. But scientific development finally proved that the law, in spite of its good points, was highly restrictive to the growth of the horseless-carriage trade, and it was repealed, for better or worse, in 1896.

Few people realize that the automobile is more than 175 years old. We are of course using the word in accordance with its generic or Latin derivation, that is, *auto*, self, and *mobilis*, movable. The self-propelled vehicle dates back to the middle of the eighteenth century, and the first "road wagon" propelled by its own engine, the Encyclopaedia Britannica tells us, is credited to Nicholas Cugnot, a Frenchman, who about 1770 built a three-wheeled carriage with a rather bulky steam power plant driving the single front wheel. Cugnot's vehicle, under a full head of steam, flew along at $2\frac{1}{2}$ miles an hour. Either this original automobile or a second model of it is still preserved in the Conservatoire des Arts et Métiers, in Paris, if the reader should care to take a look at it.

To carry the history of the automobile up to the time of my partnership with Angus Sinclair, I should add that Oliver Evans in America made a "car" in 1787; Trevithick, mentioned earlier in connection with the locomotive, built one in England in 1801; a number of others appeared in both England and the United States between 1824 and 1857; in 1875, Siegfried Narkus of Austria built a four-wheeled vehicle, it is said, powered by an internal-combustion engine;

Karl Benz, A German engineer, developed a light, high-speed, four-stroke engine of ⅔ horsepower, discovered the differential, special electric battery ignition with spark induction, and surface carburetor, and built a tricycle powered by this engine; in 1885–86, Gottlieb Daimler of Germany patented his high-speed internal-combustion engine that was to revolutionize automotive transportation; and in 1894, Krebs of France produced the first gasoline automobile incorporating many of the essential features of the modern car, which was known as the "Panhard" and which had a vertical engine under a hood at the front and a modern chassis. The automobile is not, as some might have fancied, the product of a single inventor; the Encyclopaedia Britannica lists among the European pioneers the following names: Daimler, Benz, Maybach, Krebs, Panhard, Levassor, Royce, Serpollet, De Dion, Bouton, Gibbon, and Roots; and among the American pioneers, Duryea, Olds, Haynes, Winton, Ford, King, Maxwell, Apperson, Riker, Clarke, Stanley, White, and Franklin. (If Englishmen seem to be missing from the list it may have been because of the red-flag law.) Only a very few of these famous names are still to be seen on the hubcaps and radiators of our modern mass-produced automobiles, although many are still present in a form of disguise.

The preceding brief outline brings us up to the year 1900 when I became editor of the *Automobile Magazine*. At that time there were approximately 100 automobiles in production, with 90 of them registered. In the following year the production was to leap to 1,000 and the registration to 800, the result of some intensive development by such men as Charles and Frank Duryea, Henry Ford, and Elwood Haynes in this country, and Benz, Panhard, De Dion, Bouton, and a host of others in Europe. By way of contrast, there were 25,137,000 registered automobiles in the United States in 1945, and a world total of over 45 million. So you can see that in the field of automobiles at least I got in at the beginning. But it was pretty tough at first trying to sell a magazine about automobiles when there were only 90 drivers in the whole country.

Very shortly after I had got established on the new magazine, Angus, with a great sense of appropriateness, got himself a brand-new Toledo Steamer. As editor of an automobile paper, I was expected to familiarize myself with this contrivance as quickly as possible, but since I already knew something about steam engines from the Wheelock days, all I had to learn was how to steer the thing once I had got it running. This was, of course, long before the days of licenses and driving tests, so that the perfectly logical answer to the question "Do you know how to drive?" was, in those days, "I don't know—I ain't ever tried it." When driving licenses did come many years later, they were at first strictly a means of internal revenue, and anyone who alleged that he could drive an automobile, and put up the money for the fee, was handed a license forthwith without any further proof required.

This particular Toledo Steamer, in common with all contemporary cars of that type, had wire wheels build after the fashion of bicycle wheels and fitted with single-tube pneumatic tires, as most bicycles are today. As a matter of fact, the American automobile seems to have evolved partly from the bicycle and partly from the buggy or horse-drawn carriage, with the engine mounted in the rear or under the seat, high flimsy wheels, a tiller for steering, and sometimes even a buggy-whip socket. All that was missing was a set of swingletrees and a canvas feed bag. On the other hand, the European automobiles of the same period, particularly the Panhard, had evolved a functional design that is not radically different from that of our modern motorcar, including such features as a forward engine enclosed by a hood or bonnet, hub brakes, gears and differential, and a wheel-type steering mechanism. The Toledo Steamer, a true species of horseless carriage, had a chassis hardly worth speaking of, with thin wheels which were very weak against side thrust, and which often collapsed on contact with curbstones or from any slight sideway due to erratic steering on the part of the driver.

Angus, of course, wanted to be able to drive too, although he was, as we have said, not a mechanically minded man by nature. On his maiden voyage at the helm he took me along as copilot, having a great respect for my technical knowledge and also because he probably wanted a witness in case of accident. After a backbreaking start that left my leghorn skimmer behind us in the road, Angus set off on a mad dash for the opposite sidewalk, cleared the curb in a fine leap, overran the lawn in front of the Third Congregational Church, and came to rest gently against the trunk of an old elm.

"Bravo!" I exclaimed, relaxing my grip on the seat railings. "But

I thought you would have preferred the main thoroughfare, which seems to have been laid out for that purpose."

"I was trying to avoid that delivery wagon," Angus said, pointing to a vehicle about 50 yards further down the street. "I wanted to give him the right of way."

I showed Angus how to put the Toledo Steamer in reverse. He backed away from the tree into a hydrangea bush, but finally got into the middle of the street again. "This time I'll be more careful," he promised.

We went along nicely in a fairly straight path at about 12 miles per hour, with Angus seeming to be in control of the vehicle. He even turned and smiled once or twice, saying, "It's easy, lad, when you know how," or some such remark. I was beginning to sit back and enjoy the scenery when suddenly a horse-drawn bakery wagon turned into the main street from a side alley and approached us on the left. I saw Angus grasp the tiller in a kind of panic.

"That fool horse is coming straight at me!" he yelled, pushing the stick hard over to the right and pulling open the throttle a few notches. The Toledo Steamer responded by heeling over quickly to the left, on a beeline for the startled horse. In a matter of seconds we were almost on top of the animal, whereupon with great presence of mind I reached out and pulled back the outrigger emergency brake. We slid to a stop, barely grazing the front wheels of the bakery wagon. The horse whinnied in fright, reared up on his hind legs and pawed the air wildly with his hooves, with Angus directly underneath, frozen to the tiller. It was a notable moment in the history of the automobile.

After a disturbing five minutes with the driver of the bakery wagon, who spared nobody's feelings in his summing up of the situation, we slunk off from the scene with me at the tiller and a shattered Angus in the copilot's seat. As we passed up the street towards our garage, a few interested bystanders shouted derisively, "Twist her tail, mister, she's headed for the barn!" and "Get a horse, mister!" and similar epithets that have now passed into history.

My mention of the Toledo Steamer will doubtless call to the reader's mind the most famous of all steam-propelled automobiles— the Stanley Steamer—which even the youngsters in my audience may well have seen on the city streets as late as the 1920's. The Stanley, of course, persisted longest, but the early Locomobile and Mobile, being smaller and less expensive because they were mass produced, were for a long time the leaders in the field of steam automobiles. The Locomobile, which was built in Bridgeport, was soon reconverted, as we say nowadays, into a high-grade gasoline motor car and may still be viewed outside of museums.

The steamer was not the only forerunner of the gasoline automobile, for there was also the electric-battery-powered affair, which as all of us know has somehow managed to survive to this day, in spite of the fact that a lightweight battery for automotive traction has not yet made its appearance. The earliest electrics that I can recall riding in were the apparently top-heavy hansom cabs built by the Electric Vehicle Company of Hartford, Connecticut. These seemed to have been designed with a pair of horses in mind as auxiliaries, for the driver's seat was perched high in the rear and there was a trap door in the roof for communication between driver and passengers. One almost expected a set of reins leading to the driving mechanism. Curved folding doors directly in front of the passengers' seat were opened and closed by a lever arrangement under the driver's control, and served the dual purpose of preventing the fares from escaping without settling their account and of shielding the passengers from the head-on breezes. The top-heaviness was more apparent than real because the cabs carried heavy storage batteries slung between the rear wheels, thus lowering the center of gravity to a very safe point. The cabs steered with the rear wheels, so that the maneuverability was comparable to driving a modern car in reverse.

It seems to be the general impression that the automobile, whether steam, electric, or gas, contributed something characteristically different to the principle of wheeled transportation—I mean the arrangement of the wheels and axle whereby one wheel can rotate faster than the other in turning corners—accomplished through the use of bevel gears and referred to as the axle differential. It is my recollection, however, that this method of steering was used on the horse-drawn cabs of Philadelphia that were known as "Herdics," away back in the days when I was a mere lad in the Quaker City. The front wheels of these Herdics were mounted on stub axles or knuckles, and held in much the same manner as in the automobile of the present day. There was no attention paid to "toe-in" or "camber." Each shaft or thill for the horse was fastened to the front of the knuckle instead of the modern steering arm at the rear. And the horse turned in either direction without the necessity for "cut-in" in the body of the cab, which would otherwise have been required on a vehicle that had to make sharp turns fairly often. But the arrangement caused quite a wear and tear on living horsehide, due to the sliding of the shafts against Dobbin when he turned, and the method never became popular.

The first gasoline-driven automobile I ever rode on was the De Dion, a French number that was contrived on the assumption that the front-seat passengers were more interested in seeing where they had come from than in learning where they were going. For each front passenger actually had to sit facing backward, perched upon a tool-box that served also as a seat, with one eye on the driver and the other on the departing roadway. Of course, one might swing around on the seat and face forwards, but then one would have to dangle one's legs over the front railing and thereby look quite ridiculous to oncoming pedestrians. In either position these passengers were something of an eyesore to the driver, interfering with the latter's vision even if they kept perfectly still, and more often than not they plagued the driver with silly questions like "Where are we headed now?" and "Will you let me know in time if there's a head-on collision?"

The De Dion was a rear-engine car, the power plant being a small, single-cylinder, air-cooled engine of less horsepower than that of the modern one-lung motorcycle. It was comparatively low slung when you consider the contemporary American models that were set on 36-inch wheels, and the engine was connected directly to the rear axle through suitable reduction gears. The controls were all mounted on a column that rose perpendicularly in front of the driver's seat. The particular De Dion that I rode on belonged to Winthrop Scarritt, one of the early presidents of the Automobile Club of America, and was one of the early cars which had a lower gear ratio in reverse than in first speed. I remember this because Scarritt achieved a certain degree of notoriety during a hill-climbing contest at Eagle Rock, New Jersey, by turning the car around after it had stalled and backing it up the hill to the finish line.

Duryea, Ford, Haynes, and Winton—these names are placed in

alphabetical order to avoid the necessity of stating which of them came first chronologically, but at least we can say that by 1895 each maker had built gasoline-driven automobiles and had tried them out successfully on the road. Charles and Frank Duryea have the distinction of organizing the first automobile company in the United States—the Duryea Motor Wagon Company, founded on September 21, 1895, at Springfield, Massachusetts. Duryea cars also achieved a place in history by winning America's first automobile race at Chicago, on November 28, 1895, as well as England's first automobile race from London to Brighton, on November 14, 1896. The first patent granted to a maker of automobiles in the United States went to the Duryea Brothers on June 11, 1895, and for those who are interested in patent lore we give the number—540648. On November 5, 1901, a three-cylinder Duryea car won the Eagle Rock climb.

Alexander Winton also left his mark on the automobile industry. He was the first builder of the "big" car, and one of the first to realize the necessity for providing spare parts and service "stations" in order to keep a manufacturer's automobiles in running condition after it had left the factory. I was present at the first automobile show in this country, held at Madison Square Garden on Twenty-fourth Street in New York City in 1900, and recall seeing Winton drive up in a mud-covered, weather-beaten contraption that had traveled all the way from Cleveland to New York under its own power over roads that were considered little better than cowpaths and without the assistance of the numerous signposts and markers that are such a prominent feature of the concrete or macadamized highways of today. Winton began with a single-cylinder or one-lunger, as did most of the early carmakers, but instead of being content with mere refinements only on this design, he immediately jumped to his big, two-cylinder-opposed 40-horsepower job that practically revolutionized the industry. Following this came his four- and six-cylinder cars, which for a long time were the leaders in the field of multicylinder gasoline automobiles. Winton pioneered the self-starter long before Kettering's electric device by tapping some of the compressed gas from one of the cylinders and storing it in a tank in readiness for the next start.

A car that closely resembled the first Winton was the early one-cylinder Packard, the main difference being in the shape of the dashboard. Whereas Winton's curved backward in long graceful lines, the Packard's was square or boxlike in shape. As a matter of fact, the dashboard *was* the toolbox, or vice versa. And toolboxes were a mighty important adjunct to the automobile in the days before service stations and public garages. The first such Packard I saw was the one that came to New York to participate in an early run of the Automobile Club of America over a course that extended from the old Waldorf-Astoria Hotel on the site of the present Empire State Building to the main square of Bridgeport, Connecticut—a distance of only 50 miles or so on our modern highways but the equivalent of 5,000 miles on the primitive turnpikes of the late 'nineties. The run to Bridgeport was considered a supreme test of the automobile's stamina and endurance, to say nothing of the driver's; a measure of how far the automobile has progressed up to the present is found in the fact that our modern Sunday driver thinks nothing of a spin covering twice that distance merely to pass the time away on a sunny afternoon.

This particular Packard had a body design known as the "dos-à-dos," an appellation borrowed from the French, which I translate as back to back. That is to say, the driver and one passenger faced forward and the other passenger or passengers faced backward, but with this difference from the De Dion model, that they did not have to face each other. James J. Salmon, who was an editorial assistant to Fred Miller on the *American Machinist* at one time, was my fellow passenger on the rear seat when I undertook the New York to Bridgeport run on the Packard one-lunger about 1900.

I remember this occasion very well because it was a bitterly cold December day and I had put on two pairs of long woolen drawers, a knitted chest protector, a flannel shirt, a turtle-neck sweater, a worsted jacket, a long winter overcoat, fleece-lined gloves and a set of ear muffs. This outfit was considered quite modish for winter driving in the totally unenclosed vehicles of the day. I may also have had on a linen duster over everything, although such a garment was considered somewhat of an affectation within city limits.

We left from in front of the Waldorf about 10:30 A.M., getting a hearty send-off from a handful of well-wishers and rubbernecks, and proceeded in state up Fifth Avenue, doing about 12 miles an hour. People on the sidewalks stopped dead in their tracks as we passed by and stared after us until we were out of sight. Drivers of horsecars and hansom cabs gave us a wide berth, being now familiar with the typical reaction of their draft animals to the sight of a horseless carriage. I felt very conspicuous and uncomfortable in my getup on the unprotected back seat, and too often when we stopped for traffic a brewery horse or a street-cleaner's nag would edge up to the back of the car with nostrils dilated and blow a hot breath of anger into my face. Unless we remembered to hold on tight to the handrails at all times, there was great danger of toppling off into the street each time the driver started up again. And facing backwards, with the road, the people, and other objects constantly receding from one's line of vision, tended to induce vertigo within a very short time.

At Ninety-sixth Street, just as we were approaching a long incline, the Packard let out a terrifying roar and came to a sudden stop. We all leaped off and pushed the vehicle over to the curb, while out of nowhere a crowd of curious spectators began to collect, and a policeman in a coal-scuttle hat approached, reaching for his notebook.

"It's all right, officer," said our driver, who seemed to have been prepared for some such incident. "It's just the cylinder-head gasket—she's blown again."

"Cylinder-head gasket, is it?" repeated the policeman. "I thought I heard a pistol shot, faith."

"I'll have it fixed in a jiffy," our driver reassured him as he lifted the back seat and exposed the motor. "This happens every once in a while, you know."

"And does it also happen that you have a permit to operate one of these things?"

Our driver produced the necessary papers.

"I guess everything's all in order, then," said the policeman. "Only get this contraption fixed for the love of God and get it out of here. You're collecting a crowd."

"Look at the funny man in the ear muffs," remarked a boy in our audience.

"It's one of them things that goes by itself," said another.

"Want to buy a horse, mister?" asked a third.

Our driver had taken a sheet of ordinary blotting paper out of the toolbox and had fashioned himself a new washer or gasket, which he thereupon replaced in the cylinder head. We put back the seat and climbed aboard. I noticed that the driver had not bothered to crank the engine, but had simply released the hand brake. The car, being on a slight incline, started rolling forward, and when it had got up enough speed, the driver switched on the ignition and let in the clutch. The motor started up immediately with a roar.

"That's a trick you want to remember," he said, turning sidewise toward me. "When you're going downhill you don't have to worry about cranking her up."

From my vantage point on the rear seat I saw the little crowd waving after us as we continued on up Fifth Avenue.

The remainder of the trip, strange to say, was quite uneventful, and we rolled into Bridgeport a little after 6 P.M. that evening, having been on the road a mere 7½ hours. Most of the cars that started out failed to arrive at all. But the thrill of our accomplishment had been somewhat dampened a few hours earlier when, along about 3:30 P.M. we met Albert Bostwick, the millionaire sportsman, coming back from Bridgeport in his big Panhard, which had made the trip in about 4 hours flat. The powerful French car made the American models appear hopelessly outclassed.

Speaking of the early Packard reminds me of the first Packard dealer in New York, whose name I have long since forgotten but whose very original technique of instructing new drivers remains in my memory. After the purchaser had placed an order and left a deposit against future delivery, the dealer began a two-week's course for his benefit on the intricacies of the automobile engine and the mechanics of the motor car. He first showed the prospective owner a floor sample of the car and instructed him in the rudiments of cranking the engine without getting an arm broken in the attempt. Then, as though it were a kind of parlor game, he would ask the purchaser to face the other way for a minute, while he ran around to the back and cut off the gas supply, or disconnected an ignition wire, or did other things to make the engine stop, or at least run irregularly. This he called "simulating actual road conditions." At a given signal the purchaser would turn around and then try to figure out by inspection or by tinkering just what the trouble was, and fix it if he could. Often this would involve getting "out and under," smearing one's self with grease and oil over hands, face, and clothing, or getting a stimulating shock from the storage battery. The new owners

Webb three-cylinder compound locomotive, about 1890, without side rods

The Fontaine locomotive, about 1880, with driving wheels mounted above and resting on another pair of wheels that ran on the track. Inset shows cartoon comment of the day comparing this freakish locomotive to an eccentric cyclist

First national automobile show, held in the old Madison Square Garden, November, 1900

Packard *dos-à-dos* and passengers on first run of Automobile Club of America from New York to Bridgeport, Connecticut, December, 1900

Charles F. Duryea in 1946 driving one of his early model runabouts of the late 'nineties

Angus Sinclair, shown with Mrs. Sinclair, in a 1901 model of the Toledo Steamer

Angus Sinclair's Toledo Steamer, shown on the preceding page, with the author's son Henry and grandmother, in 1901

Louis Renault in his first Renault car, about 1898. It had a 1¾-horse-power motor and wasn't intended to carry passengers

seemed to like this part of it best of all, for some unaccountable reason. A short course in driving through traffic would wind up the dealer's curriculum. I wonder how many dealers in our postwar automobiles would be capable of conducting such an educational program.

"The automobile today is, apparently, in about the position of the bicycle at the time when the diamond frame and the pneumatic tire had been accepted as final and leading features of the machine," wrote the *American Machinist* in its editorial of February 11, 1909, under the headline "The Coming Influence of the Automobile on Machine-tool Design." "Judging from the machines which may now be seen at any automobile show, they have reached a standard stage so far as their leading features are concerned. Until recently, improvements and changes which were not always improvements characterized the industry from year to year, the machine being in a fairly feverish state of rapid development. Unless all indications are at fault, this stage is now passed and automobiling business is, from this on, to become automobile manufacture, and we are led to ask if the influence of the bicycle in machine-tool development is to be repeated by the automobile."

The editorialist then proceeded to answer his own question, as follows:

To us this would seem to be not only reasonable but reasonably sure, and when the simplicity of the bicycle is contrasted with the complexity of the automobile it will be seen that the possibilities which now open up are far greater than those which existed in the early stages of bicycle development, and, for ourselves, we confidently look for rapid progress in the development of special machine tools for automobile work.

In this development (the editorial goes on), machine-tool builders must take the lead, as the automobile industry has unquestionably much to learn regarding what organized manufacture means. We have nothing but admiration for the work of automobile designers and builders. They have done a magnificent work which speaks for itself, but the conditions of the industry have heretofore made manufacture in the modern sense impossible in it, and much as we may admire the automobile people as designers and mechanics, it is the simple truth that, with few exceptions, they are not manufacturers properly so called, and many of them have the entire business of manufacture to learn. If, as we believe, the automobile industry has come to stay and to grow far beyond its present large proportions, it can scarcely fail to offer a fruitful field for the machine-tool designer and one in which he should lose no time in cultivating.

To what extent the writer of the foregoing summary of the infant automobile industry was justified, and how far his predictions came true, are things that I should like to say a word or two about in the space at my disposal. I shall try to make it interesting, but there may be those who will prefer to skip to the chapter on Airplanes or to my trip to Japan instead.

It is undeniable that in its early years the automobile industry was characterized by a state of feverishness so far as manufacturing and standardization were concerned. This was partly due to the fact that the automobile very early in its career developed into a "craze," a freak of fashion, a caprice or whim that caught on far too rapidly for its own good long before it was out of the experimental stage, and before its uses, and consequently its potential market, were thoroughly understood. As a result, manufacturers produced vehicles on a kind of "quickie" basis while there was still a great deal of novelty about them on the part of the public, and the number of different manufacturers who were doing the same thing at the same time multiplied overnight. In the beginning there was little or no research devoted to manufacturing and design problems, no apparent pooling of brains on the engineering involved, and nothing like a series of exhaustive factory tests before the product was passed on to the public. Quite the same sort of situation threatened to develop with respect to the helicopter and autogiro a few years back, but it was fortunately brought under control before a craze developed. The same sort of thing could easily have happened to the television industry in its early stages, only the greater complexities of the problem prevented premature exploitation. And one can think of other examples.

Newspapermen played up the early automobile craze in feature stories and news items in the daily press, giving great prominence to the exploits of certain millionaire sportsmen with their new horseless carriages, to inconclusive races and endurance contests, and even to the growing literature of automobile jokes intended to enliven polite discourse. One newspaper publisher, H. H. Kohlsaat of the Chicago *Times-Herald*, went so far as to sponsor an automobile race at Chicago on Thanksgiving Day, 1895, with perhaps more of an eye to the news value of such an event than to the furthering of scientific research. While it did increase the public interest in the new vehicle, it also accounted for some of the feverishness remarked by our editorial associate quoted above.

We have already noted how the American design in motor cars was a carry-over from bicycle and hansom-cab days, while European makes had already developed a functional, practical chassis and body more suited to a self-propelled vehicle. One American manufacturer was so affected by the adjective "horseless" as applied to his carriage that he incorporated in its design a wooden replica of a full-size horse, minus the hindquarters but complete with reins and harness, so that the change might not be too abrupt either for the owners or for passing quadrupeds. It was not until 1907 that Hiram Percy Maxim (whose recollections, published in 1937 under the title of "Horseless Carriage Days," make very interesting reading) showed me the first American-made automobile with the engine in front that I had ever seen. This was at the Pope Works in Hartford, where the inventor of the Maxim silencer had developed an early gas engine with four vertical cylinders connected with the rear wheels by means of a drive shaft and bevel gears, instead of the mid-engine chain-drive model that was so popular in this country at the time. It was only natural, under the conditions that I have sketched above, that scientific principles did not immediately enter into the manufacturing and design of the early automobile except in isolated instances, and that some time had to elapse before machine tools caught up with the needs of the industry.

Much of the machining on automobile parts in the early days was done by hand, and consequently nothing resembling mass production was achieved for a long while. Among the first automobile builders in New England was Harry Knox, whom I first met when he was manufacturing his three-wheeled car that was powered by an air-cooled motor. The cooling was effected by means of pins screwed into the outside of the cylinder until the latter bore a fair resemblance to a porcupine, and making these cylinders was a tedious, time-consuming job for Harry because all the holes had to be drilled and tapped by hand, one at a time.

An incident that may be worth retelling as an indication of early machine work on automobile parts occurred about 1908 during my first visit to the Acme Automobile Company of Reading, Pennsylvania, a firm devoted to producing a large, high-quality, custom-built car that was quite a slick job as horseless carriages went in those days. At this stage of automobile manufacture, the pistons were "lapped" into the cylinders. Lapping, as I have defined elsewhere as "precision finishing with abrasives," is the final stock-removing operation by means of which pieces of work are brought to desired size within closer tolerances for greater accuracy. Most lapping is done by machine nowadays, but the Acme Company was limited to hand methods at the time.

One of my first questions of the superintendent on entering the Acme Plant had to do with the kind of abrasive they were using for the lapping process.

"Oh, Mr. Colvin, I'm afraid we're not at liberty to disclose that," the superintendent replied. "It's one of our shop secrets, if you know what I mean, and if it got out, why every other automobile manufacture would be using it tomorrow. I can only say that it's a special powder of very fine abrasive quality that we discovered after a good deal of research. I'd sure like to tell you what it's composed of, but ethics is ethics, you know."

I said that I did not wish him to disclose a trade secret if it was so important, that it was merely scientific curiosity on my part which prompted the question. After a little while I got to moseying around the shop alone, looking over the operators' shoulders as is my wont, and trying to absorb some information by watching machinists in action. In due course I came to the lapping bench, where a few men were working on the pistons, using a master lap to ensure uniform abrasion. Among the miscellaneous articles on a shelf near the operators were two large, family-size cans of hand-scouring soap with the trade name Sapolio printed in large characters on the outside. I was about to say a few words in admiration of the spirit of cleanliness thus shown, when an operator suddenly reached his hand into one of the cans, scooped out a measure of hand soap, and applied it to the piston he was rubbing.

"Is this what you're using for an abrasive?" I asked, pointing in amazement to the Sapolio can.

"Sure, mister, and it's pretty good stuff, too, and only 10 cents a can." He stopped short, then added, "Cripes, I forgot—I wasn't supposed to tell anybody. Don't let on to a soul."

The superintendent came running up. "I see you have discovered our secret," he said regretfully. "Perhaps I should have told you right off, Mr Colvin—I know I can trust you not to mention it in the other shops or in the magazine. But the boss said I wasn't to tell anybody at all about it."

This situation was all the more ludicrous when shortly afterward I visited another early automobile plant in Indianapolis where they also had a " secret abrasive" for lapping that was not to be divulged to a living soul. Of course it turned out to be our old friend Sapolio. the all-purpose hand-scouring soap, or Mother's Little Helper, temporarily disguised as Ingredient X. In the same town, in a small shop near the famous speedway where motors were overhauled and tuned up for the races some years later, Sapolio was being used quite openly on main and crankpin bearings, and with great success. And still later, in 1939, I again made the acquaintance of this protean hand soap when Peter Hall, of the Hall Planetary Company, told me in a kind of stage whisper that he was using Sapolio for lapping the spindle bearings of his well-known milling machines. One thing must be said for Sapolio—it was always highly recommended as the most satisfactory abrasive for producing a fine finish, even though cloaked in anonymity.

The engine lathe and the planer began to play a larger part in the making of automobile engines about 1908, as I recall, for in that year I visited the E. R. Thomas Company's Plant at Buffalo, New York, where the famed "Thomas Flyer" first saw the light of day. The Thomas Flyer was a heavy, high-powered vehicle, one of the first to break away from the light runabout design that had so captivated American audiences in the early days. Thomas sent a car and its crew on a round-the-world tour about 1904—a trip that consumed a year's time and five or six complete sets of spare parts, but taught its makers a great deal more about the Thomas Flyer than they had known before. It was at the Thomas Plant, consisting of several buildings built around the old homestead of Grover Cleveland, that I met Clarence Buxton and Lucien Haas, the superintendent and chief tool designer, respectively, of the Thomas Company. About this time I was beginning to notice that the engine lathe and the planer were being used more and more extensively in the making of automobile engines having individual cylinders with solid heads, although I also noted that the Beaman and Smith boring machines were beginning to replace engine lathes to a limited extent.

Lucien Haas was largely responsible for the very efficient tooling of the Thomas Plant for mass production on the scale practiced in 1908, which I assure the reader did not signify 10,000 cars per day, being more like 50 cars per month. One of the things that held up a more rapid rate of production was the fact that the cylinders were made with a solid head, since the fear of leaks between cylinders and heads deterred many from attempting to make the present type cylinder block. Haas contributed greatly to the advance of machine-tool methods in automobile work through his series of articles on tool designing for the *American Machinist*, and later through his expert collaboration on our book "Jigs and Fixtures."

I have already indicated how the early "craze" for horseless carriages caused automobile plants to spring up like mushroom growths all over the country, just as hundreds of locomotive plants had sprung up in the early days of railroading. In both instances, however, the great majority faded out of the picture once the industry had become firmly established. As late as 1917 there were 127 different makes of American automobiles on the market, as compared with little more than a dozen in 1947. For the sake of the completeness of the present record, and in order to aid future scholars and research workers, I should like to give the list of American automobiles current thirty years ago: Abbott-Detroit, Allen, American-Six, Anderson, Apperson, Arbenz, Auburn, Austin, Bell, Biddle, Brewster, Bour-Davis, Briscoe, Buick, Cadillac, Cameron, Case, Chalmers, Chandler, Chevrolet, Cole, Crow-Elkhart, Daniels, Davis, Detroiter, Dispatch, Dixie Flyer, Doble, Dodge, Dorris, Dort, Drexel, Elcar, Elgin, Emerson, Empire, Enger, Fiat, Ford, Fostoria, Franklin, F.R.P., Glide, Grant, Hackett, H.A.L., Halladay, Harroun, Harvard, Haynes, Hollier, Hudson, Hupmobile, Inter-State, Jackson,

Jeffery, Jordan, King, Kissel, Kline, Laurel, Lenox, Lexington, Liberty, Locomobile, Lozier, Luverne, Madison Maibohm, Majestic, Marion-Handley, Marmon, Maxwell, McFarlan, Mecca, Mercer, Metz, Mitchell, Moline-Knight, Monarch, Monitor, Monroe, Moon, Morse, Murray, National, Nelson, Oakland, Oldsmobile, Owen, Packard, Paige, Partin-Palmer, Paterson, Pathfinder, Peerless, Pierce-Arrow, Pilot, Premier, Princess, Pullman, Regal, Republic, Reo, Richmond, Roamer, Ross, Saxon, Scripps-Booth, Spaulding, Simplex Singer, Standard, Stanley Steamer, Stearns-Knight, Stephens, Stewart, Studebaker, Stutz, Sun, Velie, Westcott, White, Willys-Knight, Winton, and Yale. A great many more names, including Brush, Duryea, Alco, Speedwell, and Waverly, had already disappeared from the scene by 1917.

To sum up, therefore, with all the advantages of hindsight over the vista of the past forty years in the development of the automobile, I think that the writer of the editorial quoted at the beginning of this section seemed to have a pretty good grasp of the situation in 1909, and certainly wasn't sticking his neck out when he predicted that the automobile industry had come to stay.

My own personal experience with various makes of automobiles was long and quite diversified. Naturally a fellow like me who gadded about all over the countryside in the role of inquiring reporter couldn't expect one car to last over a period of four decades or more. And besides the mere need for periodic replacement, there was also my inquisitive nature that prompted me to trade in the old car for a new make or model long before the old one was worn out. As a consequence, I went through a string of automobiles in a manner that would have been a credit to a millionaire playboy or a prince of the Hapsburg line. Beginning with Angus Sinclair's Toledo Steamer, which he finally relinquished to me in desperation, I started off in my own right with a Model T Ford in 1910, one of the first half hundred that Ford produced in his first year as a manufacturer of automobiles. The car was already used when I bought it, and evidently Henry had not yet got all the bugs out of his new product, for its operation was highly irregular and it thrived only on loving care and affection. It had clincher rims with 30- by 3-inch tires in front and 30- by 3½-inch tires in back, which meant that the irreducible minimum of spare tires and tubes that had to be carried along was two each. As a matter of fact a driver usually carried a rather complete line of inner tubes in the tonneau, just as though he were a salesman, because punctures or flat tires were a very common occurrence and a trip without tire trouble was something to write a letter to the editor about. The average life of the shoes themselves was not more than 3,000 miles, whereas mileages of ten times that amount and more are not unusual for the tires of today.

I then went through four more Model T's in consecutive fashion at about yearly intervals, my purpose apparently being to keep abreast of the Ford production schedule as well as I could and to learn about the latest improvements in Henry's product as they came out. I do not recall anything particularly memorable about these four except that one of them was stolen from my garage before I had even seen it, which shows that the hot car racket was flourishing even in those days.

My next venture was a Metz, which intrigued me because it had a friction drive that required a trained and delicate touch on the foot pedal in order to engage the friction wheel and thus get the car started without wearing flats on the fiber disks and getting nowhere in the process. On this particular job I once decided to try solid rubber cushion tires instead of the newfangled pneumatics, but the result was a series of broken steering knuckles that persuaded me I was better off with inner tubes in the first place.

After the Metz had lost some of its original novelty and glamour, I found myself admiring the Franklin air-cooled touring car that our local salesman was displaying very prominently in his show window. My son, Henry, who was at this time a lad of seventeen and beginning to display unmistakable signs of our hereditary trait of tinkering with machinery, had also been eyeing the Franklin covetously and learning all about it from the salesman. My sons Charles and Henry and I had done a lot of nursing of both the Fords and Metz cars. It was not very difficult for the boys to talk me into buying this distinguished-looking vehicle with its distinctive Renault-type sloping hood, because I was itching to find out how an air-cooled motor compared with the water-cooled type, and besides it was time for a change anyway.

One thing that appealed to me in the sales talk was the claim that tires could be changed with great ease because of a "quick detachable rim" feature especially designed for this model. It was not long before we had a chance to try it out. One Sunday as we were riding along the country road at perhaps 20 miles an hour the inevitable puncture occurred.

"Well, at least this won't be the tough job it used to be," I remarked to the boys, as I opened the toolbox and prepared to change tires. "What with this new engine-driven tire pump here and those quick detachable rims, it ought to be only a matter of minutes, kids."

I pried out the retaining ring about a ½-inch all around and then got a grip on it with both hands. It seemed to stick a little so I braced one foot against the hub and pulled harder. All of a sudden it came off with a *whoosh* and I went over backward with the ring halfway up my right leg. The detaching operation had been very quick indeed.

"Ha, pop, that's just what the salesman said—the rims detach quickly without the application of force. I should have told you how to take them off right."

The next step, of course, was to remove the tire from the rim. I pulled gently at first, expecting the entire wheel and axle to come off in my hands, but nothing happened. I yanked a little harder—no results. I hauled away like a navvy until the veins stood out in my neck. Finally I stopped and took a close look at the tire surface in contact with the rim, and a great light dawned on me.

The rubber of the tire seemed to have fused into one homogeneous mass with the metal of the rim, gluing the two together fast. It looked hopeless. Charles then said, "Pop, why don't you run it a few feet and maybe it will loosen up, huh?"

It seemed crazy to run a good tire while it was flat, but I was desperate now. And it worked! After we had run the car about 20 feet we stopped and found that the tire had finally broken loose and could be changed.

The Franklin, incidentally, was one of the first cars to use aluminum pistons, and as they expanded more than the cast iron of the cylinders, they were rather loose when cold, so that the car could be then cranked very easily, although a special primer helped so that we could pump high-test gas into the cylinders for starting. Another feature on the early Franklin (shared, too, by some early Fords) was a dashboard control for the needle valve on the carburetor that reduced the gas flow after the engine had warmed up and gave it a better gas mixture on hills.

I went through three more Franklins ("experimented with" would be a better phrase) over a period of about ten years and then moved on to a Buick, a Model A Ford, another Buick, a Lincoln Zephyr, a Ford V-8, yet another Buick, and a Mercury. This brings me almost up to date, although I am thinking of one of Bill Stout's Scarab II and a Studebaker at the present moment and have, of course, driven about a dozen or so other makes belonging to my sons, my friends, and my business associates. From the Toledo Steamer to the Scarab II is quite a long jump, but while driving today seems to have lost most of its spirit of adventure and excitement, I am certainly not one to pine for the good old days. Driving today is much more pleasant.

Four years before I was born, a farming couple named William Ford and Mary Litogot Ford became the parents of a son named Henry, who at the age of sixteen gave up farm work for good, walked to Detroit, got a job in a machine shop for $2.50 a week, began to build simple engines, returned for a while to the farm, married, got a job with the Detroit Edison Company as a machinist, set up a work-shop in the back of his house, and in his spare time built a gasoline motor car that ran successfully on two cylinders and 4 horsepower early in 1893. Six years later the farmer's son became chief engineer of the Detroit Automobile Company, with a small share of the stock, and in 1903 founded the Ford Motor Company with a capitalization of $100,000. In 1919, Henry and his son Edsel bought out the minor-ity stockholders of the company for $70,000,000, and in 1947 the Ford Motor Company had assets of close to 2 billions. This, in brief, is America's most famous success story, and in it is the source of many of the vast technological changes in production that have altered our way of living in the past forty years.

The growth of the Ford Motor Company has been one of the wonders of the modern world of business. According to reports, only $28,000 in stock was actually subscribed at its beginning in 1903, and of this only about $14,000 was in actual cash. The company was built up into a billion-dollar business entirely by turning back profits into new construction. It is said that Senator Couzens, one of the few original stockholders, put in $5,000 for a certain number of shares in 1903 and sold those shares in 1919 for $30,000,000, which is an astronomical percentage of profit I will not bother to figure out.

My first contacts with the Ford Motor Company began in 1907, just three years after its incorporation, when the Piquette Avenue Shop in Detroit constituted the entire plant of the company. C. Harold Wills was then making his experiments in the development of vanadium steel, one of the structural elements that made the Model T such a practical success. The qualities of this steel enabled the company to make the front axle and other rugged parts so unbelievably light that their apparent flimsiness frightened some prospective customers away.

It was on Piquette Avenue that Henry built his first six-cylinder car about 1906, which later turned out to have been an experimental venture, remaining in production only about two years. He had originally built a two-cylinder, 8-horsepower car with a chain drive, producing and selling, we are told, a total of 1,708 of these during his first year of operation. In the second year he had expanded to three different models, and for a few more years made quite a variety of four- and six-cylinder vehicles. Then in 1909 came the revolution. In that year Ford made his famous announcement to the effect that thereafter the company would manufacture only the four-cylinder Model T, with planetary transmission, and that "any customer can have a car painted any color that he wants, so long as it is black." And he kept his word—at least until 1927, when another revolution took place with the change-over to the Model A and a more flexible program of design.

In the beginning, Henry was quite averse to publicity of any kind, and many writers had tried without success to get some kind of detailed story of what was going on in the Piquette Plant for the benefit of the magazine-reading public. Whether it was simply modesty, or xenophobia, or a desire to preserve intact the secrets of the trade, I did not find out; but in 1912, C. Harold Wills, whose father happened to be a close friend of my own father, took me to his company's new Highland Park Plant just before it was put in operation and promised me the opportunity of writing it up for the *American Machinist* as soon as they had it in running order. So when in January of 1913 I received an invitation to come to Detroit as a welcome representative of the fourth estate, I lost no time in heading in that direction.

Henry had by this time evolved his revolutionary system of mass production, and whether the idea was original with him or not, the fact remains that his contribution to mass-production methods changed the whole pattern of industry and remains one of the most significant developments in the entire history of machines and machine tools. It is true that Ford builded on the foundations laid by others, and that he failed notably to credit the earlier work of men like Eli Whitney, Samuel Colt, Cyrus McCormick, and others who had achieved remarkable results with pioneer methods of mass production. It is also true that Ford, to use his own words from his Encyclopaedia Britannica article, "pioneered in the largest development of the method under a single management and for a single purpose." The single management was Ford and his son; the single purpose was to build a standardized, low-cost, dependable, practical vehicle for every adult person in the world.

I spent nearly two weeks at the Highland Park Plant, studying all the various assembly-line operations, asking hundreds of questions, speaking with dozens of engineers, draftsmen, designers, foundrymen, machine-tool operators, supervisors, and sales managers. The organization was not one-tenth of the size it is now, but it seemed vast enough even then. Ford had already attained a production rate of 10,000 cars a year, which was a fantastic figure to most readers of the articles, and in England was considered an outright falsification. Yet two years later, in 1915, Ford produced car No. 1,000,000, and not very long after that was manufacturing 10,000 cars in a single day at the Highland Park Plant.

My articles on the Ford Plant appeared in sixteen installments in the *American Machinist* during 1913 and 1914, illustrated with more than a hundred photographs of the various installations and operations, and immediately began to create quite a stir in journalistic circles. In the first place, the industrial and engineering world had been clamoring for definitive information on the *modus operandi* of the fabulous Ford Plant, and in these articles they got the news for the very first time, complete with the blessing of Mr. Ford himself. The reaction from the British technical press was most interesting. Referring to my statement about 10,000 cars a year, one organ said editorially, "No manufacturer can possibly build that many cars in one year; and even if he could, he wouldn't be able to sell half of them." Another pointed with pride to their Rover Plant in Coventry, which had then the largest production of any British plant, saying that its output of 100 cars a month was certainly the most that any reputable manufacturer could possibly produce without seriously lowering his standards. But time and Henry proved that his critics didn't know what they were talking about.

Ford and his engineers demonstrated that, given a sufficiently large demand for an article or product to make mass-production equipment feasible, great quantities could be produced accurately and efficiently at a unit cost far below any figure that had ever been dreamed of in the old days, together with tremendous savings in the amount of time and physical labor hitherto involved. Those of us who remember the old hand methods of scraping bearings, fitting pistons and piston rings, boring cylinders, and the slow and painstaking assembly methods, must realize that the practices now used by manufacturers of low-, medium-, and high-priced cars, as well as of many other industrial products, are traceable directly to the mass-production pattern established by Henry Ford.

Assembling cars on a moving conveyer is a case in point. Not one of the other car manufacturers considered it practicable at the time Henry introduced it, or when they learned about it from the *American Machinist* articles. Such a method, they said, would give the builder no time at all for the "loving care" said to be lavished on some automobiles by their makers. It was not very long, however, before most of Ford's competitors had adopted the conveyer-line assembly system when they found that it not only speeded up production but also resulted in better machining of subassemblies, thus eliminating the need for hand fitting when the parts reached the assembly line.

The impact of the Ford philosophy of wages and employee welfare, which some have called paternalism and other less euphemistic names, is still a subject of lively debate among sociologists and labor theorists. I have no intention of getting involved in either a defense or a denunciation, for I am trying hard to stick to the subject of machinery and machine tools. Nevertheless it should be mentioned that Ford's minimum wage policy of $5 for an eight-hour day had a far-reaching effect on industry as a whole and certainly raised the standards for mechanics and machinists throughout the country. It is a pity that his labor policy was not on a par with his other theories, and that for too long a time he played the role of the feudal lord with his employees, choosing to be either the kind father or the ruthless master according to the mood he was in.

Next to Henry Ford, the most spectacular figure in the automobile industry was Walter P. Chrysler. Beginning as a railroad man, Chrysler graduated to roundhouse mechanic and finally became superintendent of the Pittsburgh Locomotive Works. Here he might have remained for the rest of his life had it not been for his sudden interest in automobiles developed after a short period of employment at the Buick Plant in Detroit. After he had borrowed sufficient capital, he broke into the automobile game with two separate lines of vehicles known as the "Chalmers" and the "Maxwell," respectively. Both of these cars were pioneers in their way, but somehow managed to acquire an unsavory reputation—the Maxwell is still the butt of a well-known radio comedian's jokes—and Walter, with great good judgment, decided to liquidate both in favor of a new car with all the latest improvements, which became known as the "Chrysler."

Not long after the Chrysler had been firmly established by virtue of good performance coupled with good salesmanship, the former roundhouse mechanic startled the automotive world by bringing out a weird-looking design that he called the "Airflow." Although the futuristic lines of this number were far too advanced to suit the general public ("you can't tell which way the thing is headed," was the usual complaint), it was nevertheless the first car to use an all-welded steel body integral with the frame; the frame, in other words, had been eliminated entirely.

The Chrysler organization is probably the most closely knit of any in the automobile industry. All the models are designed in a single engineering department and very extensive use is made of interchangeable parts. Its engineers have been among the first to adopt hydraulic brakes, fluid clutch, and automatic transmission. Dave Wallace, president of the Chrysler Sales Corporation at this writing and long a close friend of mine, was the first to develop the "superfinishing" method of machining that is now used in many industries.

To conclude this sketchy outline of the automobile industry, the third member of the Big Three, General Motors, must be mentioned, if only briefly. The story of its organization and its ramifications we will, of course, politely avoid. At the Chevrolet Plant I first made the acquaintance of a former Ford employee who later achieved considerable fame in his own right. This was the Scandanavian-born production engineer Bill Knudsen, who was general superintendent of the Chevrolet Plant at the time of our meeting and who rose to the presidency of the vast General Motors Corporation, and was commissioned as a Lieutenant General, AUS, to supervise the production of war material during the Second World War. My visit to him at Chevrolet was for the purpose of securing an article on his method of extruding valves from a solid blank of round steel, the blank being heated and forced through a die which formed the stem, leaving the head with the same diameter as that of the block itself.

Charles F. Kettering, widely known as director of research at General Motors, was also the inventor of the electric starter on automobiles and developed a highly efficient air-cooled motor. At the time of my visit to Dayton, Kettering drove me all around town in a small car powered by one of his air-cooled engines. After overcoming a great deal of opposition to the idea, he finally sold it to General Motors, their intention being to use the motor on the Chevrolet. Exhibits at the Automobile Show of 1923 displayed Kettering's air-cooled engine as optional equipment on the Chevrolet, but for certain reasons of sales policy they never were actually marketed, and the water-cooled motor triumphed in the end.

I find, alas, that I have got way ahead of my story in trying to follow the rise of the automobile industry. I must return now to the year 1901, to Angus Sinclair, and to the editorship of the *Automobile Magazine.*

Our journal, after five strenuous years in which I used up ten gross of lead pencils and wore out three Oliver typewriters, was not quite as solvent as we could have wished. Whether this was because owners of cars were still too few in number, or because the embryo industry was in too chaotic a state to support a trade journal, or because my writings competed unfavorably with Mrs. E. D. E. N. Southworth's string of novels, I had no way of determining; the circulation reports showed that the *Automobile Magazine* was going unread by an increasingly large percentage of the literate population. This was intolerable, especially since I had to eat.

I made one attempt to give it a shot in the arm, and thereby brought the *Automobile Magazine* into the field of American literature, if only for a brief instant. Early in 1900, a young clerk in a Wall Street brokerage house had begun to send me sketches and short stories written around the automobile that were highly interesting but did not quite fit into our editorial policy at the time. In 1901, sensing the need for a little human interest material in our pages, I bought a story by this writer that had to do with early automobile days in the Cape Cod area. It was published in one of our early issues over the by-line of Joseph C. Lincoln. Joe, who later achieved world-wide fame as the author of such novels as "All Alongshore," "Cape Cod Stories," and "Out of the Fog," was a lovable character and a superb storyteller, and our long friendship that continued up to his death in 1944 is the source of many fond memories.

Angus Sinclair and I parted company in 1902, and I bade farewell not only to the *Automobile Magazine* but to *Locomotive Engineering* as well. It was in one sense a hard decision to make, but it was made a lot easier by Angus's slightly overbearing attitude and by my own notions of independence. For another five years I made several attempts to break into publishing on my own hook, including a disastrous venture under the trade name of the Derry-Collard Book Company on a mail-order basis, which failed for reasons too numerous to mention, and a few other projects designed to help pay off the outstanding obligations that one of my associates, in his infinite wisdom, had seen fit to saddle me with, by declaring personal bankruptcy himself.

I was therefore more or less on my uppers between 1902 and 1907, but fate in the form of John A. Hill, who must by now appear to be my guardian angel, rescued me from near poverty. In 1907, Hill proposed to me that I join the Hill Publishing Company to take charge of his latest enterprise, a monthly edition of the *American Machinist*. This was to reach out to a wider field than the weekly and to include the lowly shop mechanic who had left school in the seventh grade.

Here, at last, was the opportunity I had dreamed of since the days of my apprenticeship in the Rue Manufacturing Company. After a short wait of twenty or twenty-one years, my childhood dreams had come true.

CHAPTER SEVEN

I Join the *American Machinist*

Who would not be an editor? To write
The magic we of such enormous might;
To be so great beyond the common span
It takes the plural to express the man.
J. G. SAXE, *The Press*, 1855

"Has anybody here seen my eyeglasses?"

This was a familiar and oft-repeated query heard in the office of the *American Machinist* during the early 'nineties. The inquisitor was Frank F. Hemenway, chief editor of the paper under Miller and Moore, and one of the best steam engineers of his day. We have already seen how Frank had suggested me as editor for Alexander Luchar's new paper *Machinery*, and although I never had the privilege of working with him on the *Machinist*, I got to know him quite well in a kind of unofficial capacity.

Apart from his engineering and editorial knowledge, Frank's dominant characteristic was his knack of losing his eyeglasses at periodic intervals. How so intelligent a person with such a high regard for detail could systematically misplace these essential adjuncts and thus leave himself temporarily shortsighted may well be wondered at. It is explained by the fact that while Frank was an expert at steam engines he was something of a sloven when it came to keeping his desk in order.

Frank sat behind a handsome roll-top desk of generous proportions, an article of office furniture that was all the rage in those days. When the rolling cover was down, Frank's desk was assuredly the neatest and most methodical-looking one in the office. This was, of course, only between the hours of 6 P.M. and 8 A.M. At all other times, when the top was up, Frank's desk looked something like the Augean stables. Under the cover was a vast litter of papers, catalogues, incoming mail, unanswered correspondence, reference books, clippings, drawings, old photographs, subscription blanks, memorandums, half-finished articles and editorials, periodicals, advertisements, recipes, circulation statements, letters to the editor, small tools, paper clips, inkwells, Patent Office models, library paste, pencils, erasers, sketches for next week's layout, souvenirs, indicator cards, pipes and tobacco, out-of-date calendars, things to remember, collar buttons, slide rules, note paper, logarithmic charts, and assorted sedimentary deposits that would have fired the ambition of any archeologist.

Into this farrago Frank's current pair of eyeglasses would inevitably disappear, like twigs tossed into quicksand. He had an innocent habit of removing his spectacles, which he used only for reading, in order more clearly to see a chance visitor calling on him. When the visitor had left, the office staff waited breathlessly for Frank's probatory rummaging among his papers, followed by the stereotyped inquiry, "Has anybody here seen my eyeglasses?"

The question was purely rhetorical, and nobody felt obliged to answer. After a little more ransacking of his collection, Frank would usually get sidetracked by an accidental discovery.

"Why, here's a letter from old Charlie Kickham at Acme I guess I haven't seen before. Hm. Wants to know about pressures and temperatures and how they affect engine performance. I can't quite make out his writing, though. And here's that blueprint on the new Warner and Swasey lathe I was looking for. Now who in thunderation sent me this book on 'Home Gardening as a Means to Independence'? This must be Colvin's article on the Wilmington Shops. I thought we ran that thing last month. And here's the sample of plate steel the Hercules Boiler people sent me a while back. . . . "

And he would go on in this fashion for about a half hour until, suddenly remembering what he was looking for, he would blurt out,

"Oh, hell, I'm only wasting my time with this. Andy, my boy," he would add, summoning the office drudge, "run across to Lathrop's General Store and buy me a pair of eyeglasses like a good young fellow. Here's 50 cents. Be sure you get the magnifying kind. Try 'em on first and if everything looks blurred to you they're the ones I want. Hurry up now because I've a lot of work to do this afternoon."

When the contents of Frank's desk grew to the point where the roll top could not be closed without bursting the seams, the office staff usually got together and weeded out most of the riper items of his collection, discarding those papers and objects that were deemed to have lost most of their original value through passage of time. During the course of these periodic house cleanings, which could be undertaken only when Frank was *in absentia*, three or four pairs of eyeglasses would regularly be unearthed in the process. Whether these went into the eyeglass bank or were discarded with the other things, I never could find out.

Hemenway was not the first editor of the *Machinist*, having been preceded, as the reader will remember, by the old pioneer Jackson Bailey of whom we have spoken at length. Following Hemenway came Fred J. Miller as editor in chief, a man we have also met in preceding chapters, and who will be remembered as the unwilling protagonist of one Angus Sinclair of automotive fame.

As I have already pointed out, John Hill had signed me up to get out the new monthly edition of the *American Machinist*, which was to make its debut with the February, 1907, number. The monthly version was to coexist with the regular weekly edition, differing only in size and in its more direct appeal to the man in the shop rather than the designer or engineer. It was to be a simplified compendium of the articles that appeared in the weekly numbers, but it soon turned out that the bulk of the material was either original with me or secured from shop men who could make their work clear to less sophisticated readers.

When I joined the staff of the *American Machinist* on January 28, 1907, thereby fulfilling a lifelong ambition, I walked into the office expecting to find Fred Miller in the chair of editor in chief. I was naturally quite surprised when I found another old friend, Frederick A. Halsey, in his stead, and no sight or sign of the redoubtable Miller. I had enough politeness to refrain from asking bluntly, "How come?" But it was not long before I learned that some time previous to this, John Hill and Fred Miller had had a slight discongruity of opinion on editorial matters that gradually developed into a passage of arms in which Miller came off second best. Hence, Mr. Halsey had his chair.

Frederick Halsey was widely known at the time both as a practical

AMERICAN MACHINIST

A JOURNAL FOR MACHINISTS, ENGINEERS, FOUNDERS, BOILER MAKERS, PATTERN MAKERS AND BLACKSMITHS.

VOL. I. NO. 1.]   NEW YORK, NOVEMBER, 1877.   [$1.50 Per Annum.

Combination Lathe Chuck.

Every workman who has had experience in a jobbing or repairing machine-shop knows the make-shifts that are necessary to chuck work to the lathe spindle in the absence of a comprehensive chuck that shall act as a simultaneously-moving jaw chuck and one of independent jaws. Is a manufactory of regular

Fig. 1.

articles where one day's work

combines all the above requirements, and the accompanying engraving will make it plain to any practical mechanic.

The chuck in general appearance resembles the ordinary universal or concentric chuck, and carries either three or four jaws. (Fig. 1.) These jaws slide in radial slots on the face and are made of such a length that at every point from center to circumference in which they may be they cover the slots entirely, thereby excluding all dirt and chips. The jaws have three shoulders or steps, the outer or upper one of course much higher than the others, and when the jaws are reversed, as may be done in less than one minute, these long outer steps become the center ones, holding securely any small body, as the shank of a drill or reamer. That portion of the jaws which projects into the body of the chuck is cut into a half nut (A, Fig. 2) that engages with a screw (B), the square head of which projects through the face or rim of the chuck to receive a wrench. Below this projecting head is a bevel pinion inside the rim that engages with a circular rack or toothed ring. (C C) Now it is evident that turning any one of these screws will actuate the rack and every other screw, and so far there is nothing new or peculiar in the chuck. It is simply

Fig. 4.

other chucks, which is very desirable; fifth, the jaws can be reversed without removing any other parts of the chuck; sixth, it can be used as an independent jaw chuck, a universal chuck, or an eccentric chuck; seventh, all the working parts of the chuck are entirely protected from dirt and chips; eighth, all the parts can be removed for oiling and cleaning without removing the body of the chuck from the face-plate or spindle of the lathe, which is very desirable when large chucks are used.

These chucks are made in the following sizes:—Nine, twelve, fifteen, eighteen, twenty-one, twenty-four, thirty, and thirty-six inches, with either three or four jaws.

Our Export Business.

There is no doubt that the most direct and effectual way to introduce American machinery and tools into foreign markets is to show our foreign friends just what we manufacture and wherein the superiority over their own mechanical contrivances exists. Since the close of the Centennial Exhibition comparatively few foreigners visit the United States to make purchases of machinery and supplies, but many of them have regular representatives here who are on the alert to secure and send

from the port of New York. There must be particular fitness for such an occupation. If machinery is to be the specialty, the factor must have some mechanical knowledge as well as clear information about the state of progress in this line, in the country or countries where he designs to make his sales. Should he engage in exporting anything

from a pin to a pile driver, or from a baby

Part of page 1 of the first edition of *The American Machinist*.

mechanical engineer and as a student of industrial problems. He had been superintendent of the Ingersoll-Rand Company's machine shop at Sherbrooke, Quebec, where he inaugurated what was later to become known as the "Halsey Premium Plan" for the payment of machine-shop workmen. Seeing the abuses that so often crept into the old "straight piecework" plans, Halsey devised the method of sharing the savings due to increased production between the workmen and the company. The plan, because of its excellent results in terms of better wages for the employee and better production levels for the employer, grew steadily in popularity and was probably more widely used than any other system in its time.

Some years later Taylor and Harrington of the United States and Rowan of England proposed certain modifications of this plan which achieved a measure of notoriety but which in my opinion were not as wholly undiscriminatory as Halsey's, and certainly to Halsey belongs the credit of having been the first to break away from the rigid piecework plan which had caused so many disagreements in the old days. Halsey's premium plan probably affected wage payments all over the world to a greater extent than any other system yet proposed. At the present time there has been much attention paid to premium plans and incentive systems, notably that instituted at the Lincoln Electric Company of Cleveland.

Halsey was known too for his interest in machinery, particularly the design and operation of gearing and of valve motions. He wrote and published a number of articles on both subjects, which later appeared in book form in the Van Nostrand Science Series, and which had a great vogue for many years. But his most spectacular reputation in the field of engineering grew out of his spirited opposition to the movement then underfoot in this country aimed at making the metric system compulsory in the United States.

Now Halsey was not against the metric system as such, being too broad-minded a man to be ruled by prejudice. What he objected to in the plan, which had been framed into a bill and which was before Congress for adoption, was the compulsory feature. Under the existing laws, as Halsey pointed out in his editorial column and in public addresses before legislators and machine-tool builders, anyone who wanted to use the metric system was at perfect liberty to do so. In certain industries and types of work, he argued, the metric system might well be a decided advantage, and he was certainly not going to try to force the English system upon anybody who didn't like it. What he stressed in his arguments against the bill, and proved conclusively with a great body of facts and figures, was that the change-over to the metric system on a compulsory basis would involve in the machine-tool industry alone an expenditure of many millions of dollars without accompanying benefits of any kind whatsoever. And largely through his strenuous efforts for the cause, the lawmakers finally saw the light and brought about the defeat of the bill.

That the machine-tool builders of this country, and the mechanical industry generally, appreciated the great service Halsey had done for them in stating their case before Congress is attested by the fact that upon the defeat of the bill they presented Fred with a magnificent precision-made clock, appropriately engraved, in token of their profound esteem. This timepiece, an imposing example of the horologer's art, happened to be of the design known as the "grandfather clock." When the opposition camp, or advocates of the metric system, learned of this, they went about remarking that the selection of a grandfather clock as a gift precisely expressed the reactionary spirit of its donors. Perhaps a streamlined turret lathe would have been more fitting. I might observe in passing that there was another attempt to revive interest in the compulsory use of the metric system in 1920, and again the *American Machinist* took a leading part in the fight against the compulsory feature. And I believe the machinery industry as a whole has the same attitude on the subject that it had in 1902.

But the opponents of the metric system are confronted with its growing use in both Great Britain and in this country, especially in some automotive work. Engines for both automobiles and airplanes now use spark plugs with metric dimensions.

One of John Hill's right-hand men on the *American Machinist* in 1907 was Mason Britton, a well-known figure in the machine-tool world who had very close contacts with all the leaders of the industry, in good times and in bad. Coming to the *Machinist* in 1901 as an eighteen-year-old stenographer (most of the stenographers of that day were of the male sex), Mason rapidly rose to a position of importance and responsibility, becoming in fact the mainstay of the paper and of the Hill Publishing Company itself for a considerable period before its merger with the McGraw Company. He and I were in very close contact during our long association with the magazine, and it is gratifying to report that we always worked together in complete harmony, even though our ideas on some subjects were not entirely identical. During the Second World War, Mason was one of the top members of the Machine Tool Division of the War Production Board, and he finally resigned from the McGraw-Hill Company in July, 1944, to become the American member and chairman of the Machine Tool Committee of the Combined Production Resources Board. In addition to his other duties, he was also a consultant of the Surplus War Property Administration in Washington, and later became Foreign Economic Administrator toward the close of the war. Although we were proud of his significant contribution to the war effort, those of us who knew him best on the *American Machinist* were filled with genuine regret to see him leave the paper after so many years of service. He is now (1947) President of the Metal Cutting Institute.

In 1907, the senior associate editor of the *Machinist* was a young man named Frank A. Stanley, who had come to the paper a number of years earlier after quite a long practical experience in machinery both in this country and abroad. Beginning work in a cartridge-loading plant in Connecticut in the late 'eighties, he then went to Brown and Sharpe, and finally to Pratt and Whitney. In the middle of the 'nineties Stanley traveled to England, Ireland, France, and Germany to supervise the installation of machine tools of various kinds, returning to this country at the turn of the century to take up editorial work on the *American Machinist*.

While I had met Frank several times before I joined the paper's staff, it was only gradually that we were drawn together by our work, and perhaps by our common New England ancestry; but it was not long before we had formed a close friendship that has now lasted almost forty years.

For some time prior to 1907 I had been guilty of composing various and sundry small books on certain phases of machine-shop practice, and had furthermore succeeded in getting these offerings published. The very first book that I ever imposed on the reading public was a small, 4- by 6-inch paper-bound volume of eighty-eight pages, entitled "Machine Shop Arithmetic," published by the Practical Publishing Company, a pseudonym for Colvin and Cheney, who split the profits fifty-fifty, in 1895. I have hesitated to mention this up until now because, while the book seems to have been well received, it was by no means an outstanding event in the publishing world of its day, and besides it sold for only 50 cents a copy. Following this modest beginning came another small book, handsomely bound in black limp leather, bearing the title "The Compound Locomotive," which my former employer Angus Sinclair brought out over his imprint in 1900.

The year 1905 saw the publication of yet another little book of mine, "Link Motions, Valve Gears, and Valve Settings," which appeared under the name of the Derry-Collard Company, a publishing firm that A. Leighton Donnell and I brought into being and then promptly interred. Donnell and I were probably the first to adopt the plan of selling books by mail on approval (a technique later developed very successfully by the McGraw-Hill Book Company, Inc.), but we soon discovered to our regret that such a venture required a great deal more fluid capital than either Donnell or I were able to lay our hands on. Before the Derry-Collard Company folded completely, I managed to publish a fourth volume known as the "Railroad Pocket-Book, A Quick Reference Cyclopedia of Railroad Information," in 1906, and considered myself lucky to sell the publication rights subsequently to a London firm called the "Locomotive Publishing Company," who ran the book through several editions.

By the time that I knew Frank Stanley on the *American Machinist*, therefore, I had had sufficient experience with the writing of short books on machine-shop subjects to realize that what was most needed was a larger, more comprehensive handbook covering the whole field of machine-shop practice. I had actually been working on and off for three years compiling material for just such a handbook when I met Frank in 1907, but upon discovering that he had

wide experience in machine work along slightly different and com-
plementary lines, I proposed that he collaborate with me on the new
project. Frank consented and we went to work in earnest, the former
contributing a good share of material that I would otherwise not have
had access to. We finished the manuscript in the summer of 1908,
and apparently carried along by our own momentum, proceeded
immediately to a series of nine short manuals on various practical
hints to the machinist.

The first edition of the "American Machinists' Handbook"
appeared in October, 1908, bearing the imprint of the Hill Publishing
Company. It so happened that the elder Charles Churchill of London
was in our office when it appeared and bought the very first copy
from John Hill himself. With this auspicious beginning, together
with the energetic cooperation of Martin M. Foss, then in charge
of the book department of the Hill Company and later president of
the McGraw-Hill Book Company, Inc., the "Handbook" went
through eleven printings totaling 36,000 copies in the first edition.
While this may seem a modest enough figure compared with the
sale of Harold Bell Wright's novels of the same period, it was considered a pretty good showing for a technical book. The "Handbook," incidentally, is now in its eighth edition and has sold slightly
over 600,000 copies to date, and while it has not yet been translated
into a foreign language it has been sold in nearly every country in
the world.

In 1908, also appeared the series known as the "Hill Kink
Books," now long out of print, by Stanley and myself, covering
general repairs, press tools, patternmaking, milling machines, jigs
and fixtures, drill presses, and other machine-tool work of a rather
elementary nature for the practical machinist. Stanley has also collaborated with me on such books as "Running a Machine Shop,"
"Turning and Boring Practice," "Drilling and Surfacing Practice,"
"Grinding Practice," and "Gear Cutting Practice," all of which are
still in print and doing well, and he has also his own work "Punches
and Dies" in the current McGraw-Hill *Catalogue*.

Although Frank Stanley left the *American Machinist* many years
ago because of ill health (which has now been fortunately restored),
we have been in close touch with each other ever since. And although
he has been living in California for about twenty-five years, the width

of the continent has not prevented occasional visits between us, augmented of course by a fairly steady correspondence. Each revision of the "Handbook" has necessitated almost constant consultation between its authors, and the revisions of the auxiliary books on which we have worked together keeps us in constant touch with each other. We have been joint authors of so many works that our names seem to be firmly linked together in the minds of mechanics in various parts of the country, to the extent that each of us is frequently asked, "And how is your friend, the other Handbook Twin?"

Next in service seniority on the *American Machinist* in 1907, after Miller, Halsey, and Stanley, was the very unusual Ed A. Suverkrop, a man who combined the qualities of an excellent mechanic and experienced writer with the unpredictable temperament of the satirist and merry-andrew. "Suver," as we called him, had a fine technical background, had traveled widely as an engineer on ocean liners to South America and to the Far East, and was a great admirer of precision workmanship. At the same time, he was an irrepressible wag, full of quips and cranks, sallies of wit, and often stinging repartee. Most gagsters I have met have minds as devoid of content as some of their hoaryheaded jests, and grow tiring in a very short time; but Ed Suverkrop was the brilliant exception, for he knew more about the world in general and machinery in particular than several dozen of his contemporaries, and when he wrote about precision methods in engineering he commanded the respect of the entire machine-tool world.

Possibly because he appreciated his own abilities, Ed Suverkrop felt he could indulge his antic sense of humor with some degree of justification. I remember one occasion having to do with the Johansson gauge blocks that we mentioned in another connection a few chapters back. "Suver" had become deeply interested in these precision gauges when they were first introduced into this country, and after writing a series of very interesting and informative articles on them for the *Machinist*, he developed a method of his own for manufacturing gauge blocks of a similar design. While he was deeply engrossed with this project, he happened to meet the superintendent of a well-known machine shop one day, who promptly said, "Well, Mr. Suverkrop, I've been reading your articles on Jo-blocks and they're very interesting indeed. Tell me, is it true that you're working on a design of your own?"

"Yes," answered Suverkrop concisely. "Only I'm going to call mine 'Su-blocks' instead. Or do you think 'Krop-blocks' would be better? The matter of euphony is very important, you know."

"Oh, indeed, Mr. Suverkrop—I see what you mean, 'Su' and 'Krop'—very clever indeed. Ha! But speaking seriously, just how do you intend to make your blocks—how do you get those millionths of an inch tolerances?"

Suverkrop looked at his questioner in dead earnest for a moment and then said, "Of course you realize it's a closely guarded trade secret at the present time. I'll tell you if you promise on your word of honor not to divulge it to a living soul. Will you promise?"

"Certainly, Mr. Suverkrop. You know me. Mum's the word!"

"All right. Now listen carefully. Let's say we're going to make a ½-inch block. First I take an ordinary piece of ¾-inch steel and cut off about 7/32 inch with the shaper. That's just the preliminary rough work."

"I see."

"Then I prepare a chemical bath in a large open vat, made from my own secret formula. I can say that it is mostly muriatic acid combined with sodium fluoride, methyl acetate, and a few complex hydrocarbons. Do you follow me?"

"Oh, yes sir. Very clearly. Then what do you do?"

"Then I take a lot of these roughed-out blocks and suspend them by means of counterbalanced chains directly over the vat so that the blocks barely touch the surface of the liquid. By carefully adjusting the counterbalancing apparatus I then immerse the blocks in the acid to the required depth. The acid does the rest."

"How do you mean?"

"Eats away the surface of the block, of course. Cuts it down until it's exactly ½ inch plus or minus oh-triple-oh-two. But you've got to have the weights set just right, and of course everything depends on the strength of the acid bath. Now don't breathe a word of this to anybody, will you?"

"Oh, no, Mr. Suverkrop," replied the very much confused superintendent, "and I sure appreciate your telling me about it. Personally, I think you're a real genius." The superintendent afterwards told me he honestly believed this was the way Suver made his gauge blocks.

Thinking about Ed Suverkrop brings to mind another humorist of the machine-tool world, an engineer named George Markland, who was head of the Philadelphia Gear Works for many years and a prominent figure in the American Gear Manufacturers' Association over a long period. George, who always enjoyed a joke even when it was on himself, told me this gem about Suverkrop:

It seems that Markland, in the early days of the Philadelphia Gear Works, was quite interested in his company's advertisements and was always thinking up new and arresting layouts. One of his designs showed the Philadelphia Gear Works *Catalogue* fastened to a post by the tang of a common-cut or bastard file. He sent this prize layout around to the *American Machinist* with a note saying that he thought some such caption as "Keep Our Catalogue on File" would be pretty good, but that he was open to suggestions from the editor. Suverkrop got hold of the drawing and wrote back to Markland as follows:

> Dear Mr. Markland:
>
> I have seen your advertising layout showing the gear catalogue pinioned to a post by means of a bastard file. Your suggested caption seems to me a trifle flat, and the play on words too obvious. I therefore offer you the following, which I think is more subtle and far more appropriate: "The Bastard Who Uses Our Gears Gets Stuck."

No one enjoyed the joke more than Markland himself, and he and the nimble-witted Suverkrop became fast friends for life.

In order to relieve the occasional monotony of "straight" shop reporting, Suverkrop and I were often assigned to ferret out unusual items of interest that might liven up a page where necessary. On a tip from a constabulary friend of mine, I traveled to an obscure little shop in New England that specialized exclusively in the making of handcuffs, and wrote up a brief but absorbing article telling how these essential aids to law enforcement were fabricated. Not to be outdone by a newcomer, Suverkrop went out into the hinterland and came back with a kind of nature-study piece about one James Crans, an artistic blacksmith who fashioned lifelike roses, complete with foliage, out of odd bits of iron, rivaling, in design at least, the carefully bred prize specimens of his contemporary Louis Van Boeckel of Belgium.

Suverkrop finally resigned from the *American Machinist* so that he could devote all his energies to the commercial manufacture of his precision gauge blocks, but after beginning on a small scale in the Taylor and Fenn Shops in Hartford, he died before the venture had a chance to succeed.

The editorship of an established magazine must take into account the principle of succession, and in somewhat the same manner as the patriarch of old appointed from his deathbed a favored lieutenant to take over the leadership of his people, so was the editor of the *American Machinist* obliged to nominate a likely candidate from the ranks to succeed him when the time came. The nomination was not always openly announced, although it was often tacitly assumed by the members of the staff.

While Fred Halsey was editor in chief, everybody assumed that the logical successor was Frank A. Stanley, the senior associate editor of the *Machinist*, and a thoroughly capable man for the post. A year or so before Halsey approached the age of retirement, however, a newcomer named Leon P. Alford, a graduate of Worcester Polytechnic Institute, was added to the staff in the capacity of associate editor. Alford, although a fine engineer with practical machinery experience gained at the United Shoe Machinery Company, soon became a source of friction to most of the men on the paper because of his attitude of assumed authority and even overbearing manner toward his equals on the editorial staff.

We learned later that this unfortunate situation was due largely to Fred Halsey himself, who had permitted us to go on assuming that Frank Stanley was going to be editor in chief in a short while, whereas Halsey had privately appointed the new man, Alford, as his successor, feeling that only a college graduate could handle the job properly now that science was taking over everything. When we learned the facts, we were ready to forgive Alford for his authoritative ways, for we realized that he was merely putting on a sort of dress rehearsal for the big job ahead. And Frank Stanley was going to resign anyway, because of ill health.

Alford gradually broadened out into a very likable personality after he became editor in chief in 1910, and following a fine career in that post, he resigned in 1917 to go with the Ronald Press; some years later he became dean of engineering at New York University, succeeding Joseph W. Roe. We remained very good friends until his death in 1942. It was during his regime that I spent four months at the Springfield Armory in 1916, making a study of the methods and operations used in making the Springfield rifle, so that other manufacturers could learn how they were made in case the government suddenly gave them an order for ten thousand or so, and other shops would be called on to make them. That was just before the First World War, and I see I am getting ahead of myself.

We must now take a step backward a few years to 1902, so that we may chronicle from the beginning the rise and development of the National Machine Tool Builders' Association which, after the American Society of Mechanical Engineers and the various technical magazines in the field, was one of the most effective means of coordinating and organizing the machine-tool industry in the United States.

Although the building of machine tools was one of our earliest industries and was absolutely essential for the construction of all types of machines used in other industries, it may seem strange that it was not until 1902 that a move was made to form a national association of machine-tool builders in this country. This apparent neglect was largely due to the fact that most of the shops building machine tools in the early days had been started up by lone mechanics who possessed more ideas and mechanical skill than business acumen and experience. These early shop men were of necessity an unorganized band of lone-wolf inventors whose main purpose was to put their mechanical ideas into what they believed were marketable machines. Each manufacturer naturally felt that his machine tool was the best of its kind, that those of his competitors were, *ipso facto*, somewhat inferior products and not to be trusted too far. They were rugged individualists, these pioneer toolmakers, who had not yet realized the truth of the old adage that in union there is strength.

An excellent historical outline of the formation of the National Machine Tool Builders' Association, here reproduced in part, was written by my old friend August H. Teuchter, head of the Cincinnati-Bickford Tool Company of Ohio, and presented at the twenty-fifth anniversary of the association. This outline is so clear and concise that it may with considerable profit be read by all mechanically minded young men of the present generation, many of whom have little or no conception of the confusion of ideas existing in the industry at the turn of the century.

The National Machine Tool Builders' Association (writes Mr. Teuchter) grew out of a little meeting, held in New York in the spring of 1902, of seventeen lathe builders who were called together at the invitation of William Lodge, president of the Lodge & Shipley Machine Tool Company of Cincinnati, to talk over their mutual problems in a friendly way. There were reasons a-plenty for earnest consideration of the situation that confronted these seventeen builders, and, in fact, the whole machine-tool industry, at that time.

The competition of twenty-five years ago was a bitter rivalry. Business judgments were founded on hearsay and rumor—mostly a jumble of misinformation. The shrewd buyer who was willing to employ such methods found that it served his purpose to sow seeds of distrust and enmity among competing sellers. Definite standards of business practice among the members of any given industry were rare. In the face of "business-at-any-cost" policies of the majority, it was a difficult matter for the smaller, weaker companies to formulate sound policies or adhere to good business practices. For the machine-tool industry, whose problems were so different, so little understood, and so much

An early chain-feed lathe, about 1840

The lathe which turned engine parts for Ericsson's Civil War ironclad, *Monitor*, launched
January 30, 1862

Early milling machine in Silver and Gay shop, said to be the inspiration for Frederick Howe's later machines

Frank A. Stanley, about 1925

American Machinists' Handbook

AND

DICTIONARY OF SHOP TERMS

A REFERENCE BOOK OF MACHINE SHOP AND
DRAWING ROOM DATA, METHODS AND
DEFINITIONS

BY

FRED H. COLVIN, A.S.M.E.

Associate editor of the *American Machinist*, Author of "*Machine
Shop Arithmetic*," "*Machine Shop Calculations*,"
"*The Hill Kink Books*," etc., etc.

AND

FRANK A. STANLEY

Associate editor of the *American Machinist*, Author of "*Accurate
Tool Work*," "*Automatic Screw Machines*,"
"*The Hill Kink Books*," etc.

1908

HILL PUBLISHING COMPANY

505 PEARL STREET, NEW YORK
6 BOUVERIE STREET, LONDON, E.C.

*American Machinist — Power and The Engineer — The Engineering
and Mining Journal*

Title page of first edition of the *American Machinists' Handbook*, 1908

MACHINE SHOP
ARITHMETIC

A Pocket Book containing some of the problems
of everyday shop life and the way in
which they are solved.

BY

FRED H. COLVIN

AND

WALTER LEE CHENEY

Editors of **MACHINERY**.

THE PRACTICAL PUBLISHING CO.
65 North 18th St., East Orange, N. J.
1895

Title page of *Machine Shop Arithmetic*, 1895

The Maxim flying machine, as illustrated in *Machinery* for August 10, 1894

Professor Samuel Pierpont Langley and his pilot, Charles Manley, photographed just prior to the unsuccessful launching of Langley's aerodrome on the Potomac River, Washington, D. C., October 7, 1903

Side view of the engine developed by Charles Manley for Professor Langley's aerodrome showing arrangement of timing gears more difficult than those of industries not so far removed from the consumer, it was hard even to determine what was good policy and what was not.

Mr. Lodge had given these matters especial thought. Early in the history of his own business, he had discerned greater opportunities in specialized production, and by 1900 had become one of the leaders in the manufacture of lathes. Here again, the peculiar problems of the machine tool industry became intensified when the field was narrowed down to but one of its products. The rapid expansion of all industrial enterprise through the 'nineties had been reflected in the growth of the number of machine tool shops. Particularly throughout the Middle West many new shops had sprung up, all eager to take what business could be had on any terms, regardless of the effect on their own business or on the industry as a whole. The future did not look inviting. A demoralized industry cannot go forward, and demoralization appeared to be lying in wait just around the corner.

Mr. Lodge and others of the lathe group were convinced that fear and distrust arising out of ignorance of competitors' policies were strongly contributing elements in the threatened demoralization; that the substitution of a friendly spirit of cooperation was the first step necessary in combating the unsound practices and evils that were promising to choke off their industry's progress; so a meeting was called. The seventeen manufacturers who responded, unanimously endorsed the association idea, and out of that meeting grew the National Machine Tool Builders' Association, the object of which, as stated in the Constitution and By-Laws adopted in 1902, is "To promote the interests of the National Machine Tool Builders in the direction of good fellowship, and the liberal discussion of subjects pertaining to the sale of machine tools."

The first officers elected were as follows: President, Joseph Flather, of Flather & Co., Inc., Nashua, N.H.; first vice-president, William Lodge, of the Lodge & Shipley Machine Tool Co., Cincinnati, O.; second vice-president, W. P. Davis, of the W. P. Davis Machine Tool Co., Rochester, N.Y.; secretary, P. E. Montanus, Springfield Machine Tool Co., Springfield, O.; treasurer, Enoch Earle, of P. Blaisdell & Co., Worchester, Mass.

Good fellowship was the central thought of the plan—good fellowship and a friendly interchange of ideas. Out of this it was hoped would emerge a universal adoption of those policies or practices found to be good and beneficial to the whole country.

It might be interesting (continues Mr. Teuchter) to review here the names of the firms who were represented at that early meeting: American Tool Works Co., Cincinnati, O; P. Blaisdell & Co., Worcester, Mass.; Bradford Machine Tool Co., Cincinnati, O.; W. P. Davis Machine Tool Company, Rochester, N.Y.; Draper Machine Tool Co., Worcester, Mass.; Fairbanks Machine

Tool Co., Springfield, O.; Flather & Co., Inc., Nashua, N.H.; Greaves-Klusman & Co., Cincinnati, O.; Hendey Machine Co., Torrington, Conn.; R. K. LeBlond Machine Tool Co., Cincinnati, O.; Lodge & Shipley Machine Tool Co., Cincinnati, O.; Prentice Bros., Worcester, Mass.; Rahn, Mayer & Carpenter Co., Cincinnati, O.; F. E. Reed Co., Worcester, Mass.; Schumacher & Boye, Cincinnati, O.; and Springfield Machine Tool Co., Springfield, O.

In October, 1902, the first annual meeting of the association was held in Cleveland, the membership having grown to thirty-three companies representing builders of lathes, milling machines, drilling machines, shapers, and grinding machines. Every one of the thirty-three member companies was represented at the meeting.

The first paper presented before the association at its first annual meeting in 1902, by Fred A. Halsey, dealt with the metric system (!), and a resolution was adopted by the association opposing the system because of the enormous first cost of new equipment required to conform to the new standards, the cost of maintaining a double standard for repairs and renewals, and the consequent increased cost of the product to the consumer.

This is the first record of a united effort on the part of the machine tool builders, acting together as an industry, on a question of interest to all manufacturers in the country. It represented the awakening of an industry consciousness—a realization of a new power that from that time on was to make its own place in the nation's business.

Standardization of parts, that we look upon as a question of our own time, was earnestly advocated by Mr. Lodge in a paper before the association at the annual meeting in 1903, when the new association was but a year old. It was about the time of the introduction of high-speed steel, when an unprecedented revolution in design was imminent. Commenting on the radical changes that were being foreshadowed, Mr. Lodge advocated the adoption of standard parts that would facilitate interchangeability of face-plates, chucks, and tools.

In 1908, when revision of the tariff was a question of national concern, machine tool builders, through the association, secured a separate classification for the industry under the heading "machine tools," volunteering at the same time a reduction in the tariff on machine tools. The reduction held until after the (First) World War, when the Tariff Committee restored the percentage as a protection against a possible flood of foreign-made tools brought in at depreciated currency prices, and the consequent weakening of an industry indispensable to the national defense.

Thus far Mr. Teuchter, and I owe him a debt of gratitude for providing the foregoing excellent summary.

Foreign trade was one of the early topics of discussion, as Mr.

Teuchter points out, and in 1906 the United States government sent Capt. Godfrey L. Garden to study conditions abroad. The following year John Hill, intent on keeping his *American Machinist* readers well informed on the current scene, sent J. Wallace Carrel to Europe for several months on a similar mission.

The subsequent history of the N.M.T.B.A. is a story of steady growth and increasing service to the industry. Realization of the need for better business methods led to securing the services of Ernest F. DuBrul as general manager and of Frida F. Selbert as secretary, with offices in Cincinnati, in the fall of 1920. DuBrul made a very complete study of the ups and downs of the machine-tool industry, and following his well-considered recommendations, business practices were improved and the industry as a whole strengthened.

About this time, in connection with the work of the American Society of Mechanical Engineers and the American Standards Association, progressive members of the N.M.T.B.A. began to sponsor the standardization of certain features of machine-tool construction. This had proved highly beneficial to makers as well as users of machine tools. Among the standards thus far adopted are spindle noses for milling machines and for lathes, including the tapers of all machine spindle holes; slots in machine-tool tables, tool-post openings, screw machine tools, and other parts; so that many tools and fixtures can now be used on different machines without loss of time.

It has been my privilege to work on a number of these committees of the American Society of Mechanical Engineers with representatives of the different machine tool builders. This has helped to maintain acquaintances and friendships begun many years ago, some of them made before any real idea of the need or value of standardization was apparent.

Ernest DuBrul resigned as general manager of the association in 1931, being succeeded by Boyd Fisher and later by Herman H. Lind. Tell Berna became manager in 1936 and holds the post at the present writing. Mrs. Selbert, a most capable secretary, is probably more familiar with the details of the organization than any other officer, past or present, of the association. It is to her that I am indebted for most of the historical material presented above.

As many of my older readers will recall, the period from about 1902 to 1914 saw the rise of a crusade of so-called "scientific" management, and the much overworked word "science" was bandied about, as it still is today, by people who had not the slightest idea what it actually means. Science was in a fair way to becoming another religion or cult, if one could judge by the columns and columns of space devoted to the "popularized" variety in the increasing number of Sunday supplements; and the worst of it was that very few readers knew that science was merely a body of knowledge obtained and verified by rational thinking, and not a new deity that periodically spoke in oracles from the mountaintop.

The trend to scientific management, under these conditions, naturally brought in its train a fair number of charlatans and thimble-riggers who figuratively set up their medicine shows in the public square and sold flummery and hocus-pocus in the name of science to the uninformed multitude. The field of industry was certainly not immune, and quite a few mountebanks passed themselves off as efficiency engineers and scientific managers, thereby selling numerous business executives quite a shoddy bill of goods. Very early in the game the *American Machinist* organized a countercrusade which, while acknowledging the good points of honest scientific management, began to debunk the quacks and imposters who posed as efficiency experts.

One of the most sensational exposés in this direction was made by the *American Machinist* as early as 1882, and although it relates more to the problem of ethical business methods than to scientific management, it may serve to indicate the editorial policy of that magazine throughout the years.

It seems there was a clever adventurer named John Fink who, as Damon Runyon would say, put himself away with several well-known manufacturers as being an upright and ingenious inventor of a patented cutting compound for use on various kinds of machinery. He was a slick dresser and the prototype of today's high-pressure salesman, weaving a kind of hypnotic spell over his prospects before he unloaded several gallons of his formula, collecting anywhere from $50 to $700 for exclusive shop rights, and making a quick dash to the railroad station to catch the next express out of town. If the customer needed a lubricant instead of a cutting compound, Fink was always most ready to oblige, selling the identical formula at the same prices and with the same dexterity. He carried about with him several reams of testimonials from well-known concerns and any quantity of filled and unfilled orders, so that the client usually felt like a fool for not having signed up long ago and thus getting the jump on his competitors.

The *American Machinist* one day got hold of a sample of Fink's alleged patent all-purpose-lubricant-and-cutting-compound, and found it to be a cheap mixture of lime, French chalk, potash, water, and third-grade oil. It was of course absolutely worthless for either purpose, and even destructive to machine parts. Among the victims, the *Machinist* learned, were such reputable concerns as the Baldwin Locomotive Works, Brown and Sharpe, Cambria Iron Works, Hoopes and Townsend, and Pratt and Whitney. Fink, with the brashness common to the high-class swindler, threatened to sue the *American Machinist* if it "published anything that might be injurious to his business"! But the exposure was made in the magazine's columns, and Fink was indicted in Detroit in 1885 for fraud.

I had read a little about Fink's get-rich-quick scheme at the time, but in 1885 I was more interested in the business of making injectors. Nearly thirty years later, in 1915, my memory of the event was suddenly jogged into activity when a shop superintendent for a Texas railroad told me that an elderly, well-dressed gentleman named Fink had just offered his company the exclusive shop rights to a patented formula to be used as a cutting compound or lubricant, as the case may be, and that the railroad company was on the point of laying out a good deal of cash for the privilege. After very little investigation I discovered that history was about to repeat itself, for, believe it or not, it was the same operator Fink of my younger days, doing business at the same old stand. Counting on the passage of thirty years to dull the memories of men, Fink had not even bothered to improve on his formula, feeling no doubt that what was good enough for one generation was good enough for the next. I promptly wrote up another exposé and Fink was again taken out of circulation.

These and many other frauds were persistently sought out and exposed by the *American Machinist* in the interests of the machine industry. Even the advertising copy that came in was carefully scrutinized by experts in various fields so that advertisements of doubtful character might be eliminated. Not infrequently the advertisements of old and perfectly reliable manufacturers had to be edited in order to remove the possibility of misinterpretation as to the action of the tool or machine advertised. We weren't taking any chances of being accessories either before or after the fact to any disingenuous projects of the Fink variety.

This very sketchy account of my early years on the *American Machinist* makes no attempt to record in detail the development of the machine-tool industry during 1907–14, the period roughly covered in this chapter. I have made no mention of the panic of 1907, the discovery of the North Pole by Admiral Peary, the *Titanic* disaster, the outbreak of the First World War in Europe, the early beginnings of radio in the work of such men as Dunwoody, Fessenden, and DeForest, the development of electric ship propulsion, the mercury-vapor lamp, the gyroscope compass, and the airplane. In the next chapter I hope to make up for some of these oversights by presenting the story of the airplane as one interested spectator saw it unfold.

CHAPTER EIGHT

From Maxim to the Jet Plane

The birds fly,
An' why can't I?
J. T. TROWBRIDGE,
"Darius Green and His Flying Machine,"
1869

Daedalus made the first flying machine, so the Greek legend tells us, but his son Icarus spoiled everything by going after the all-time altitude record before his wing structure had been properly flight-tested.

The Wright brothers do not follow immediately in the history of aviation. The indefatigable Leonardo da Vinci left numerous sketches and much cryptic writing on the subject of flying before the year 1500, although he apparently did not produce a working model of an airplane. Sir George Cayley in 1706 made what was probably the first helicopter, consisting of two windmills made of gulls feathers that rotated about a vertical axis. Whether or not it flew is uncertain. This brings us to a fellow named Stringfellow.

John Stringfellow, an Englishman, was one of the first serious students of mechanical flight who realized that it was impossible for man to fly by imitating the flapping motion of birds' wings—which is what nearly all the early experimenters had tried to do. In 1842, Stringfellow constructed a model airplane, now in the Science Museum, London, which bears a startling resemblance to our modern pusher-type monoplane, and which was the first model airplane that actually flew. Unlike the flapping-wing type of machine, his model was so constructed that the supporting force or lift was obtained by means of a stationary wing, while the motive power or propulsion was supplied by two four-bladed propellers mounted on the

157

trailing edge of the wing. It is true, of course, that another Englishman named William Henson also constructed a very similar monoplane with two-bladed pusher-type propellers in the same year, but although he equipped his model with a 25-horsepower steam engine, we are told that the machine never left the ground. The year 1842, however, marks a great turning point in the history of aviation, for from that time on the basic principles of mechanical flight began to be more closely studied and more widely understood.

Getting down to my own times, I must not fail to mention the German inventor and engineer Otto Lilienthal, who was probably the first aeronaut to pioneer in gliding or motorless flight. He, too, got off to a bad start by studying too closely the flapping motions of birds, but later arrived at a stationary arched wing that permitted him to make over two thousand glides of varying distances in complete safety. Interest in the principles of flying received enormous stimulus in America from the pioneering work of Lilienthal, who wrote a book called "The Flight of Birds and the Art of Flying" in 1889, but whose brilliant career was cut short in 1896 when his machine was upset in flight, killing its pilot.

Then there was Octave Chanute, a French-American engineer who followed up the work of Lilienthal in gliding, and who also published a book on the subject entitled "Progress in Flying Machines" in 1899. Chanute sought to improve the earlier methods of balancing the craft in the air, believing that the shifting of the pilot's body from one side to the other was not a very dependable means of maintaining equilibrium, and accordingly worked seriously on the design of a flexible tail and movable wings. He seems to have begun his aviation career too late, however (he was sixty when he started), to have accomplished anything of great importance to powered flight, although his book was eagerly read by the Wrights when they were feverishly seeking to evolve an engine-driven airplane. It has been said, and rightly so, that Chanute's framed-truss biplane glider, with rudimentary fuselage and tail, gave the Wright brothers their main ideas of construction.

We cannot yet come to the Wrights and their tremendous achievement without first mentioning another great pioneer, Samuel Pierpont Langley, American physicist and astronomer, who was the first to demonstrate the practicability of mechanical flight on May

6, 1894. I know that from this point on I am getting into a matter which is still highly controversial, and I shall do my best to stick to the accepted facts and to my own recollection as an observer and reporter of contemporary events in this field.

Before entering the Langley-Wright controversy in full panoply, I should like to return for a moment to the magazine *Machinery* which, the attentive reader will remember, I helped bring forth to the light of day in September, 1894. In that memorable Volume I, Number 1 (copies of which I trust have been preserved by biblio-philes and collectors of rare items), I illustrated the pentaplane designed by Sir Hiram Maxim and known as the "Maxim Flying

The "eolipile." This was a primitive form of jet propulsion operated by an alcohol lamp that heated a water-filled metal ball; the back-pressure of the escaping steam drove the vehicle forward. (*From Harper's New Monthly Magazine, August, 1869.*)

Machine," because I believed it to be an item of general interest to the reader. I was somewhat taken back by several irate "letters to the editor" in which I was roundly criticized for "taking space in a sixteen-page paper to print such nonsense," because the Maxim flying machine "was only a freak by an erratic inventor."

Maxim's plane, which was damaged early in 1894 before it had made a successful flight, was a huge affair 90 feet long with a wing spread of 104 feet. It was built with four sets of horizontal wings placed one above the other, with a fifth pair of wings on top, canted at an angle of about 25 degrees. According to E. W. Roberts, a Cincinnati engineer who joined Maxim at Baldwyns Park, Bexley, England, on July 10, 1894, and who was with him until the tests were abandoned—due to the approach of winter and the shutting off of funds by the directors of the Maxim-Nordenfelt Company—the Maxim flying machine was to achieve in flight the effect of a biplane with 4,000 square feet of lifting surface. Roberts, whom I got to know fairly well, told me that there were two steam engines of 160 horsepower each, and one 17-foot propeller with a 16-foot pitch on each engine. The plane, he said, weighed 7,800 pounds, or nearly 4 tons—the largest heavier-than-air machine to be constructed for many years to come.

Steam engines, of course, were used at that time because the best internal-combustion engine available weighed 20 pounds per horsepower. The steam plant, complete, weighed but half of this. Gasoline fuel was used, being first heated to 40 pounds pressure in an auxiliary boiler and giving a solid blue flame when it reached the main boiler, which carried 300 pounds of steam per square inch.

Maxim's machine was not intended for free flight, but only to test the lifting power of the wings. The structure ran on steel rails 8 feet apart and when the final tests were made had overhanging wooden rails 30 feet apart to prevent capsizing and to limit the lift. On the final test, according to my informant Roberts, the machine lifted about 12 inches from the rails and flew about 200 feet at a speed between 40 and 45 miles per hour. The lift of the wings was so much greater than had been expected that the wooden rails above the outrigged wheels were not strong enough and were torn away before the end of the 1,800-foot runway was reached.

It should be remembered that no claims of "free flight" were made for the Maxim machine; but Maxim had apparently worked out the problems of the design of wing surfaces, lift, pull of the propeller, and other important features, which, had his data been followed up at the time, would certainly have produced a flyable airplane.

And now let us examine the Langley controversy.

Although my first-hand information concerning the work of Professor Langley in aviation came long after his death, it came from the man who had worked very closely with him in this field and who was at the controls of his man-carrying aerodrome when it dropped into the Potomac on October 7, 1903. This was Charles Manley, a young engineer who had collaborated with Langley on the construction of some of his early passengerless models and who designed and built the gasoline engine used in the final plane. Manley, whom I first met when he was bringing out his hydraulic variable-speed transmission and demonstrating it, told me the complete story of the Langley experiments during a ride from Hammondsport to Buffalo during the early days of the First World War.

After Langley had been elected secretary of the Smithsonian Institution at Washington in 1887, he divided his time between the study of the solar spectrum and the study of the theory of flight, gradually devoting more and more of his energy to the latter investigation. He got off to a good start by discarding most of the then prevailing theories as to how birds fly, and constructed a huge "whirling table" by means of which "It was possible to construct machines that would give such velocity to inclined surfaces that bodies definitely heavier than air could be sustained upon it and moved through it with great velocity." Following these preliminary investigations Langley set to work building several model flying machines, and on May 6, 1896, succeeded in getting his heavier-than-air steam-driven aerodrome off the ground. This model, weighing 26 pounds and with a wing spread of about 13 feet, flew a distance of over half a mile in about 90 seconds on two separate occasions; later in November of 1896 a similar aerodrome covered about three-quarters of a mile at about 30 miles per hour. "Never in the history of the world," says the Encyclopaedia Britannica, "previous to these attempts, had any such mechanism, however actuated, sustained itself in the air for more than a few seconds. He thus paved the way for others who have achieved success with man-carrying machines."

These successful experiments, inasmuch as they took place along the Potomac in Washington in full view of a large number of people, attracted great interest all over the country, and with Langley's great prestige as secretary of the Smithsonian Institution, it was not long before the United States government agreed to subsidize further experiments by granting him the sum of $50,000 to produce a successful man-carrying aeroplane.

The problem of obtaining a light but efficient power plant now became uppermost in the minds of Langley and his assistant Charles Manley. Despite Maxim's earlier demonstration of what could be done with steam, they felt that an internal-combustion engine was necessary if a man's weight was to be added; accordingly they both traveled to Paris to interest DeDion, then a successful builder of small motors for his well-known voiturette, in building a 30-horse-power motor for the new plane. DeDion, however, who had been through enough grief in manufacturing his low-powered motors (known as "corn-poppers") flatly refused to consider the proposition —he was fed up with troubles of his own, so why take on any more headaches?

The only alternative was to approach Dr. N. A. Otto, the cele-brated gas-engine builder of Germany. Dr. Otto, inventor of the four-stroke cycle which bears his name, said he would be perfectly willing to construct an engine of 30 horsepower—except that he could not come anywhere near the weight limit required. So the Otto engine was also out of the question.

Not the least bit downcast, Langley and Manley returned to the United States determined to build an engine of their own if nobody else seemed willing to try. Manley began work on a single-cylinder experimental motor, which, if it were successful, would be developed into a five-cylinder radial engine for the plane itself.

His modest description of the way in which he surmounted the many difficulties involved kept me completely absorbed all the way from Hammondsport to Buffalo, and made the train ride seem all too short. No spark plugs were available, he told me, so he had to make his own. In order to keep costs as low as possible he made his experi-mental cylinder with only a single wall and with no water jacket. During the running tests on the engine he was obliged to wrap turkish towels around the outside of the cylinder while an assistant played a stream of water from a garden hose on it in order to keep it relatively cool. Even with this cooling system, the engine could be run only 2 or 3 minutes before it got too hot. But the tests showed Manley that the motor was practical, and he went right ahead and built his five-cylinder, 30-horsepower engine within the weight limit he and Professor Langley had set.

When the plane, or "aerodrome," was finally completed, it be-

came Manley's job to fly it. To members of the present generation
who have grown accustomed to hearing about army or civilian test
pilots taking up a new type of plane almost every other day, this may
seem to be something of a routine chore. I must ask the reader to
remember the simple fact that no one since the beginning of the
world had ever flown an aeroplane before. There had been, of course,
glider pilots and balloonists before Manley, and model or full-scale
airplanes without pilots, but this was to be the first flight in history
of a heavier-than-air, man-carrying flying machine. It took a considerable amount of courage as well as complete faith in one's
convictions.

On October 7, 1903, Langley's plane was placed on the barge that
was to serve as a launching platform and was towed out into the
middle of the Potomac River near Washington. When all was ready,
the catapulting mechanism was released, the plane started moving,
and just as it reached the end of the launching rails, it nosed over and
plunged into the river.

Manley survived the ducking, of course, and stated emphatically
that if he had been able to get the plane into the air he could have
flown easily enough. He was sure, he said, that the plane caught on
the rails just before leaving the barge and not only checked his forward speed but also nosed the machine over and down. The fact is,
as everyone will agree, that the 1903 Langley aerodrome did not fly,
and this spectacular failure, after so great a build-up, is said to have
grieved Langley so much that he died prematurely in 1906 of what is
sometimes called a broken heart.

In March, 1914, Walcott, then secretary of the Smithsonian
Institution, contracted with Glenn H. Curtiss to attempt a flight with
the Langley plane and thus prove or disprove that it would have
flown if it had been properly launched. The corollary, naturally, was
that if Langley's plane was proved capable of flight in October, 1903,
the achievement of the Wright brothers in December, 1903, would
have to take second place. And most important of all, Glenn H.
Curtiss, who in 1914 had been declared an infringer of the Wright
patents by the U.S. Court of Appeals, would be in a position to have
the decision reversed and secure the original patents in his own right.
And this is where the great controversy comes in.

The 1914 tests of the Langley aerodrome resulted in the machine being lifted into the air several different times for intervals not longer than five seconds. On the basis of these tests, the Smithsonian Institution stated in 1914, 1915, 1917, and 1918 that Langley's plane was the first heavier-than-air machine capable of maintaining sustained human flight. These statements were certainly not calculated to make the Wright brothers feel very happy, and as a consequence Orville Wright sent the original Kitty Hawk machine to England in 1928 rather than to the Smithsonian.

It is only recently that the whole truth about the controversy has come to light, in a very factual article by Dr. C. G. Abbot, current secretary of the Smithsonian Institution, which appeared in the January, 1943, issue of the *Journal of the Aeronautical Sciences*. This paper, approved by Orville Wright in 1942, proves conclusively by detailed structural analysis that the plane flown by Curtiss at Hammondsport in 1914 was by no means the same plane that was unsuccessfully tested by Manley in 1903.

For one thing, the 1914 model was launched by means of hydroplanes attached to the machine—a device that hadn't been invented until 1909—whereas the 1903 aerodrome was catapulted from a barge. Secondly, the propellers and the motor had been modified, the former "after fashion of early Wright blades." Thirdly, the system of control had been greatly modified, with important changes in the ailerons, rudder, and steering wheel. Finally, the size, area, aspect ratio, camber, leading edge, covering, and other details of the wings had been altered to a considerable extent in the 1914 version.

Summing up the controversy, Doctor Abbot writes:

Speaking for the Smithsonian Institution . . . I sincerely regret that statements were repeatedly made by officers of the Institution that the Langley machine was flown in 1914 "with certain changes of the machine necessary to use pontoons," without mentioning the other changes included in Dr. Wright's list. I point out that Assistant Secretary Rathbun was misinformed when he stated that the Langley machine "without modification" made "successful flights." I sincerely regret the public statement by officers of the Institution that "The tests of 1914 showed that the late Secretary Langley had succeeded in building the first aeroplane capable of sustained free flight with a man." Leaving to experts to formulate the conclusions arising from the 1914 tests as a whole, in view of all the facts, I repeat in substance, but with amendments, what I have already published in Smithsonian Scientific Series, Vol. 12,

p. 227, 1932: The flights of the Langley aerodrome at Hammondsport in 1914, having been made long after flying had become a common art, and with changes of the machine indicated by Dr. Wright's comparison as given above, did not warrant the statements published by the Smithsonian Institution that these tests proved that the large Langley machine of 1903 was capable of sustained flight carrying a man.

I hope, along with Dr. Abbot, that this finally lays to rest the long controversy as to who was the first man to fly a motor-driven, heavier-than-air flying machine. And now we can get on to the story of the Wright brothers.

It was not until a year after I had joined the staff of the *American Machinist*, or approximately five years after a certain long-to-be-remembered afternoon in December, 1903, that I saw one of the Wright brothers piloting a motor-driven flying machine on Governor's Island. My son Charles, who was fifteen years old at the time, witnessed the flight with me, and had no idea then, of course, that he would later become president of the Institute of Aeronautical Sciences and a world authority on aviation affairs—nor, for that matter, did his father—but I feel that this is as good a place as any for a slight plug for Charles.

The Wright brother we saw in action was Wilbur, who as everyone knows was the elder and who died prematurely in 1912 without knowing of the tremendous strides that his and his brother Orville's invention were to take in the next forty-odd years. The story of these two inventors, from their amateur beginnings in the bicycle shop at Dayton, Ohio, through their intensive self-education in the theory of flight by the method of trial and error, their study of Chanute's and Langley's published writings, their development of an 8-horsepower automobile motor and suitable propellers for their power plant, their successful and tremendously significant test flight of twelve seconds over the wind-blown sand dunes of Kitty Hawk, North Carolina, their exhibitions at Le Mans, France, and finally to their present enduring world-wide fame, is certainly too well known even by people who do not read books to justify my retelling it here. All I can hope to add to that story are a few side lights from my own personal observations and recollections.

It was in 1909 that I first visited the Wrights in Dayton—or to be more accurate, Wilbur Wright himself, for Orville was visiting Europe at the time in connection with their budding aviation business. By that time they had abandoned the use of a catapult take-off device that was operated by the dropping of a heavy weight in a huge framework structure that looked something like a cross between a guillotine and a gravity pile driver.

Wilbur, who was very cordial in dealing with gentlemen of the press, showed me all around their plant, which consisted for the most part of a small wooden shop where they assembled their flying machines. At that time they were building their tiny motors in a converted frame dwelling rented for the occasion, although at first glance I thought it was their own home. What had formerly been the living room, kitchen, and dining room had been transformed into a kind of compartmented machine shop, complete with lathes and drills and other necessary appurtenances, and in these quasi-domestic surroundings the early Wright airplane motors were built and tested; and they ran.

Observing my great interest in aeronautics in general and in what the Wrights were doing in particular, Wilbur went into considerable detail to explain the operation of the several component parts of their flying machine, including the mechanism for warping the fabric wings in order to control equilibrium, the crossed bicycle chain driving the two propellers in opposite directions, and the extensive series of tests the brothers had made to determine air pressures and wing lift. I was very much absorbed in it all when suddenly Wilbur interrupted himself and said to me, "Mr. Colvin, I might talk on like this for days, but there is really only one practical way for you to understand the idea of flying, so that when you write this up in your magazine your readers will get the feel of it."

"I guess you mean that I should fly in a plane myself?"

"That's it exactly. It is too late this afternoon, but the first thing tomorrow morning, if the weather is right, I'll take you up with me in our latest model and we'll fly around so you can get the feel of it. What do you say?"

Reader, think of the opportunity that presented itself to me! To fly in the latest model flying machine, piloted by Wilbur Wright, the celebrated coinventor of the world's first man-carrying airplane! Think of the stories I would be able to tell my children and grand-children for years to come—that I had flown with the great Wilbur Wright a scant six years after his great triumph at Kitty Hawk! You will say that it took me less than three seconds to reply, "I'll be waiting for you at sunrise, Mr. Wright!"

But I did not say that. I said that I was sorry but I had to be in Cincinnati early the next morning for a special appointment.

Now there are probably a good many readers who will conclude that this was a very thin excuse, indeed, to cover up a morbid fear of leaving terra firma even under the aegis of one of the world's foremost pilots, and that in so answering I displayed an altogether reprehensible lack of imagination, to say the least. The record does look bad, I will admit. But the actual fact, doggone it, is that I *did* have to be in Cincinnati early the next morning for a very special appointment. Any other interpretation of the record is a base canard.

Few realize or appreciate the amount of painstaking work that preceded the first successful flight at Kitty Hawk on December 17, 1903. Wilbur and Orville Wright, who had formed what they called the Wright Cycle Company, on Third Street in Dayton, Ohio, began studying the possibilities of flight as early as 1896. They were at that time building the Van Cleve bicycle, named after an ancestor who had settled in Dayton a hundred years before. They began by studying the writings of such men as Stringfellow, whom they learned to admire after they began to experiment with gliders, as well as Chanute, Lilienthal, and Langley, who was also an early enthusiast.

Having studied the available data on gliders and wing surfaces, which was indeed very meagre, they decided to build a glider them-selves which would embody the best design features they had been able to learn about from various sources. Next came the selection of a place to conduct their experiments, where conditions were favor-able and where they would be reasonably secluded. They consulted the Weather Bureau in Washington and found that the coast of North Carolina had the strongest and most constant winds, as well as sand dunes that could be used to give sufficient elevation for launching. The postmaster, by the way, is said to have recommended the dunes as a soft landing place just in case! So Kitty Hawk and the Kill Devil hills were selected, and thus were destined to become the shrine of American aviation.

It was early in 1901 that they made their first glider test at Kitty Hawk. And though the few observers felt that the tests were successful, the Wrights did not consider them very satisfactory. They felt that they hadn't got the performance they had been led to expect from the data of Lilienthal and others. Returning to Dayton, they started some new air-flow experiments of their own, which led to their building what may have been the first wind tunnel ever constructed. It was at least original with them and I have not found data regarding any having been built before.

Their first tests, however, were made with model wings mounted on a bicycle wheel, the latter being suspended horizontally on a spar that was stuck out in front of a bicycle. The cyclist, or would-be aeronaut, was supposed to pedal at as nearly constant a speed as possible. Then came a blast of air from the throat of a square tube that played on wing models suspended in the air stream. Both brothers kept detailed diaries in which they recorded all the tests.

This embryonic contraption was superseded in October, 1901, by a miniature wind tunnel, 6 feet long and 16 inches square, having a glass top so that the action of the air on the wing models could be observed. The air went through what they called a "wind straightener" at 40 feet per second, which is about 27 miles an hour as near as I can figure it.

Balance of the craft was obtained by the principle of using the normal air pressure on a plane surface to measure the lift of an airfoil. Wing models were mounted on heavy cross-stream bars so linked that the lift on the model tended to move it across the wind stream. The drag in the normal plane would tend to resist the movement. When lift and drag balanced, the rate of lift to the resistance of the normal plane was shown by a pointer attached to the linkage.

Tests were carried on with about 200 models made of sheet metal, each model being tested at fourteen different angles of inclination, from zero to 45 degrees. Tests were also made with varying aspect ratios from 1:1, to 1:12. All these results were carefully tabulated and were later to contribute to the success of their first powered plane.

The principle of wing warping, used on the Wright's early gliders as well as on their first powered plane, and which later was to become the basis of a protracted patent controversy, was developed as a result of watching the action of birds in the air. Their second glider was not so efficient as the first, for they had not yet analyzed and digested the results of their various experiments. But the third glider, which made twenty-five successful flights on September 19, 1902, was satisfactory enough to warrant their going ahead with the idea for a powered plane. On the twenty-fifth flight however, the glider was wrecked in landing, but fortunately without injury to Orville, who was at the controls, nor did it deter them from going ahead.

With this experience and the results of their hundreds of tests to guide them, they went back to Dayton to build their first man-carrying, powered, heavier-than-air airplane.

These details of their experimental work seem to me all the more interesting because of the Wrights' complete lack of technical training. Few bicycle mechanics would have had the ingenuity or the perseverance to have carried through such a series of tests and experiments, especially in the face of the criticism and ridicule that accompanied any mention of flying at that time.

As with too many of the developments which have been made in this country it was necessary for them to go abroad to secure the recognition due them. Approval by England, France, Germany, and Italy came before people in the United States really appreciated what had been developed in their own land by ordinary mechanics who possessed vision and perseverance. The Wrights felt that String-fellow had come the nearest to designing the first really practical plane, and it is said that Wilbur expressed the opinion that, if provided with a suitable motor, the Stringfellow plane was capable of piloted flight.

Another young man who began life as a bicycle mechanic and became one of the most foremost figures in aviation was Glenn Curtiss, whom I also knew personally as the result of numerous visits to his plant at Hammondsport, New York, in search of material for *American Machinist* articles. Curtiss, the reader will remember, figured in the flight-testing of the Langley aerodrome in 1914, the results of which were for a long time a rather controversial subject as I have indicated earlier in this chapter.

A visit to the Curtiss Plant, perched on a hillside overlooking Lake Keuka and circumscribed with vineyards, was nothing short of a revelation to a groundling like myself who had never flown except over the handle bars of a high-wheel bicycle. Here, when the weather permitted, powered flight was a solid reality, although it often required only a mild breeze to make taking off or landing quite unsafe in those days. As early as 1910, Curtiss had made a sound beginning in what was then large-scale airplane production, and by 1914 had developed the Hammondsport Plant into a highly efficient airplane factory judged by the standards of the time.

Here I met bluff old John McNamara, who was the guiding spirit in the actual building of both engines and planes, and Lawrence Sperry, son of Elmer Sperry of gyroscope fame and a daring young aviator in his own right, who had recently won the French award for stabilized flying by leaving the cockpit of his plane in flight and walking out on one wing. My son Charles, who worked at the Curtiss Plant in the summer of 1913, flew almost daily with Sperry over Great South Bay on Long Island to check the device that they were both working on in 1916 and which is now known as the "automatic pilot." We were all very much grieved when Sperry was lost in the English Channel after the First World War as a result of engine failure on his "flivver" plane.

Curtiss built many planes for the British before the United States became involved in the First World War, but, if I may be permitted to probe into an old sore, he was apparently discriminated against by our own country's air procurement personnel. This, to me, was one of the more unsavory happenings of that somewhat confused era, and I do not propose to go into it at any length. To those who may be further interested in the details, I merely make the suggestion that they look up the court-martial proceedings and the investigation made by Charles Evans Hughes at the time. Hughes, who at one time had been John A. Hill's lawyer, afterwards became, as we all know, the Chief Justice of the U.S. Supreme Court.

Shortly before the outbreak of hostilities in 1914, Curtiss was busy constructing for Lieut. John Cyril Porte a special flying boat which was to be used on a transatlantic flight that had the backing of Rodman Wanamaker. Curtiss took much personal interest in the venture, and during one of my visits to his Buffalo plant for the *American Machinist*, he spent considerable time with me, pointing out the special features of the new craft. It seemed of monstrous proportions to me then, looking indeed like the airplane of the future, with a wingspread of over 70 feet; but it would be a mere toy in comparison with the flying boats in use in 1946, such as the Mars or even the lesser PBY, the work horse of the Navy during the recent war.

Although the contemplated flight of Lieutenant Porte was never made, this early Curtiss flying boat served as a model for many other craft that were actually built and gave a good account of themselves in the First World War. This boat that Curtiss displayed to me with such great enthusiasm was the forerunner of the small fleet of Navy flying boats which made the first ocean crossing in 1919, and among the officers in charge of the flight was a Commander Richardson, whom I had met and talked with at Hammondsport in the early days of 1912.

Curtiss, as I have been trying to indicate, was a real pioneer in the field of airplane construction, and with the benefit of machine tools and a well-designed plant, came very close to building airplanes on a mass-production basis. He certainly deserves lasting fame for the "OX" airplane engines that he designed and built. Although these engines are now completely out of date from the standpoint of design and efficiency, they were indeed the backbone of all of the training planes used during the First World War, and moreover were the first practical examples of lightweight, air-cooled engines. I feel that they belong in the same category as the Ford Model T, in the sense that both were a monument to simplified design and both gave herculean service in the early days of the two industries.

Speaking of the OX engines reminds me of an incident that I saw happen in the test room of the Curtiss Plant during one of my early visits in about 1915. A Curtiss OX engine under test was registering something over 85 horsepower and behaving beautifully. An inspector for the British government, which had intended to purchase a fair quantity of such engines, was present in the test room, observing the performance with great interest. At the end of the run he approached the test chief eagerly.

"My dear fellow," he said, "I should like very much indeed to purchase this particular engine for His Majesty's government. Will you be good enough to let me put in a claim for it now? I can see that it is a superb motor in every respect."

"Oh, well now, Mr. Humphreys," the chief answered, "I'm afraid er . . . I'm afraid this one's already been spoken for by another party. Somebody else has already bought it, practically. But we've got another one outside just like it—let me show you."

"The one outside, sir, does not happen to interest me at the moment. It is *this* motor that we are standing in front of which my government wishes to purchase. I shall enter a claim for it immediately."

"Sorry, Mr. Humphreys, but that there motor is sold."

"Sold? But don't you realize, my good man, that your company has agreed—contracted, I should say—to supply the British government with the engines it orders? Doesn't my government have a priority over all other purchasers at the present time? How can it have been sold?"

"That's the way it is, Mr. Humphreys. This here one's sold. But the one outside is just as good—maybe even better."

The inspector went on fuming and demanding his rights, but the test chief won out in the end. When Humphreys had left I went over to the chief and asked, "Who's the important customer that got first crack at the motor, Harry?"

"There wasn't any customer, Fred. I had to tell a lie to that inspector. I just couldn't sell him that motor, honestly. I lied to save his skin."

"How come?"

"Well now, Humphreys has been inspecting engine parts here for the past week or so, and some he marks O.K. and others he marks Reject. Now this motor we just tested was built nearly 100 per cent from the parts he has Reject written on, with his initials C.H. after it. Suppose we sold him the motor and it got to England and came in for overhaul. What would those officers do to him? They'd probably make a buck private out of him the next day and put him to work digging latrines. I had to lie to keep him out of trouble."

I cannot leave Glenn Curtiss at this point in our chronology without quoting from one of the advertisements that he ran in several issues of the old Aero Club of America *Bulletin* in 1912:

> *On* the Water, *Over* the Country—*Faster than 60 Miles an Hour!* Glenn H. Curtiss' new "aeroyacht" marks the high spot of exhilarating sport *with* safety. For speed and pleasure it puts motor boating and automobiling out of the running. It's a revelation to the red-blooded sportsman.
>
> Curtiss New Model Hydro-Aeroplanes start from and alight on both land and water. They are thoroughly practical water and air craft and combine durability with safety. Simple in construction, they are quickly mastered and easily handled. You, too, can become a successful aviator. A knowledge of practical mechanics is not necessary.
>
> "Aeroyachts," as the new hydro-aeroplanes are called by enthusiasts of the wonderful sport, are priced at a moderate figure. Cost of tuition applies on purchase. Know all about these Curtiss Hydro-Aeroplanes. Write today for full information. Training grounds in New York and California. Curtiss Aeroplane Company, Hammondsport, N.Y.

Let us back up a couple of years to 1910, the year that saw the first world's air meet at Belmont Park, Long Island. The *American Machinist* had begun to follow the growth of aviation at an early date in its history, and had sent Leon P. Alford to Newfoundland in 1908 to observe the experiments of Alexander Graham Bell, of telephone fame, with his various forms of cellular wings or airfoils. And when the first air meet was held at Belmont race track in the fall of 1910, our paper made a very detailed study of the planes exhibited and flown, printing lengthy articles on them with numerous half-tone illustrations. As I look back over the thirty-seven years that have elapsed since then, I realize that the planes then exhibited were nothing short of remarkable both in design and in performance.

One must remember, of course, that the engines that powered these planes were, by present-day standards, very crude and of very low horsepower. The Wright motor was a four-cylinder in-line engine, developing perhaps 60 horsepower at maximum, and the Curtiss OX engine, although of V-8 design, was of about the same rating. And another early engine in the same power class was the Hall-Scott, built on the Pacific Coast.

Perhaps the best-known engine at the 1910 aviation show was the Gnôme, a French seven-cylinder air-cooled radial engine that revolved with its propeller about a stationary crankshaft; it had a kind of imitator in another French motor of very similar design whose name, La Rhône, rhymed not too exactly with Gnôme. These revolving engines produced a very noticeable gyroscopic effect in flight, making it difficult for the pilot to change the direction of the plane from left to right, and besides they acted rather like a lawn sprinkler and threw castor oil all over the plane and its aviator.

But these were by no means the first radial engines, or even the first revolving-motor radial engines. I clearly remember seeing in 1898 an illustration in the *American Machinist* of a radial, air-cooled motor mounted on a platform and held by a man at either end. The engine, built by the Adams-Farwell Company of Dubuque, Iowa, was designed for use in automobiles, and was mounted directly over the rear axle of the car, with its cylinders revolving around a stationary crankshaft. Correspondence with the Adams Company in 1944 revealed that as early as 1903 they had developed an airplane motor and had held the original patents on air-cooled, revolving-cylinder motors, antedating both the Gnôme and LaRhône motors mentioned above. In an old circular the Adams Company stated that they did not bring suit for infringement because "they were glad to have outside help in breaking down prejudice against that type of motor." The Adams-Farwell motor, incidentally, was in all probability the very first to adopt the principle of contrarotating propellers, one being attached to the revolving cylinders and the other rotating on the fixed crankshaft. These propellers tended to neutralize the gyroscopic effect that was so troublesome on the French motors.

But to return to the Belmont Air Meet of 1910. By far the most interesting feature of the meet was the races. These followed the oval course of the race track itself, or at least a fair approximation of it, and the planes were flown at a very low level—hedge hopping, we would now call it—barely missing the grandstand and the spectators each time they flew past it. There was also what was known as a "slow" race in which the idea was to see how slowly the pilot could fly his plane without stalling it; this handicap was won by an Englishman piloting an old Wright biplane at about 30 miles per hour.

Two French planes that were outstanding because of their extremes in size were the Demoiselle and the Antoinette. The

Artist's conception of primitive heli-copter built in 1706 by Sir George Cay-ley, as it might have appeared in flight.

Demoiselle, appropriately named, was a very tiny affair with small, butterflylike wings and diminutive motors, and the extreme range of its ceiling was not more than 40 feet. In fact, one is tempted to say that it barely left the ground. The Antoinette, on the other hand, was a huge monoplane with large, tapering wings with a total spread of 46 feet, and powered by a sixteen-cylinder Panhard-Levassor engine, built by the makers of the then well-known Panhard auto-mobile. The Antoinette at an altitude of over a thousand feet looked like a sizable dragonfly as it was maneuvered by its pilot Hubert

Latham, who was a reckless flyer but perhaps the only man who could handle the Antoinette properly.

On the second or third day of the meet, the relation between meteorology and flying was forcibly brought home to the aviators as well as the spectators. The day was a typically gusty fall day, with occasional ground winds of 10-mile velocity or so. A sudden gust of wind stronger than the rest caught up with a number of grounded planes and overturned them like so many leaves or pieces of cardboard, causing great consternation among pilots and owners of the craft. It will be recalled by some old-timers that it was a sudden gust of wind that completely wrecked the Wright brothers' first glider on December 17, 1903, after it had come to rest on the ground following its fourth successful flight. While this may well point out the flimsiness of the early craft, we should remember that the far heavier Navy Hellcat bombers have to be lashed to the carrier deck in stormy weather, and that it is by no means impossible for a heavy gale to upset a B-29 bomber on the ground if it hits it just right.

On that same windy day of the Belmont Meet a well-known flyer by the name of McCurdy went up after an altitude record in a Wright biplane. In spite of the wind, or maybe because of it, he got up to the desired altitude (it was certainly less than the record of 11,642 feet made the following year by Lincoln Beachy), but at that point his troubles began. Up there the wind was a good deal faster than it was on the ground, and when McCurdy turned the nose of the plane around and headed for the race track, he discovered a curious fact— the wind was blowing his plane backwards! The head wind was not merely reducing his air speed, but actually making it an increasingly negative quantity! We on the ground could see McCurdy high in the air, headed valiantly toward the field but getting further and further away all the time. I learned afterward that he finally landed on a farm many miles distant on the eastern end of Long Island.

Another event of the 1910 meet was indeed striking, if I may use that word in its literal sense. A French aviator was a contestant in the 100-mile endurance race that meant countless laps around and around the race track. He was flying a Blériot monoplane, a very fast and tricky plane in those days, and, as has been mentioned before, he flew very low. Nearing the end of the race he unfortunately ran out of gas, and complications immediately set in. For the

Blériot monoplane did not lend itself very readily to dead-stick landings, and furthermore the Frenchman was not high enough to pick out a good spot to land or to avoid hitting the crowd of spectators. He thought fast and decided to attempt the impossible.

On his last lap around the field the Frenchman singled out a sturdy-looking telegraph pole not very far from the grandstand and headed his speedy little monoplane straight for it. It looked as though he had chosen suicide as the simple way out. At the last instant before collision he nosed the plane over slightly so that the center of the left wing struck the telegraph pole with full force. The impact tore away the wing and sheared off a 6-foot section of the wooden pole, leaving a splintered stump in the ground and the upper section of the pole hanging from the wires overhead. The plane spun violently around, landing abruptly a short distance away.

Of course, we all were certain that the daring Frenchman had been killed outright, or at least so badly broken up that it would be only a matter of hours before the undertaker was called in. But lo and behold, he emerged whole and unscathed from the wreckage of his plane, and a half-hour afterward he was being driven around the track with only a small white patch on his forehead, in order to demonstrate to the spectators that flying wasn't so dangerous after all.

Blériot planes, I might add, won all the speed contests in this first Belmont Air Meet of 1910. The American flying machines were still a long way from their present position of world supremacy.

No sketch of the history of aviation would be complete without at least a passing reference to lighter-than-air aircraft, and while I do not propose to bore the reader with an account of the Montgolfier achievements and of ballooning in the Civil War, I should like to say a word at least about dirigibles.

Dirigibles came largely into the public eye during the First World War when the Germans used them to bomb London and particularly Trafalgar Square, with little or no military effect as far as the course of the war was concerned. The Germans, capitalizing on the researches and experiments of Count von Zeppelin, started off on a dirigible-building spree that did not end until the fate of the *Hindenburg* in 1937 ultimately convinced them that perhaps dirigibles were an outmoded and impractical form of aviation.

The first dirigible I ever saw was in New York City in 1910, at the time of the Belmont Air Meet just described. The craft was moored off Riverside Drive near Grant's Tomb, and drew a large crowd of spectators. From this point Capt. Thomas Baldwin took off on a flight to Albany—at least he said he was going to fly to Albany, but he actually wound up in a meadow a few miles below Dobbs Ferry. Some skeptics expressed doubt that he expected or intended to reach the state capital, because he left Grant's Tomb shortly before noon and did not even bother to take a ham sandwich along as provisions.

Shortly after the signing of the Versailles Treaty, the United States received from Germany a dirigible known as the "ZR3" as partial reparations. It was later rechristened the *Los Angeles*, and enjoyed a very long life until it was retired as an experimental hangar ship about 1938. The fate of the *Shenandoah*, the *Akron*, and other large dirigibles is, of course, too well known to be discussed here.

Before the ZR3 or *Los Angeles* had first heaved into my field of view, I recall seeing about 1917 one of the first Goodyear blimps, or semirigid dirigibles, piloted by Ralph Upson, a former free-balloon pilot. He navigated the ship from the factory at Akron to the city of Cleveland, where he achieved fame and notoriety by landing the blimp on the roof of the Statler Hotel. I was on the Statler roof at the time in the capacity of guest observer, and it seemed to me a feat of great skill and daring, because the landing stage was very small, there was a fairly strong breeze, and two or more passes had to be made before the landing was accomplished.

One of the more interesting experiments in lighter-than-air aircraft was an airship familiarly known as the "tin blimp," shown in an adjoining photograph. It was built in 1929 by the Detroit Aircraft Company, and I had the privilege of seeing it under construction as well as in the air over Lakehurst, New Jersey, which is about 18 miles from my home. My friend Ralph Upson was chief engineer on the project and had a great deal to do with the whole idea.

Technically known as the "ZMC-2," this dirigible was not actually made of tin, but of aluminum sheets that were ninety-five ten-thousandths of an inch thick—pretty thin stuff, you will agree. It contained no gasbags or ballonets, but held the helium gas directly inside the metal skin itself. The sheets were shaped so as to give the proper contour, and were fastened by rivets driven by one of the most ingenious machines I have ever seen. The seams were made with three rows of staggered rivets, driven simultaneously from three strands of wire 0.035 inches in diameter. All three rows of rivets were driven at the rate of 135 rivets per minute. The wires were then cut off, used as punches to perforate the sheets, and headed on both sides. There were twelve rivets to the inch holding the sheets firmly, with a sealing compound on the sheets at the joints. The body of the blimp was practically gastight, and leakage of the helium was never a problem. The so-called "tin blimp" was 149 feet 9 inches long, 52 feet 8 inches maximum diameter, and weighed 8,800 pounds. Powered by two Wright radial engines of 220 horsepower each, it was used for training lighter-than-air pilots for a long time before it was retired for old age.

The Second World War saw the use of dirigibles confined to patrol of the sea lanes, especially during the early days of the war when German U-boats were a real menace to our shipping. In view of the advances made in the past two or three years in plane construction and performance, it seems doubtful that the dirigible now has the future once predicted for it. Still, predictions are always dangerous, even the one I have just got off myself.

And having thus taken a quick look at a part of the history of aviation, without touching upon the vast subject of the mechanics of the airplane industry itself, we can again gather up the loose ends of this rambling autobiography by turning back to the *American Machinist* and the year 1914. Before we do that, however, I would like to mention briefly a forgotten phase of motor development, although it is not too closely connected with the subject of aviation. I mention it here in the belief that it may possibly save a certain amount of useless expenditure in experiments that have been tried and abandoned in the past.

I am thinking particularly of the engine known as the barrel, cam, or wobble-plate type, the first of which I recall seeing at an exhibition of the Franklin Institute about 1885. This engine had been invented by a Daniel Kemp West of London and was patented about 1871. The engine, built in this country by the Colt Patent Firearms Company for marine use, developed 75 horsepower and was designed for compounding. So far as I know, this was the only engine of its

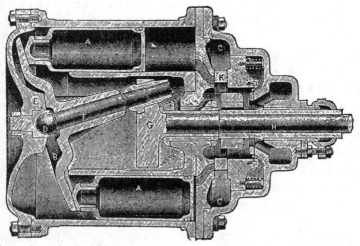

Woodcut of a Colt "wobble-plate" engine, from the *American Machinist*, October 23, 1880—forerunner of many similar designs.

type built for steam operation. The advent of internal combustion engines, however, gave a new lease on life to the idea, and others have been attempted since, including Arnold, Torbert, Herrmann, and other similar engines. Many an engine designer was, and still is, intrigued with the possibilities of placing such an engine in commercial use in spite of all of the previous failures.

CHAPTER NINE

Machine Tools and the First World War

The only war I ever approved of was the Trojan War—it was fought over a woman, and the men knew what they were fighting for.
WILLIAM LYON PHELPS, A Sermon, 1933

The hardest part of writing even a short biography, at least for an old codger like me, is trying to preserve some semblance of chronological order instead of skipping around here and there at random as people and events crowd in on my overworked memory. Just wait until you're on the verge of eighty, dear reader, and see how much trouble it is keeping your thoughts in order as you look back over the crowded years. Sometimes the trouble is that I remember too much, and want to put too much trivia on the record; at other times I find I have omitted much that may be considered important to readers of this chronicle and have thereby lessened whatever historical value it may have. Well, anyway, let's get on with the story, now that the apologies are out of the way. I was about to say a few words about machine tools and the First World War.

During the fall of the year 1914, soon after hostilities had got off to a good start following the little incident at Sarajevo and von Ludendorff's advance into Belgium, the machine shops in the United States began to be deluged with orders for machine tools and for the materials of war themselves. As the German guns began to bombard Antwerp and as the British and French were doggedly holding the line at Ypres in November, 1914, American shops were hard at work turning out rifles, shells of various sizes and kinds, fuses and detonators, and a variety of other small war matériel.

The *American Machinist* naturally devoted much space to the description of the manufacturing methods—many of which had been improvised almost overnight in order to meet sudden emergencies—that were being employed in the various shops that had foreign contracts. The articles served the purpose of instructing plant owners and superintendents in the kind of work being done and thus helped prepare the shops for work of this sort in the event that the United States should be drawn into the war. In spite, however, of the well-intentioned but vain promise made by the Wilson campaign to "keep us out of war," the spring of 1917 saw us entering the conflict practically unprepared, except for the machine-shop and munitions experience we had gained by having worked on numerous contracts for the Allies.

Some of the improvised methods, especially in the Canadian shops, were both ingenious and fascinating. One that I recall was the drawing of fairly large cartridge cases on a planer, instead of on a press, because the latter was not immediately available. But it was in the matter of specifications that perhaps the greatest amount of improvisation, not to say mystification, was evidenced. The British, Russian, and Serbian contracts undertaken by American shops really enhanced our knowledge of military inspection practices, and demonstrated, if demonstration were required, that too often the set of specifications had been drawn up by someone who had only an academic knowledge of manufacturing methods and a rudimentary idea of costs.

One outstanding example of specification trouble was encountered in the making of a fuse which screwed into the nose of a British shell and which was turned out in tremendous quantities. The British orders were so large that the various contractors found it advisable to form themselves into a sort of Fuse Makers' Association (of which my good friend George T. Trundle Jr., then with the Multigraph Company, was the chairman). The fuse in question was made of brass, with a threaded portion about 2 inches in diameter and about 1½ inches long, and it had a rather fine thread. This thread was inspected by measuring its outside, or crest, diameter, which was held to very close limits—so close, in fact, that I recall seeing a huge lot rejected for being only a few thousandths of an inch too small. But in this case, the wily manufacturer simply rolled the threads up to the required outside diameter, and they passed a second inspection, although the thread form had been distorted by this

Wilbur Wright piloting his 1902 glider

The first Wright airplane motor, of horizontal design with vertical valves at right angles to the head, about 1903

Three-quarter view of the Wright brothers plane flown for the first time on December 17, 1903
Orville Wright standing in front

First "hydroaeroplane" built by Glenn H. Curtiss, shown on its first successful flight in San Diego Bay, California, January 26, 1911

Early Curtiss "OX"-type engine, used on several different models of Curtiss airplanes, about 1913–16

Early Curtiss plane outside hangar at Hammondsport, New York, about 1913—note tricycle landing gear

Capt. Thomas Baldwin taking off from Grant's Tomb, Hudson River, bound for Albany, New York, in 1910

First flight of the ZMC-2, familiarly known as the "tin blimp," although actually made of aluminum sheets, August, 1929

operation and the fit was hardly as good as it had been before. The importance of the pitch diameter (and I add this only for those who know what *that* is) was not then appreciated as it is now. Yet, because the only duty of the thread was to hold the fuse in the shell tightly enough to withstand the initial stress due to firing, and could be used only once, the thread fit was actually not very important, and a thread length one-third of that specified would have been entirely adequate. Similar criticism, of course, might easily be made about many other specifications of all nations in wartime.

I remember also the rifle that hung in the chief inspector's office at the Eddystone Plant at Remington. The inspector, whose name I fortunately do not recall, told me that every piece that had gone to make up the rifle had been rejected as unfit by a number of inspectors. The joker was that this very rifle when assembled turned out to be a fairly first-class weapon and made a good record on the test range. "I keep that rifle hanging up there," the chief inspector told me, "as a shining example for inspectors who are inclined to be a bit too fussy about their work. But at the same time I am certainly not encouraging sloppiness either."

Early in 1916, when it began to look as though nothing short of the Kaiser's abdication and the scrapping of all of Germany's *unterseebooten* would keep this country out of the war, the U.S. War Department decided, very wisely, that detailed information should be available to all potential manufacturers concerning the methods used in making the Springfield rifle (then the standard arm for our infantry) in the event that large quantities should be required in a hurry. The War Department, represented by Maj. Gen. William Crozier, surveyed the possibilities of getting this information compiled and aggregated promptly and came to the conclusion that an editor of the *American Machinist* might be able to handle the job properly. So it was arranged with General Crozier that none other than yours truly should go to the Springfield Armory and tackle the job of gathering the information.

In August of 1916 I was accordingly given office space in the Armory by its able commandant, Col. W. S. Peirce, who was assisted by Maj. G. H. Stewart and Capt. R. R. Nix, all of whom gave me their utmost cooperation in the work. Aided by a local assistant named Harry R. Johnson, and a very efficient secretary, I was able to complete the research end of the project in about four months. Beginning with the barrel, we studied the rifle piece by piece and meticulously followed the operations being performed. We reported on the kinds of material used, the tools and cutters, feeds and operating speeds, cutting lubricant, heat-treatment, and the time required for each separate operation. This detailed informa-

The "Hotchkiss Revolving Cannon" from The *American Machinist*, December 13, 1879; a forerunner of the modern machine gun.

tion then appeared in the *American Machinist*, first in successive issues, then in a special edition, and finally came out in book form. The concise and effective method of presenting the data, incidentally, was planned by John H. Van Deventer, then managing editor of the paper; the many hundreds of illustrations and detail drawings were executed by Arthur Ormay, a clever draftsman then in charge of the illustration department.

Much of the machine equipment at the Springfield Armory, unfortunately, was very antiquated in comparison with contemporary standards. The speeds and the feeds were almost leisurely and the methods employed were of about the 1890 vintage. Perhaps the greatest handicap on some of the parts, however, was the design and the materials indicated in the specifications. Regardless of the use of a particular part in the operation of the rifle, or the stresses to which that part was subjected, the designers of small arms insisted on having forgings throughout. Such parts as the band that held the barrel on the stock, the butt plate, or the swivel which carried the strap for slinging the rifle on the shoulder were required to be machined from drop forgings, which meant machining them all over.

These and other obvious inefficiencies began to bother me as I lay awake nights mulling over the problem, and one day while I was still actively engaged on the research I requested and obtained an interview with the Secretary of War, Newton D. Baker, who happened to be staying at the same hotel in Springfield while he visited the Armory. I told the Secretary Baker of some of the practices I had observed which didn't seem quite right to me, and pointed out where they could be improved upon.

"It may be that you are entirely right about some of these points, Mr. Colvin," the Secretary of War said. "But it will require a little more investigation before we can come to any definite decision or make any extensive changes in our present methods and machinery. You know as well as I do how difficult it is to make overnight changes in procedure once it has been established. Moreover," he added, "if these West Point officers, who use the rifles and train other men how to use them, do not know how to make rifles, who in the name of reason does?"

Secretary Baker's logic was a bit irksome here, and I replied:

"Mr. Secretary—Anna Held, the current toast of Broadway, uses perhaps a box of face powder a day—but Colgate hasn't made her its factory superintendent on that account."

Secretary Baker grinned and saw the point.

"I would suggest," he said, "that you prepare for me a detailed report covering all the points you have in mind and setting forth your recommendations as to how the manufacture of these Springfield rifles can be expedited."

"Certainly, Mr. Secretary," I replied. "I shall get to work on it immediately."

"Oh—one very important point—make sure you mark your report Confidential, since it will necessarily be a classified document in the military sense—and see that it is addressed to me personally."

I agreed to do exactly as Secretary Baker requested. In my report I pointed out that there was not a tolerance on a single part of the rifle excepting the thickness of the bayonet blade—which was held to 0.002 inch when a $\frac{1}{16}$ inch would have made no difference whatever; that because of the lack of tolerances, the assembly of the rifle was of course selective, and considerable fitting was necessary; that the design of some of the nonessential parts, such as the bands for holding the barrel to the stock and the butt plate, should be made of strip steel in a punch press rather than drop-forged; that the stocks should be completely finished on a sand belt instead of being sandpapered by hand as called for in the specifications; and that there was room for numerous other improvements and simplifications. I addressed the report to the personal attention of Secretary Baker with high hopes of seeing at least a few of my recommendations adopted.

The very next thing I knew was the *American Machinist* received a hotly worded note from General Crozier stating, in effect, that this person Colvin had proven to be not quite the man for the job of reporting on the Springfield rifle, and that somebody else—anybody—should be sent down immediately to replace him. And when I entered Colonel Peirce's office the following day he politely informed me that he had been ordered by General Crozier to "curtail my visits" to the point where I would be actually debarred from the Armory.

When the initial shock had worn off somewhat, I made a bee-line for Secretary Baker's office, prepared to defend my rights even if it meant death at the hands of a firing squad. I asked the Secretary to explain the situation.

"It seems, Mr. Colvin, that your report arrived while I was out of town," he said, "and inadvertently my secretary turned it over to General Crozier as a matter for his attention. This was, of course, an error of tact, and I deeply regret the incident."

I was still angry, and I said, "If General Crozier issued that order solely because he resented my criticism of the present setup —which, Mr. Secretary, I have no need to remind you was made at your own request and addressed to your personal attention— then his action only proves the point I was trying to make, namely, that there is a great need for officers around here who know modern production methods more than they know military regulations. I might point out that unless the general can prove that I am hindering the production of arms or am actively engaged in sabotage, he is acting without authority in issuing such an order, since, like myself, he is merely a hired assistant reporting to the Secretary of War." Indignation seems to have lent strength to my oratory.

Secretary Baker indicated that he was very sympathetic with my viewpoint and regretted sincerely the position I had been placed in by the incident. A few days later I was informed that General Crozier had issued another order rescinding the first one, and that I was to be permitted to visit Springfield Armory and all other arsenals as before. The news of the incident leaked out, however, not only in official circles but also in the local press at Springfield, and it was something of a *cause célèbre* for a while. But this is by no means the end of the story.

When we entered the war in 1917, it was decided to use the Enfield rifle, after all, instead of the Springfield, changing the chamber of the Enfield to fit the Springfield cartridge. This change was made presumably because there were several shops in this country already making large quantities of Enfields for the British, and it was considered more feasible for these shops to expand their present production rather than convert to the Springfields. Nevertheless there were a number of serious and inexplicable delays due, according to the rifle manufacturers, to the inability of certain Ordnance officers to decide on some of the minor details of design and production.

War was declared by President Wilson via Congress on April 6, 1917, and sample rifles that functioned satisfactorily were submitted early in June. Yet as late as August of that year I found, as a result of a personal inspection tour, that the Winchester Arms Company, which should certainly have been in production by that time, was placidly marking time, awaiting the go-ahead signal from Washington. Orders for rifles had been expected every day for a period of weeks, but since no orders were being received the men were simply standing by idle and, of course, being paid full-time wages for doing it. No rifles could be produced without orders from headquarters, and the only order received from Washington up to that time were merely, "Stand By." I took several photographs in the plant of groups of men playing cards, reading newspapers, and otherwise killing time during regular working hours while the war was already four months old and we were still losing it.

The facts and photographs I brought back from this visit to the Winchester Plant formed the basis for a scorching editorial in the *American Machinist* by managing editor Van Deventer. We did not print the photographs, but indicated that we had them on file as evidence in case anyone should think we were imagining things. My old antagonist General Crozier, having learned in advance from the grapevine that the editorial was coming out, went to considerable pains to have that issue of the *Machinist* suppressed or impounded, but freedom of speech triumphed in the end and the editorial came out on schedule.

The editorial that caused all this commotion appeared in the August 16, 1917, number of the *American Machinist*, in what one might call a very spectacular format. It occupied a full page in 16-point type, with generous sprinklings of boldface, italics, and display lettering. Facing it, on the left, was a blank page, with the following notation in the center:

> The editorial this week is so important that we omit from this page anything to detract your attention from it.

And this is what Van Deventer said:

HOW CAN OUR BOYS FIGHT WITHOUT GUNS?

This editorial is not an attack on any individual, but on a system.

Suppose, Mr. Manufacturer, with emergency orders filling your shop, you should discover that through a lack of executive decision your workmen had been forced to kill time by playing checkers and cards during working hours! What would *you* do with the man responsible for this condition? Would you accept *any* excuse from the official who exercised full authority?

Scores of skilled rifle makers in one of our best-known American plants have been for weeks and are today retained on the payroll, killing time with checkers and cards during working hours, simply because certain officials have been unable to arrive at a decision regarding details.

This work is being done on a "cost-plus" basis for our Government, so that you and I must pay these men for killing time. But this is of small

Cartoon entitled "Playing the Kaiser's Game," intended to occupy the blank page in the August 16, 1917 issue of the *American Machinist*, referred to on p. 188, but never published.

moment compared to the inexcusable and dangerous loss of time in making our new army rifles.

These mechanics are not responsible for this condition. The shop management is not responsible for it. Somebody is. Who is it?

England was forced by bitter experience and delays of this kind to eliminate Bureaucratic control of all munition manufacture, and place this work in the hands of those qualified by experience to decide quickly between the essential and the nonessential.

Experienced engineers and works managers are the men who should decide upon specifications, manufacture and inspection.

We have not published these facts without due deliberation. But we believe that truth in this matter is more important than the personal feelings of well-intentioned officials whose duty it is to decide on specifications, but who are incapable of coming to a decision.

Months after war has been declared—months after the type of our rifle has been determined—it is a crime against our boys who will bear rifles at the front to permit American rifle makers at home to pass week after week playing checkers and waiting for something to do.

At the bottom of the page, in 6-point type, was the following:

The above statement is based not simply on editorial knowledge of the facts, but on incontrovertible proof, photographic and otherwise, in the possession of the editor.

Publication of the facts in this form brought down a storm of censure on *American Machinist* scribes and made me about as popular with the Ordnance Department as the proverbial skunk at a garden party. General Crozier flatly refused to have anything more to do with me, and I had great difficulty in getting to see his right-hand man, Gen. John S. Thompson. The result was that I was "requested" to meet a committee of Ordnance officers so that they might show me the error of my ways, point out how I had got things all confused in my mind, and demonstrate how my view of things was exactly the reverse of the true situation. "For how," they reasoned, "can this magazine writer, this little man who has probably never fired a gun in anger in his life, know anything about rifles or any other kind of weapon? What can he know about military strategy, or supply, or echelons, or any of the other things we learned at West Point? He means well, no doubt, but he simply doesn't understand the problem."

The meeting was held in the office of Frank A. Scott, chairman of the General Munitions Board, who was on leave of absence from the Warner and Swasey Company of Cleveland. General William S. Peirce, who had been promoted from the rank of colonel since my acquaintance with him at the Springfield Armory, together with three other officers of equal rank who had been in charge of various arsenals at one time or another, composed the committee. In the face of all that brass, I, a civilian with the simulated rank of buck private, should have been duly chastened and repentant. But of course I wasn't.

"Mr. Colvin," one of the brigadiers began, "we mean no personal slight when we say that your knowledge of firearms cannot be as extensive as ours, for we have made it our life study, so to speak. Whatever delays you may have observed, and we admit there have been some, stem from the urgent necessity of securing interchangeability of parts on these rifles—a problem which we are working on night and day and which will be solved in the very near future. Then you will see how production will begin to roll."

"But, General," I replied, "What about the tens of thousands of Enfield rifles that some of these very plants we are talking about have already manufactured and shipped to British troops? There didn't seem to be any great problem there."

"You are forgetting, aren't you, that those rifles had a different bore and a different chamber from those now being designed for our own troops."

"I don't see how that detail makes any difference," I replied, forgetting to add the "sir."

"Well, it does, and you must take our word for it."

"Just what do you mean by interchangeability?" I asked, turning to one of the older generals.

"Interchangeability—harrumph—er, by interchangeability is meant that feature of a rifle, or 'piece,' as it is called, whereby a part of one rifle can be replaced with its corresponding part from another rifle—a very important advantage in modern warfare.

"For example—we have an infantryman in the heat of battle whose piece—rifle, that is—becomes disabled or defective for some reason—the trigger jams or the bolt freezes or the front sight gets knocked off. If these and other parts of the rifle are interchangeable with those of every other rifle, he has merely to stoop down, remove the corresponding part from the piece of the nearest fallen comrade, replace it on his own rifle, and continue firing on the enemy."

I almost laughed out loud.

"Why in the name of—for Pete's sake, General, why wouldn't the soldier grab the *whole* rifle from the 'fallen comrade' instead of acting like a crazy fool and trying to make complicated repairs under fire? Is the enemy going to call a truce while our men sit down on the battlefield and take their guns apart?"

"The example I gave," the general answered coolly, "was perhaps not too well chosen. The more complicated repairs would of course be made behind the lines by specially trained crews, who would thus salvage thousands of rifles that would otherwise be lost."

I had to let that one go by, for I could see that in a minute or two we would be off on the subject of logistics, or the strategy of counterattack, or how Blücher could have avoided the staggering losses to his army in the Napoleonic campaign of 1814. I decided to backtrack a bit.

"There is no argument," I began, "that interchangeability is a highly desirable feature on this particular rifle, although I cannot help thinking that while we are talking here, Ludendorff is making nice headway on the Western Front"—I got an icy stare all around at this—"but supposing that we want interchangeability, can anyone here tell me why we shouldn't set limits on all dimensions to obtain it?"

No one answered, and I turned to Frank Scott with all the ardor of an evangelist or a temperance lecturer. "Frank," I said, "as an official of the Warner and Swasey Company—which, gentlemen, is one of the leading machine-tool builders in this country—will you kindly tell the committee about the necessity for tolerances on each part of the rifle if we want to have interchangeable manufacturing?"

Frank Scott very obligingly backed me up with a short but pellucid account of limits and tolerances, and when he got through I pointed out as politely as I could that not a single dimension of the Springfield rifle showed a tolerance on any drawing then in use. I then added that it was somewhat ironical, nevertheless, that bayonets were being rejected for variations of only 0.002 inch in the thickness of the blade. (One hardheaded officer, by the way, who had seen service in France, conceived the brilliant idea of using the bayonet scabbard as the "go" gauge and thus salvaged many blades that had been discarded.)

After much discussion the committee meeting finally wound up, and although no immediate agreement was reached, it served to stir things up in the Ordnance Department, and it was not long before Winchester and other plants were turning out our rifles in quantity. General Thompson, who was later to achieve fame as the inventor of the sub-Thompson machine gun, or tommy-gun, went to bat with me on several additional points. Although none of the reasons he advanced for the Ordnance Department's stand seemed very cogent to me, he was at all times a square shooter, and he and I became good friends after the smoke of the first clash had cleared away and we began to understand each other's viewpoint.

Editor Van Deventer had by no means shot his bolt with the philippic of August 16. A little over a month later, in the September 20, 1917, issue, Van struck out in a double-page spread as follows:

WANTED—A MASTER HAND.

One of the main indications of a well-ordered business is a thorough coordination of its various activities and a hearty cooperation of its different departments. And this is of vital importance in time of business stress or in critical periods.

Yet this coordination and cooperation, which are so vital to the vigorous prosecution of the war to a speedy finish, are notably lacking in many of the preparations that are now under way.

Work is being duplicated by different committees; gauge inspection is being scattered instead of centralized; the army and navy bid against each other for delivery and occasionally in price; red tape, seniority and precedent stand in the way of the hearty cooperation that makes for the most efficient conduct of any business.

We do not question the motives of any of the men who are engaged in the work. But hell is said to be paved with good intentions. What we need now, and will need for two or more years to come, is Results. . . . England solved the problem by appointing Lloyd George as Minister of Munitions. Not because he understood the theory and technicalities of artillery and ammunition, but because he knew how to use the technical talent that was available, because he knew how to tackle a big problem in a big way and to get things done.

We entered the war April 6, 1917. Look up the serial number of the Springfield rifle of this date and the serial number of the Springfield today and see how many have been delivered during these vital five months. Ask the Ordnance Department how many of the new U.S. Enfields are ready for the National Army that is now gathering. Ask the Ordnance Department how many Lewis machine guns, the discarded American invention whose merits were recognized abroad but not at home, are ready for use. Ask the Ordnance Department how recently and how many times the gauges have been changed for the new rifle cartridge. And with all of these questions, ask them—WHY.

Is it not time we profited by England's example, when we know that delay means the loss of precious lives and added cost of the war?

. . . A master hand is needed in the shape of an open-minded executive with wide experience in co-ordinating different departments and in handling big business problems in a broad way. . . . With such a man in control, we feel sure that Congress can be depended on to be extremely liberal with appropriations. It is not to be blamed for questioning appropriations as long as the present unsatisfactory and inefficient methods continue.

We are all stockholders in the great corporation known as the United States of America. Let us insist on applying at least as good methods as we demand in our own business, which becomes insignificant in comparison. *The time has come to put the right man in charge of all munitions and end the inevitable delays and inefficiency of the present system.* [Italics mine.] The right man will utilize all the experience of valuable men now in the work and as many more as may be necessary.

Delays mean needless loss of life, unnecessary sorrow and suffering, and war taxes that may be avoided.

General Crozier and a few others, however, never forgave me or the *American Machinist* for our dastardly attack, but I have not once lain awake nights worrying about it. An important point is that the *American Machinist* assured all its readers that the Winchester management were in no way to blame for the situation that was thrust on them, and I should like to repeat that same fact here. It seems likely, on the other hand, that our exposure of the delays in securing the new rifles, as well as of other inefficiencies, hastened the retirement of General Crozier as Chief of Ordnance.

It is a matter of historical fact, of course, that the cause of this confusion was traceable to deeper sources. In December, 1917, Congress, urged on by the hostile criticism of such men as Theodore Roosevelt and Leonard Wood, began a prolonged investigation of the administration of the War Department, up to and including its Secretary, who had, in an unguarded moment, *expressed his happiness at our unpreparedness*, saying that it put us morally far above our adversary. Then, after an appropriation of $640,000,000 for aircraft in July, 1917, the Secretary of War had promised that in a year's time we would have 20,000 fighting planes in France; but, as Senator Lodge pointed out in the spring of 1918, we hadn't a single fighting plane in France, or a finished gun with a complete round of ammunition, of a caliber above 6 inches. Secretary Baker defended himself before the Senate by saying that no army of similar size in the history of the world had ever been so quickly raised, trained, and equipped as ours, and that all kinds of arms had been provided for every American soldier in France in 1918. President Wilson came to the support of his Secretary of War and praised the War Department for its "extraordinary promptness and efficiency." But nevertheless the Congressional investigation was followed shortly by a considerable shake-up of the bureaus in the War Department, and I think no one will now contend that this did not result in increased efficiency.

After the retirement of Major General Crozier as Chief of Ordnance, Col. Charles C. Wheeler was appointed acting chief during the strenuous fall and winter of 1917. Colonel Wheeler had previously been in command of the Watertown Arsenal in Massachusetts, where I had been a frequent visitor ever since 1895, and here I met Maj. C. C. Williams, Major Shinkle, and Major Westbrook, all of whom were to be seen later in Washington during the war years—Major Williams eventually being picked by Gen. John J. Pershing to accompany him to France with the first American Expeditionary Force, the one that landed in Europe before any of us here knew that the troops had left our shores.

In something less than a year, Williams, promoted to the rank of major general, returned to Washington to take over the Ordnance Department, which had grown to tremendous proportions in the interval following Crozier's retirement. Our friendship was renewed immediately on his return, and I was very happy to be of some service to him and to his department in securing information in many fields of research without the handicap of being connected with the department in any official capacity. For only in that way could I get at the facts that were not published in the official bulletins. Few people, perhaps, realize the size and the complexity of the problems that confronted General Williams's department at that time, and the serious difficulty of obtaining unbiased and factual information. Certainly no encomium from me is needed to testify to the splendid way in which Williams handled the task, both during the war and in the years that followed, up to his retirement.

In charge of procuring airplanes for the government was Howard Coffin, ably assisted by his contact man Curtice Hitchcock, and it was through the latter gentlemen (who, by the by, was a partner of Reynal and Hitchcock, the New York book publishers) that I finally made my first airplane flight, after putting it off for eight or nine years as hinted at in the preceding chapter. Hitchcock and I were two of a small group who journeyed to Camp Borden, a few miles north of Toronto, to study Canadian methods of servicing and repairing trainer planes. These were mostly all Curtiss J-4's (or "Jennies," as they came to be known in popular parlance and in fictional romance of the day) and of course this greatly simplified the problem of overhaul and repairs.

At that time the engines—Curtiss OX5's—were given a top overhaul after twenty-five hours in the air and a complete overhaul after fifty hours. How far the design and construction of aircraft engines have progressed in the past thirty years can be appreciated by the fact that modern airplane engines in transport service are overhauled only after 600 to 700 hours of continuous service.

My first flight was nothing if not unspectacular, and if I was scared silly at being up so high—3,000 feet or less—I certainly am not going to admit it at this late date. The plane was of the old open-cockpit type and I thought the breeze was going to blow my head off at first, but after a while I got so I could even look over the side of the cockpit without getting dizzy, except when the pilot made a steep bank or an air pocket boosted the plane several feet without warning. Flying in the pressure-sealed, air-conditioned cabin of a modern stratoliner is far less thrilling than that early flight of mine in the old Jenny biplane. You really felt more like a bird on the wing in those days.

This visit to Camp Borden resulted in several articles for the *American Machinist* over my by-line, intended for use in air training centers in this country, and while the articles were, of course, passed by the censor before I left Canada, I still remember with a tinge of regret that I had to pay duty on the portable typewriter that I had brought along for recording my impressions and suggestions.

My work as Washington correspondent during the First World War can best be characterized as hectic, although I never found that it lacked interest. At General Williams's request I inspected a goodly number of munitions and ordnance plants, and even studied a set of proposed plans for the erection and equipping of a huge gun-overhaul plant in France. But the latter, fortunately, never was needed because of the sudden collapse of German resistance in 1918. Airplane and navy-yard work was covered in my nonofficial visits, and during one of these I recall seeing the single test cylinders of the Liberty engines at the U. S. Bureau of Standards, which eventually led to their development and manufacture by Ford, Lincoln, Cadillac, Marmon, and Packard.

One of the outstanding developments in the design of this famous airplane engine was the way in which Ford, under the guidance of Harold Wills, produced forged tube cylinder blanks for all the makers of Liberty engines. Although some have contended that the Liberty motor was inexplicably long in developing, and that it was found to be unsuitable for the lighter fighting planes, I still feel that it represented a considerable achievement at a time when mechanical production was in a state of constant turmoil and confusion.

Before the development of the Liberty Engine, all steel cylinders had been made from a solid billet. The Gnôme cylinders, as I saw them made in Brooklyn, were bored and turned from a solid blank weighing about 95 pounds, whereas the finished cylinder weighed but 6 pounds. The army officials first planned on making the Liberty engine cylinders in the same fashion. Harold Wills of the Ford Company was quick to realize that this would present an impossible situation, both as to securing machine tools and to the amount of time it would require, to say nothing of the flagrant waste of steel in wartime.

Accordingly, Harold took a steel tube, long enough and thick enough to make two cylinders. These blanks were cut in two parts at an angle of about 30 degrees. Each cut end, after being heated to forging temperature, was closed in with suitable dies in a heavy press, thus creating a closed-end cylinder, as the design called for. In many cases the opening welded solid, but the angle of the cut was so designed that this was a trifling matter, for the opening, if any, came where one valve-seat opening was cut in the cylinder.

It was said that Ford was so confident that this method would be adopted that he piled up many thousand forgings before the Army had actually accepted these blanks for the cylinders. He was then in a position to supply all the other manufacturers of the Liberty motor with these cylinder forgings.

One of the anomalies of the Liberty motor production story is that there was universal accord among pilots and plane builders alike that Ford's Liberties were uniformly the best of all. This was a considerable surprise to a lot of people in the business, for how could a plant which specialized exclusively in making the lowest priced car on the market really turn out a first-class airplane engine? Mass production even then was still associated in the minds of many with inferior quality, as though the more one made of an article the shoddier it became. One feature of Henry's Liberty engine program appealed strongly to me. He did not guarantee to make every part strictly interchangeable; only the subassemblies that would be replaced as a unit in case of overhaul. Strict interchangeability of all parts, especially of those subject to wear, is seldom economical, as many manufacturers know very well. Selective assembly saves time and money, and replacements must allow for wear in any case.

A word or two should be said about the development of airplanes generally in the First World War. Despite the fact that the Liberty motor was a pretty good engine, our record as manufacturers of airplanes during this very critical period was something really to be ashamed of, as almost everyone knows who has done a little reading on the subject or who was around at the time. If I were asked to give one single reason for our astonishing failure to build airplanes, even after France and Great Britain had shown the way, I would think first of a group of men from the Middle West who dominated the procurement program, who sold the air service an airfield that had to be abandoned because of its being under water after a heavy rain, who prevented an equitable or sensible distribution of orders, and who in some way kept their names out of the report on *Air Service in America's Munitions*, written by Crowell, then Assistant Secretary of War, and approved by Secretary Baker. This volume is still available at the Government Printing Office in Washington and is a masterpiece of optimism, especially as far as airplane production was concerned. To those who recall the discrepancy between the promised 22,000 planes and the pitiful few that were actually produced, it reads like a fairy story.

The reader interested in these details will do well to study the testimony collected by Charles Evans Hughes in 1918 in this connection. It will be recalled, perhaps, that this investigation (on which I was called by Hughes as witness) was made as a result of surveys conducted by the famous sculptor Gutzon Borglum at the request of President Wilson.

It may also be remembered that Col. Jesse Vincent was acquitted by court-martial as not being responsible for the questionable practices brought to light by the investigation. And just before any of the other persons in high places were to be brought to trial, Secretary Baker ordered the entire case dismissed. Those of us who had known Baker as a good mayor in Cleveland and as a square shooter in the early days of the war, could only feel that he knew about the evidence which had been collected and that it was certain to convict some of those whom he felt (for reasons not evident on the surface) he had to protect.

The few planes that were finally built were an outstanding example of shoddy construction and defective workmanship, and they were so dangerous to fly that many of our aviators deliberately crashed them behind the lines, knowing that it was certain suicide to take them into combat against the Germans. These planes were familiarly known among Allied fliers as "flaming coffins," because they almost always caught fire at the slightest pretext and brought the pilot to an untimely end even before he had made contact with the enemy. It will be remembered by those familiar with the story that none of these planes were ever returned to the United States at the end of the war, but were deliberately destroyed in order to prevent their glaring defects from becoming too widely known in this country.

I had followed the failure to secure satisfactory planes very closely, and had visited the various airplane plants to learn more about the underlying causes. I traveled so extensively around the country that I was spending the greater parts of my nights on sleeping cars during this period. When I had gathered sufficient material, I wrote out a long article for publication in the *American Machinist* which I titled, "WHY WE HAVE SENT BUT ONE BATTLE PLANE TO FRANCE." While this article was still in page form and had not yet appeared in the magazine, I decided to show it to the chairman of the board that had been appointed to investigate the background and activities of the men in charge of airplane construction. The chairman read the article in my presence and said, "What you have written here, Mr. Colvin, is mostly all true and checks with what the committee has found in their investigation. The situation is of course serious and demands immediate correction, but I can assure you that steps are being taken right now to rectify the errors that have been made. Production will soon be moving ahead, and there will be no recurrence of these inefficiencies."

"That sounds very reassuring," I told him. "In view of what you say, maybe I ought to hold up the publication of this article, because we have no intention of beating a dead dog, so to speak, so long as we know it's really dead."

"I was going to ask you to do just that," the chairman said. "I know you or your magazine do not want to cause a sense of distrust on the part of the public, or give comfort to the enemy. Don't publish the article, and I can assure you that the faults you have discovered are already being corrected and will not recur to hold up airplane production. What do you say?"

For answer I grabbed the telephone, asked for long distance, and soon was talking to Van Deventer.

"Hello, Van—Fred talking. Listen—you've got to kill that story of mine on the airplane scandal about sending only one plane so far to France. What? I know, Van, but I've just been assured by–by a person in a very authoritative position here that everything's been changed and the facts in that article don't apply any more. It's all water under the bridge, they tell me, and they say if we print the article we'll only be stirring up more confusion and we won't really be helping the war effort any. O.K.? You might run that piece by Stanley on typewriter parts as a filler instead. All right, I'll tell 'em here that you've killed it."

The chairman was very gratified and thanked me profusely.

The chairman was also the most uninformed official I have ever met, or else he was the greatest prevaricator in all my experience, for, as everyone knows, nothing whatever was done to correct the scandalous condition of our aircraft industry and the whole project remained a public disgrace to the very end of the war.

I know I am getting out on a limb when I say that this has been partly attributed to the policy set by none other than Gen. John J. Pershing. "Black Jack" was of course entirely innocent of the deplorable state of American airplane manufacturing, but it is true that he sent word to the United States from his headquarters in France to the effect that, come what come may, America must produce better planes than the French Spads—quite a large order in view of the current state of United States aircraft production. The net effect of Pershing's well-meant message was that American manufacturers found themselves aiming at what proved to be an impossible ideal, and instead of building hundreds and even thousands of the best American design then current, the brass hats decided to wait for the "better" airplane, which, of course, never materialized. And American aviators continued to fly the French Spads until the Armistice was signed.

If the reader feels glum about all this, I suggest that he contemplate the story of American aircraft in the Second World War, which I shall attempt to discuss when I come to it in Chapter Eleven. It is a much more hopeful story.

And I really want to say something about machine tools in the First World War.

The pressing need for war materials for both our own army and that of the Allies created a great demand for machine tools in this country, and the problem of how to obtain them became quite serious. Every possible and conceivable pressure was brought to bear on the manufacturers of machine tools in order to secure priority of delivery. The various departments of the U.S. Army fought with each other to make a display of their alleged efficiency, and the same held true in deals involving the Army and Navy at the same time. For example, the Navy had a number of spare airplane motors that the Army needed for some LWS scout planes because no motors could be obtained from the manufacturers. The Navy refused to release its spare motors, thinking it the better part of valor to hold on to what they had so as not to be caught short-handed, and this sort of thing went on until the whole matter was referred to Secretary Baker and Secretary Daniels.

The same lack of cooperation was apparent between different branches of the Army. The general in charge of gun carriages happened to have a number of acquaintances among machine-tool builders, and perhaps tried to corner the market on all the machine tools available, at the expense of the general who was in charge of building the guns themselves. Nobody seemed to realize that the gun carriages were useless without the guns to go with them.

As a result of this bickering and rivalry between departments, a Machine Tool Division was established with George Merryweather as chief, in order to secure the best possible distribution of the machine tools being produced. With him was Abe Einig, from the Motch and Merryweather Company, and Arthur J. M. Baker, an Englishman whom I first met when he was with the Cincinnati Milling Machine Company.

George Merryweather, one of my long-time friends, had a most difficult task laid out for him, but he turned in a splendid performance. His knowledge of the machine-tool industry, his insight into the whole problem of manufacturing machine tools, his ability to judge character and qualifications, and his acute sense of downright honesty, made him the best possible choice for the job. He was affable, if that means he knew how to get along with people on their own terms, but he was also firm and outspoken whenever the kid-glove method wasn't applicable. George and I spent many hours, often far into the night, discussing and analyzing the various production problems as they arose, and my admiration and affection for the man increased in proportion to the amount of time I spent with him. His humorous and at times whimsical manner, his use of striking similes and parables, and his trenchant sarcasm (when required) made him a character long to be remembered by everyone who came in contact with him. George has, unfortunately, passed on to his reward, but I have recently had the privilege of knowing his son, George Jr., who was a lieutenant in the Navy in the Second World War.

One of the more interesting developments arising from the demand for machine tools in the manufacture of war equipment was the "shell lathe," designed by my old friend Lucien Yeomans, and built under his supervision by the Amalgamated Machine Tool Company of Chicago, a firm that was born in wartime. Speaking only approximately, this peculiar lathe consisted of a heavy cast-iron headstock and a tailstock tied together by large, ground steel shafts. In this lathe, then, holes were cored in both castings to receive the steel shaftings and to allow plenty of room for pouring type metal around the shafts. The castings were lined up in a fixture—the shafts properly positioned in the rough holes—and the pouring of the type metal locked them into a substantial lathe bed. The steel shafts also formed the *ways* of the lathe, and the result was a very rigid lathe that could be built in a few hours and could handle shell work with the best of them.

Well, what about the women?

Except for Kate Gleason, I haven't talked about women much in this rambling narrative, but not because I wasn't interested in the subject. Only because the fair sex (or weaker?) does not enter into the history of machine tools until this very point in our chronology. Mrs. Charles A. Beard will probably be in a position to correct me on this, but women in industry, if we except sweatshop labor and the textile field, hadn't figured prominently as operators and artisans until circumstances forced a radical change in the early years of the twentieth century. To be exact—mechanized war, even in its embryonic, 1917 form, was the opening wedge that has since proved to be a new and promising gateway to careers for women in industry.

I might go on to amplify this thesis for several pages, but, in order to save time and space, I should like to quote from an article I wrote that was published in the *American Machinist* for September 20, 1917, under the title "Women in the Machine Shops."

We are such creatures of habit, and are so slow to grasp new or different phases of an idea which may not be new in any sense, that we are a bit shocked at the thought of women running machines in the shop. Yet, we have not been at all disturbed by seeing women in the textile mills or in paper-box factories, and we quite forget the fact that watch factories and typewriter shops have for many years employed women in large numbers.

. . . The draft will take thousands of men out of our shops; and in order to maintain production, this loss must be met from the most available source. Therefore, we must utilize women on as much of the work as possible, after training them to do it.

I went on to discuss the problem of lowering the standard of wages allegedly caused by the infiltration of women into men's jobs, spoke about the question of where to get the right type of woman for the particular job, how to teach them, and what shop changes it would be necessary to make where women were around instead of men. After discussing such problems as woman's capabilities, shop facilities such as lavatories, rest rooms, and lunchrooms, maximum hours per week, and related questions, I launched into the following discourse on what the women should wear around the shops— although certainly this was outside of my province, if anything ever was:

In nearly all the shops visited, no attempt has been made by either the management or the women themselves to wear anything but the usual costume. Skirts are as a rule short, but at least no shorter than many seen on the street. [This, in 1917, would mean not more than an inch above the ankle.]

Dark clothes naturally predominate, and large aprons or even outer skirts are quite common.

Some, however, consider it a good plan to wear out old clothes of all kinds; and a few fancy waists and other dressy gowns are to be found, very much as the men formerly wore out their frock coats and other fancy suits.

A few shops encourage the girls to wear a small, neat cap to protect their hair from dirt and also keep in the stray locks from possible danger. This is particularly true in grinding and polishing rooms, even though exhaust fans are provided.

The Worcester Pressed Steel Co. has encouraged its shop girls to wear overalls, believing them to be safer, more comfortable in every way than any sort of skirt can possibly be. The company first purchased three pair of neat and well-made women's overalls and offered them to the first three girls who would wear them at their work. Quite naturally, three of the younger girls were the first to accept the offer, and as a result practically every girl in the machine shop is now wearing overalls and liking them in every way. They are fully as modest as the average dress, allow perfect freedom both standing and sitting, without fear that an undue amount of hosiery is exhibited to the passer-by. Very stout girls do not take kindly to them, but even they fall into line after the good points [!] of the overalls become apparent.

One feature to be guarded against is not to allow the girls in the office to snub the shop girls, or otherwise make them feel that they are in a different class, particularly from any difference in the occupation or dress. This question of social caste is one that must be carefully handled if the best classes of women workers are to be obtained.

While I do not wish to change the subject too abruptly, I should like to mention the fact that in March of 1919, my eldest son Charles founded the now well-known Pioneer Instrument Company and set up his office in a rented room in downtown Manhattan. His brother Henry, after he had recovered from a siege of typhoid fever contracted at the Langley Field research station during the war, joined Charles in his work. How well they progressed in developing their new business is indicated by the fact that they equipped the *Spirit of St. Louis* in 1927 with their recently perfected earth-inductor compass and other types of flying instruments before Lindbergh took off for Paris on his famous flight of May 20. Soon after reaching Paris, Lindbergh was thoughtful enough to cable Charles, telling him how well the instruments had functioned. The Pioneer Instrument Company later moved into a factory of its own in Brooklyn, and in 1929 the brothers sold out their interests to the Bendix Corporation.

Charles has continued his direct contacts with aviation up to the present time, but Henry branched out into the field of plastics, and has now become an authority on several phases of plastics manufacture and design. To carry the genealogy a little further, Henry's son Henry, III, (familiarly known as Ted) now represents the family's interest in aviation again, after having served as an ensign on the old battleship *Mississippi* during the tail end of the Second World War. Ted is now deep in research work for the Kollsman Instrument Company, and so as the years roll by, the old-timer can now shine in the reflected glory of his progeny.

Well, I think I have covered the First World War as well as I am able. Of course, I have not mentioned such things as the action at Heligoland Bight, the Scarborough raid, von Spee's south Pacific raids, Coronel and the Falkland Islands battles, Togoland and the Cameroons, the Battle of Dogger Bank, the Dardanelles campaign, the Battle of Jutland, Admiral Jellicoe, the pocket at Cambrai, Caporetto, the Arras and Saint-Quentin sector, the Battle of Lys, the second Battle of the Marne, the capitulation of Bulgaria, von Ludendorff's resignation, and the signing of the armistice of November 11, 1918. I purposely avoided them because I know nothing about them beyond, as the late Will Rogers was wont to say, what I read in the newspapers. And anyway, I am saving my strength for the chapters on Japan and the Second World War and the future of the machine-tool industry. I am thinking of a supplement to the present autobiography to be written when I am ninety years old, so that I must leave something untold now.

CHAPTER TEN

Tour of the World in Eighty Days

---

*Traveling is one way of lengthening life, at least
in appearance.*
BENJAMIN FRANKLIN, "Letters," 1767

I have brought this story up to the close of the First World War, and as a sort of breather between two world conflicts, I thought I would talk about my travels in this chapter, although the strict chronology of this autobiography may be somewhat strained thereby. When I say travels I mean of course those made outside the continental limits of the United States, for, as the reader can probably surmise by now, I got around quite a bit on home territory as a roving editor of the *American Machinist*. The travels I am going to talk about in the present chapter were partly a kind of vacation from the machine-tool world—the glorified Cook's tour I had been promising myself ever since I was twenty-one, but which I did not actually achieve until I had left my youth some distance behind me.

We must go back to the year 1911. In September of that year I embarked on the German fruit steamer, *Prinz Joachim*, bound for Panama and the Caribbean. It might be advisable, perhaps, to make a slight correction to what I have said above—this first trip was mostly in the line of duty, as I was supposed to gather material for an article or two on the construction of the Panama Canal, which was then about one-third completed. But I considered it as a kind of vacation, too.

I traveled with an acquaintance named Nathan Rockwood, whose mother had been a girlhood chum of my own mother back in Sterling, Massachusetts. On the way down to Panama the boat anchored offshore of one of the smaller Caribbean islands and took on several hundred native laborers bound for Colonel Goethals's big project. They were herded aboard like cattle, vaccinated in production-line fashion by the ship's doctor, and then packed into close quarters below decks. But they didn't seem to mind it in the least.

We also stopped at Santiago, Cuba. I recall that it was a bright, sunshiny morning when the *Prinz Joachim* nosed her way into the 7-mile-long strait that connects Santiago Bay with the ocean. And as I entered the bay I could not help thinking of Admiral Cervera and how he had hidden his Spanish fleet here in June, 1898, finally leading it through the channel on July 4 to swift destruction at the hands of Admiral Sampson's American warships. And it was in this channel that Naval Constructor Richmond P. Hobson and his men purposely sank the American collier *Merrimac* in a vain endeavor to bottle up Cervera's squadron in the harbor.

We went ashore for a day in Santiago, somewhat thrilled, I must confess, at visiting the most recent battlefield in American history, for in those remote days we were still thinking of war as an interesting phenomenon and not as the stupid and fantastic tragedy it really is. We climbed up the slopes of San Juan Hill, still fresh in our minds as the scene of Lt. Col. Theodore Roosevelt's exploits as leader of the 1st Volunteer Cavalry or "Roughriders," as they became known journalistically. I was also thinking of the stirring accounts of this "major battle," written by Richard Harding Davis and Stephen Crane, so that I had what might almost be called a romantic attitude towards the subject. I could not hear the rumblings of the great holocaust that was to follow in three or four years, nor could I imagine that war was to be the constant preoccupation of civilized nations for the next generation. If some writer of the H. G. Wells school had predicted that in forty years or so great nations would be annihilating each other in a push-button war of rocket projectiles carrying atomic-powered explosives, I would have said that pure fantasy had reached its extreme limits, or that the writer was a mental case. I would not say so now.

The city of Santiago, built on the east side of the bay on sharply rising ground, gave me my first taste of old-world atmosphere, and I was immensely intrigued with the steep winding narrow passageways that were known as streets, the tropical and polychromatic architecture, the high, barred windows overlooking the exiguous thoroughfares. Exactly as I had been told by the novelists and playwrights who went in for Spanish locales, there was nearly always a señorita behind each of these barred windows; she would be, I reasoned, under the strict surveillance of a stately duenna watching her from within; the fair señorita was merely being allowed to look upon the outside world without participating in it. My reasoning received a sudden jolt when one of these señoritas called out to me:

"Hey, Americano! *Muchachas!* You like! *Viente centavos, toda la noche!*"

But these were not pure Castilian señoritas, I am told.

After a brief stop at Kingston, Jamaica, we left the *Prinz Joachim* at Colón, the northern end of the proposed Panama Canal. This was the goal of the trip for Nathan and me, for it was our business to study and report on what was being done on the construction of the canal—it had been under way for five years, or ever since the Isthmian Canal Commission had reported in favor of the lock system rather than the sea-level system, and Congress had given the go-ahead signal to Col. George W. Goethals of the Corps of Engineers. Nathan had to report from the civil-engineering angle for *Engineering News*, while I was supposed to cover the maintenance of mechanical equipment for the *American Machinist*. President Roosevelt (T. R., of course) had issued an executive order in January, 1908, which placed supreme power in the hands of Colonel Goethals, giving him all civil, military, and other powers in the canal zone, and making the members of the Isthmian Commission subordinate to him. In other words, Colonel Goethals was head man.

Our first move, naturally, was to seek out the Brooklyn-born West Point graduate (who was made a major general in 1915 and served as quartermaster general during the First World War), so that we might secure the necessary credentials that would allow us to visit all the widely flung parts of the immense project without being shot at for trespassing. George Washington Goethals proved to be a very cordial gentleman, affable in spite of the tremendous pressure under which he and his men were working, and the net result of our interview was that Nathan and I were given passes, personally signed by Colonel Goethals, that gave us the right to visit any spot serviced by the Panama Railroad. In addition to this,

Colonel Goethals placed his private car at our disposal so that we might make a preliminary inspection trip.

In case I may have given the wrong impression by using the phrase "private car," let me hasten to explain exactly what Colonel Goethals' personal conveyance actually was. It was a 1908 touring car (the make I do not remember) from which all the original finery had been unceremoniously ripped out and replaced by rough wooden seats, an unpainted wooden roof, a few two-by-four up-

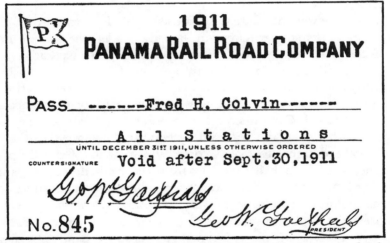

Railroad pass signed with original autograph and facsimile signatures of Colonel George W. Goethals, builder of the Panama Canal.

rights, and little else. The sides were completely open to the elements and the wheels had been equipped with flanged rims instead of tires so that the car could be run on top of the railroad tracks. The whole thing was very typical of the plain, straightforward way in which Goethals worked.

His driver, an experienced noncom, certainly knew the entire project almost as well as Colonel Goethals did. With a preliminary and perhaps unnecessary warning to us to hold on tight to the two-by-fours, he started off on a ride that for thrills was the equal of any roller coaster then in operation at Coney Island. The construction men had had little time to worry about grades when they laid this railroad, and there was little or no ballast under the ties because the route was subject to change without notice.

We went down into the cuts where huge steam shovels were at work loading the long trains of cars with earth fill to be dumped at Gatun in order to create the enormous dam that resulted in Gatun Lake. The flat cars with their dirt load had the right of way over everything on the road, and just in case anyone was inclined to forget this important fact, there were signs all over the place reading, DIRT HAS THE RIGHT OF WAY. This was impressed on us throughout the trip, for we probably spent half of the time on a siding behind a mudbank while trains heavily laden with excavated earth and rock crawled past us on their way to Gatun. And even on the main line of the Panama Railroad, passenger trains were sidetracked in order to let the dirt trains through.

Neither Nathan Rockwood nor I had realized the size of the railway operations necessary to build the canal. All the articles we had read when we were priming ourselves for the journey did, indeed, stress the tremendous efforts being made to "make the dirt fly," but none of them had hinted at how the dirt was to be disposed of once it had been removed from the cuts. It was a revelation to learn that the railroad of the canal alone had more locomotives and more cars than had the well-known Boston and Albany line in New England. Moreover, we learned that it took an extensive repair shop and some 1,200 men to keep this equipment in operation. But this was not all. To maintain the scores of steam shovels and other earth-moving equipment required a still larger shop with 1,800 more mechanics—in other words, 50 per cent more than the number required to keep the railroad in running condition.

Steam shovels took a lot of punishment. Earth under the track had a nasty habit of sliding out and overturning them even when they were standing idle. As though this were not enough, huge banks of soil, seeming to resent being disturbed after centuries of complacency, would suddenly turn into landslides and bury several of the great shovels completely out of sight. In many instances these landslides occurred so swiftly that the shovel operator and crew were buried with their machine. It is small wonder that none of the early schemes for the construction of the canal ever got to first base.

For there were many others who attempted to build the Panama Canal before George Goethals came on the scene. As early as the year 1550 a Portuguese navigator named Antonio Galvao wrote a book telling how a canal could be cut at Tehuantepec, Nicaragua, Panama, or Darien, and the following year the Spanish historian de Gomara implored Philip II to undertake the project immediately. Of course nothing came of it. In 1698 William Paterson, founder of the Bank of England, set up an ambitious scheme for a settlement on the Isthmus of Darien, the construction of a canal, and a monopoly on world commerce, but disease and lack of funds made him abandon Darien soon after his expedition had landed. The Spanish government revived the project in 1771–79, during which period surveys for a canal were made at Tehuantepec and Nicaragua, but again it came to naught. From 1825 to 1887 numerous concessions were granted to private citizens of the United States and Europe for the construction of a canal, but nobody every got beyond the planning stage.

Ferdinand de Lesseps, whom we spoke about in an earlier chapter, entered the scene about 1880, under the sponsorship of an International Congress of 135 delegates from France, Germany, Great Britain, and the United States, and work actually began on a sea-level canal between Colón and Panama, but, as Goethals himself points out in his Encyclopaedia Britannica article, de Lesseps's management was "characterized by a degree of extravagance and corruption rarely if ever equaled in the history of the world." Work was finally suspended in 1889.

The United States had naturally become seriously interested in the proposed canal by this time, realizing that it might become a vital part of the country's defenses, and after the Spanish-American War, Congress created the Isthmian Canal Commission to make a detailed study of the project. In 1903, following the declaration of independence of Panama from Colombian rule, this country signed the Hay-Bunau-Varilla Treaty with Panama, giving us the "use, occupation, and control" of a strip of land 10 miles wide on which we might build the canal. And finally, in 1907, the Isthmian Canal Commission was reorganized, as we have already noted, and Col. George W. Goethals was appointed engineer in chief. When the canal was declared officially finished and open for business in 1914, a total of approximately 240,000,000 cubic yards had been excavated, and we had spent something in the neighborhood of $367,-000,000. A small sum, however, when one considers what we spent on the Second World War and the development of the atom bomb.

But to return to our travels. For the eight days of our stay in Panama we followed a strict routine. Carrying a camera and an umbrella (both of which were in very frequent use), I would leave Panama City at 6 A.M., headed for the nearest town where there was a machine shop or mechanical activity of any kind. The visits to the shops gave me background material for several articles in the *American Machinist*, and I used up dozens of films photographing equipment and sundry details of working conditions. One of my days thus spent was devoted to an examination of the many dredges used on the canal work, some of which had been built and operated by the French under de Lesseps. And the shops at Balboa, on the Pacific end of the canal, contained a great deal of other machinery, as well as corrugated roofing and siding sheets, brought over by the ill-starred Gallic engineer.

The ruins of the old city of Panama, destroyed by Sir Henry Morgan in 1671, were an object of special interest to us. Most of the old tower, so widely seen in pictures, was still standing, and adjoining it were the foundations of what was presumably a monastery. Few traces of the walls remained, and these were mostly hidden by a tangle of tropical vines. It was hard to realize that this was all that remained of a once-thriving city of 20,000 inhabitants. For, according to some accounts, Panama City was the metropolis of the west coast during the early Spanish regime, and served as a fitting-out place for the Spanish raiding expeditions against Peru and other South American countries in the sixteenth and seventeenth centuries. From here they carried priests and missionaries to spread the gospel to the benighted heathen, bringing back (as a mere incident of their journeys) the gold of the Incas, armies of slaves, and loot of all kinds, and leaving a broad swath of death and destruction in their wake.

It was unbelievable, too, to stand on the Pacific side of the Isthmus and recall how the Spaniards themselves were later despoiled by Sir Henry Morgan's piratical band. Having spent days in traveling just a few miles across the Isthmus, and having seen the wildness of the jungle growth of the Caribbean side, I could not quite comprehend how a small band of men, even half-savage pirates, could force their way across and capture an established and strongly fortified city. This appears even more incredible when we realize that it was not until 1941 and the Second World War that a highway of any sort was put across this narrow neck of land. The raid of Sir Henry Morgan and his fellow pirates will always stand out in my mind as one of the most difficult and daring undertakings in history.

The good ship *Prinz Joachim* picked us up again and took us back to Santiago, Cuba. From there I traveled by rail to Havana while Nathan Rockwood returned, somewhat reluctantly, to New York. In Havana I stayed at the Hotel Seville, and I mention this detail only because it was here, in the year 1911, that I saw my first dial telephone, which many good people believe was not developed until the late 'twenties. I have often wondered why Havana had a dial system long before any city in the United States, and perhaps some executive of the A.T. & T. will care to enlighten me on this point.

The high spot of my visit to Havana, after I had gone the usual rounds of the railway shops, the marine repair shops, and the maintenance shops of the large sugar "centrals," was a trip aboard the battleship *Maine*, which, it is claimed, was sunk by a person or persons unknown on the eve of the Spanish-American War with a loss of 266 lives—and which was just being raised from the mud of Havana harbor when I arrived. Just how the explosion which sank her occurred may never be known or at least made public, but the first American Board of Inquiry, having examined the wreck a month after the explosion, reported that it was caused by an exterior mine, because of the upheaval of the ship's bottom. This report may have been colored somewhat by existing sentiment and jingoism, and I believe that few or none now know whether the explosion was internal or external, accidental or perpetrated. We all know, however, that it precipitated the Spanish-American War, brought T. R. into prominence, gave unscrupulous beef packers a chance to purvey putrid meat to the Quartermaster Corps at fancy prices, taught us something about malaria, gave us a taste of imperialism, brought us Puerto Rico and (for a time) Cuba, and gave us a colony on the other side of the earth—the Philippine Islands.

The author, his secretary, and Harry Johnson, at the Springfield Armory, September, 1914

The Adams-Farwell six cylinder rotating airplane engine, built between 1915 and 1918

A planer of unusual design, found in a Cuban "sugar central," about 1911

Part of the superstructure and the stern of the battleship *Maine*, photographed as it was being raised from Havana Harbor in 1911, following its sinking on February 15, 1898

The decks and superstructure of the *Maine* were covered with a heavy incrustation of barnacles and other sea growth, as can be seen in the picture I took of it at the time. The silt and mud were being cleared away as I stood watching the operations, and every now and then a workman would knock his shovel against a skull or a section of vertebrae, in the manner of Shakespeare's grave-digger in *Hamlet*. It was not a very pleasant sight to behold.

The following evening I boarded the steamer for Key West, and my first trip abroad was soon at an end.

Three years later I was on my way to Europe, accompanied by my wife, in the year 1914—just before the outbreak of the First World War. We left New York in a raging blizzard on St. Valentine's Day, which was of course a pretty piece of symbolism. Railroads were blocked by snowdrifts, and we reached the ship twenty minutes late. Our trunks and baggage had been put off the ship and the gangplank was just about to be drawn in when we arrived. If we hadn't telephoned from Hoboken, we would have been left behind. The captain apparently didn't believe in letting the elements keep him from his appointed rounds, even if it meant leaving a few passengers stranded.

New York City disappeared completely in a whirl of swift-flying snowflakes as soon as we reached midstream. It seemed impossible that we should ever find our way down through the channel in the white wilderness; but we made it, only to run into an 80-mile hurricane at sea that lasted three days and three nights. There was a foot of snow on the decks, the ship pitched and tossed in the gale, and it was a very rough passage indeed. I was beginning to wonder what insane desire had prompted me to voyage on the broad Atlantic in the dead of winter when I could have remained comfortably at my own fireside with a few back numbers of the *National Geographic*, but the storm gradually subsided, the snow was cleared from the decks, and faint rays of weak sunshine began to brighten the last few days of the trip before we raised land.

At London we went first to the old Morley Hotel, facing Trafalgar Square, because all the guidebooks said that was the proper thing to do if one wanted atmosphere, but before long we transferred to the Strand Palace, which was more within our means and less crowded with tourists. The first Sunday there was almost like a spring day, and we could not resist having tea out of doors in near-by Kew Gardens.

"Wonderful weather, isn't it, dear?" I said to my wife. "All of these tales about London fog and climate are probably grossly exaggerated."

"I wouldn't be at all surprised," she answered. "I have always thought it was merely a literary device used by detective-story writers to create local color. Look at that blue sky overhead."

That night the fog crept in on stealthy feet and blotted out everything within the radius of a man's arm. In the morning it began to rain gently at first, and then in bucketfuls, and the rain kept falling all that day and the next, and the day following, and the day after that, and the day after that again, and every night, and it rained, rained, rained for four solid weeks without ever a letup. We were continually soaked to the skin, and it was cold, and our clothes never dried out, and I said one day, "To hell with this place. I'm going back to Sterling, Massachusetts, where the weather is not so damned unreasonable." But we stayed on.

Of course I had to make a tour of the British machine shops on this busman's holiday of mine. I never stopped to think that my wife might not get such a tremendous kick out of this tour as I, but her interest was nevertheless considerable, and the more she saw the more her interest grew. She never tired of hearing me expound on the virtues or disadvantages of the British lathe *versus* the American lathe, or of listening to some of my long-winded explanations of machinery operation, even though she knew no more about it than the back of my hand. She was a great gal to have around.

One of my first visits was to the Napier Automobile Plant, which was largely a "custom" shop. They told us that about half of their customers bought the bare chassis only and then had their own carriage builder make the body. This was apparently a revolt against the mass-produced, standardized, run-of-the-mill variety of automobile that Henry Ford had successfully introduced in America. The custom-made job was personalized, more expensive, and showed that the owner was a man of distinction. More often than not a coat-of-arms was emblazoned on one of the doors. This did not affect the car's performance, though.

From London we traveled to Coventry, a famous old town that has since been almost completely destroyed by the *Luftwaffe* and is still being painfully rebuilt by the hardy survivors of one of the heaviest air raids before the days of atomic warfare. Coventry, which traces its existence back to the foundation of a Benedictine monastery by Earl Leofric and his famous spouse, Lady Godiva, is about 900 years old, and there were still some portions of the ancient Roman wall, built in the sixth century A.D., in a fair state of preservation.

Coventry, though of great antiquity, is by no means a sleepy, moss-covered hamlet. As early as the sixteenth century it was famous for its dyeing industry, and acquired such a reputation in that field that the phrase "as true as Coventry blue" became a household expression in the British Empire. Before the First World War it had flourishing automobile, bicycle, and textile industries, with a good beginning in the manufacture of telephone and other electrical equipment. And in the war that ended in 1945, Coventry had such a leading position in the manufacturing of all kinds of light and heavy equipment that Marshall Goering's supermen singled it out as the number one city to be destroyed from the air.

It was here that I saw the great Alfred Herbert Plant, the Crossley Gas-Engine Works, the Humber Motorcycle Plant, the Rover Automobile Plant, and the Webster and Parks Machine Works, where a unique double-table vertical boring machine was made—the only one of its kind I have ever seen. The owners, officials, foremen, and operators of every shop I visited went out of their way to be gracious to me, and in nearly every case the usual formality of asking "Do you have an appointment?" was waived in order to save the time of a visitor from the United States. The books and articles I had written up to this time had evidently paved the way for my visits, and it was indeed flattering to have a fair number of people tell me that my name was well known in machine-shop circles as the co-author of the "American Machinists' Handbook" and divers other publications along that line. In more than one shop I was told that the "Handbook" was the ultimate authority on many questions of design and operation of machine tools and related equipment, although this may have been merely an expression of politeness—it is hard to say.

Our next stop was at Birmingham, in the northwest of Warwickshire, a fairly recent town when compared with Coventry—it is little more than 600 years old and did not become commercially or industrially important until as late as the seventeenth century. Birmingham, as everyone who has looked in an encyclopedia knows, is renowned for the art of metalworking in all its varied forms—brassworking, ironworking, jewelry, gold, silver, small arms, buttons, hooks, pins, and screws and nails in enormous quantities. Every machinist is familiar with the Birmingham wire gauge, and many scriveners of the past generation knew that the best pen nibs came from Birmingham. Besides being a leading center of railroad-car manufacture, Birmingham is also well known for its production of automobiles, tires, and accessories. It is a curious coincidence that another and much younger city named Birmingham is even more famous industrially, particularly in the manufacture of steel and pig iron, but *this* Birmingham is located in Alabama, U.S.A., and hence we cannot talk about it here.

In Birmingham (England) I made the usual tour of the machine shops, and among them I recall Ward's, makers of turret lathes—known, by the way, as "capstan" lathes in British terminology—as well as the shop of the Gear Grinding Company outside the city, where H. F. L. Orcott had established a plant for grinding gear teeth, based on the operation of the Detroit company of the same name. Frank Cooper and Hugh Purdy of the Buck and Hickman office took me on a very pleasant automobile trip through the English countryside in early April, and while I do not pretend to be a student of literature, I could not help recalling the lines of Browning that I had read in school, "O to be in England, now that April's there." Spring in the English countryside is really something to wax poetic about.

Our trip took us to Leicester, the county town of Leicestershire, located on the river Soar, which my guidebook tells me is a tributary of the Trent. Leicester is another of the really ancient English towns,

dating back to 120 A.D. during the Roman occupation, and flourishing way back in the ninth century as the seat of a bishopric. Hosiery
was its main trade before the Second World War, but I am not sure
what is going on there now. At the time I am speaking about—
1914—one of the most important sights from my point of view was
the plant of Taylor, Taylor, and Hobson, the famous makers of
lenses and other optical equipment. I was particularly interested
because of the progress being made here in the field of precision
measurements. The senior Mr. Taylor, who was the managing
director of the firm, showed us every kindness, going so far as to
invite my wife and myself to his home for luncheon. The last time I
heard from Frank Cooper—it was in October, 1946, I think—he was
enjoying fine health in Scotland at the ripe old age of ninety-four,
having retired as head of the Buck and Hickman Company in
London. I recommend the machine-tool field, or even its peripheral
activities, to everyone interested in living beyond the allotted threescore and ten.

The city of Manchester lies 189 miles northwest of London, and
I have no need to tell anyone that it is the most important center
of the cotton industry in the world, and a close runner-up in the field
of manufacturing of heavy and light machinery, weaving and spinning mills, locomotives, and other industrial accessories. Naturally
the Manchester district—comprising the city itself and its neighboring towns and villages—gave me the opportunity for a full-fledged
field day in my chosen subject, for there are few cities in the world
where so much diverse and interesting machinery is gathered
together in a relatively small compass.

To be consistent in my account of English cities, I should state
that Manchester, or Mancunium as it was known to the Romans, was
chartered in the year 1301 by Baron Thomas Gresley, and that
cotton, in its modern sense, was first processed and woven there
about 1620. The purpose behind my mentioning all these statistics
is merely to present a better perspective of the situation.

Apart from the engrossing details of the operation and layout
of the numerous shops, I recall particularly the labor-relations attitude of Hans Renold, owner and president of the Hans Renold
Plant at Manchester, which was renowned for the silent-chain device
it manufactured for power drives. Hans, who took me on a personally

conducted tour of his plant, wanted to know at the end of our visit if there was anything further on which he could enlighten me.

"Yes," I spoke up glibly. "Do you have any trouble with the unions—I mean, what is your policy, generally, in dealing with organized labor?"

"I am very firm on that subject," Renold replied with some feeling. "I make it a strict rule never to hire a man if he belongs to—" he paused momentarily—"if he belongs to no union whatsoever." His artful phrasing caught me a little off guard. He went on.

"I will not employ a man who hasn't guts enough to belong to a union, and I *mean* that," he said, slamming fist against palm for emphasis. "A lot of workmen are afraid to join a union now because they think they'll lose their job when the boss finds out. But let me tell you unionism is a good thing and it's on the rise. We employers have all had our unions for a long time now, only we disguise them under the name of 'associations.' Why shouldn't the men have theirs? Then all of us—employers and workmen—can get together and agree on terms that will apply to everyone concerned. The individual worker hasn't a chance by himself—he knows that—but at the same time the boss is much better off when he has to deal with the workers as a group. It's only reasonable, don't you think?" Hans Renold was a full generation ahead of his time in the field of collective bargaining.

It was in Manchester, also, that I ran across another unusual labor-relations situation, at least from our present point of view. The American manager of the British Monotype Company, whose shop I visited, told me of an experience he had had recently that helped him understand the meaning of class distinction, a subject he had been entirely unfamiliar with hitherto.

The foreman of his grinding department was about to resign for reasons that have no bearing on the story. He went to his most capable assistant, a man whom he considered the best grinder in the shop, and spoke somewhat as follows:

"Mister Hawkins, you might know that I intend to leave my place here on the first of the month. The chief has asked me to recommend someone for the job, and I think you are easily the best choice. How do you feel about it?"

"Well, sir, I deeply appreciate your kindness . . . the honor . . . you are very kind, sir."

"I'll tell the chief you'll take it, then?"

"Oh, sir—give me a little time to think about it, won't you? I've got to think it over and talk with the Missus. Tomorrow—I'll let you know tomorrow morning, sir, and thank you again for thinking of me."

The next day the foreman sought out Hawkins and inquired, "You've come to a decision, Albert?"

"Yes sir, I have," said Hawkins.

"Then you'll want to see the chief about the arrangements?"

"I don't think that will be necessary, sir. I . . . I don't want the job, if you don't mind, sir."

"Don't want the job? Why, man, it will mean a rise of two pound six a week to start—and more after that when you've been at it a while. Are you daft?"

"It's this way, sir," said Hawkins. "If I may say it myself, I'm known as the best grinder there is in these parts. Mrs. Hawkins and myself are right at the top of our own group—the other grinders and their families and friends, I mean—the kind of folks in our own circle. They look up to me, sir, as being the top of the grinders' class, and everyone is very respectful to us.

"Now if I was to take this foreman's job, sir, I and the Missus couldn't be familiar with the grinders' class any more, and all of our old friends would feel they had to stop seeing us because we would be out of their circle. But then we'd be only at the bottom of the foreman's class, you see, and nobody in *that* circle would want to have anything to do with us for a long time at first because we'd only be newcomers.

"So the Missus and I talked it over last night and we came to this decision, sir. Thanking you just the same for the compliment, it just isn't worth it for me to be promoted to foreman. I think I should stay as I am."

Passing from this example of class distinction (which has largely been wiped out by the recent war), I turn to recall my visit to the Whitworth-Armstrong Plant where I became greatly interested in the huge lathes employed in the turning of big guns and shafting for naval vessels. There were many large, hollow-spindle lathes made of cast iron, with holes through the spindles ranging from 18 to 24 inches, and for those in the know, these were impressive figures for cast-iron bearings.

This led me to look into the possibilities of cast iron for machine bearings, and ever since that time I have remained a convert to its use in this field. When the bearings can be made of sufficient size and are carefully lubricated until they wear into a glazed surface, cast iron proves to be an excellent material for the purpose. For those who may wish to know the reasons for this, it is that the average grade of cast iron is porous enough to retain a good quantity of oil on its surface, and is therefore almost self-lubricating.

Speaking of cast iron reminds me of another story that takes us back to the 1890's. Photomicrographs were just coming into use then as a tool for research workers in metallurgy whereby the molecular pattern of steels and other metals could be studied. An old friend of mine, who shall be nameless, became seriously interested in the new technique and made several very fine photomicrographs of steel sections.

But he was also a wag with a very odd sense of humor. Asked to exhibit his work in this line at a meeting of prominent metallurgists, my friend prepared a very impressive-looking print and submitted it to the gathering. The photograph was passed among the scientists and engineers present, all of whom studied it avidly and made excited comments.

"Excellent detail!"

"Notice the granular structure!"

"And the carbon particles in suspension!"

"And the fault lines in the lower portion!"

"It may indicate crystallization!"

"It is an exceptional grade of steel!"

"It is at least a 50-diameter magnification!"

"What can we not learn from this technique!"

These and similar remarks were bandied about for a while until finally the chairman of the committee, addressing my friend the photomicrographer, announced, "And now we will hear from the man who made this remarkable photograph—photomicrograph, to be exact. Will you tell us, sir, exactly what grade of steel this represents, and whether it is carburized, austenitic, casehardened, or otherwise?"

My friend sensed that things had gone too far.

"Look, fellows—don't get sore, but that picture isn't a photomicrograph at all."

"Not a photomicrograph?" said the chairman. "But how do you photograph a section of steel without a microscope?"

"It isn't even a steel sample," my friend confessed, looking around for the nearest exit.

"Then what kind of metal is it?"

"It ain't even metal. It's—it's a life-size shot of—of a sugar cookie!"

"*Yoroshiku gozaimasu!*"

That, or something very similar to it, was the expression that greeted us on our arrival in Tokyo.

The Tokyo interlude brings us forward to the year 1929, for I had been asked to act as delegate for the Society of American Automotive Engineers at the World Engineering Congress held in Tokyo during October of that year.

A good number of my readers will be wondering why in the name of heaven the World Engineering Congress decided to hold its meeting in Tokyo when there were so many other places available. The veterans of the recent war, particularly those who fought through Okinawa, Iwo Jima, Buna, Hollandia, Aitape, Tarawa, Saipan—and those few who came back from Bataan and Corregidor, Wake Island, Guam, and a half-dozen other spots in the Pacific— will wonder why I should even devote part of a chapter to my visit to Japan.

My only excuse is that I hope the account which follows may give the reader a better insight into the problem of what we are to do with Japan in the years to come, by setting forth the impressions of one traveler who saw the Japanese people some twelve years before

Pearl Harbor, a few years before their government had embarked on a large-scale plan of conquest and imperialism. If I seem to be treating the Japanese too generously, judged by 1941–45 standards, I hope it will be remembered that in 1929 the Japanese people were still in the Lafcadio Hearn stage and all of us thought they were one of the pleasantest races of mankind on the face of the earth. During the recent war many commentators quoted the Encyclopaedia Britannica article on Japanese moral characteristics—written in 1932—to the effect that "the Japanese are essentially a kindly hearted, laughter-loving people, taking life easily and not allowing its petty ills unnecessarily to disturb their equanimity." This was considered a great joke in the light of Pearl Harbor and subsequent developments. But it shows how far you can go wrong in sizing up the character of a group of people so complex as the Japanese. I don't think the average Japanese businessman wanted war.

In order to follow the story in the subsequent pages with any degree of impartiality, the reader may wish a further reorientation on the subject of Japanese relations circa 1929. In spite of Japanese aggression in the Chinese-Japanese War of 1894–95 and the serious economic penetration of Japanese immigrants into American territory, there was a great deal of rosy optimism about Japanese peaceful intentions as early as 1909. In 1908 it was stated that there were more than 60,000 Japanese in California who did not intend to become American citizens, but planned merely to make money and return to their homeland. The state legislature of California proposed certain enactments designed to limit the entry and residence of Japanese immigrants in 1909, but this was followed by a great outbreak of indignation not only in Japan but also in the United States. In the *American Machinist* for January 21, 1909, the American Locomotive Company had a long letter published which stated that United States interests would suffer greatly from the proposed "anti-Japanese legislation," in view of the fact that "the Japanese are highly sensitive, quick to resent the insulting attitude assumed by the authors of the bill now pending in the California legislature."

The letter stated in defense of its position that our business with Japan had continually increased from 1903 to 1907, and quoted export figures for railway materials and iron and steel manufactures of from $23,150,000 to $40,350,000. The letter further stated that the exports of locomotives from the United States to Japan and her dependencies had increased from thirty-nine in 1901 to 270 in 1907. The communication closed with the following exhortation:

> It occurs to us, therefore, that you could, through the editorial column cf your paper (the *American Machinist*), remedy to some extent the damage already done to American interests, by publicly assuring our Japanese friends that the American people as a whole hold them in the highest respect and esteem.

The reader will understand, therefore, in what frame of mind I voyaged to Japan in October, 1929, and will perhaps excuse me for not suspecting them at every turn. But since even General Mac-Arthur seems to have faith in the Japanese people, perhaps I should not excuse myself too much.

Well, anyway, let's get on with the story. My wife and I left New York very appropriately on the anniversary of my birthday—my sixty-second birthday, by the way—October 5, 1929. In Chicago we stayed over with our old friends, the Jack Morrows—"Jack" being the pseudonym for Lester C. Morrow, formerly an associate editor of the *American Machinist* when I was just a beginner, and now editor in chief of *Factory Management*, as well as consulting editor of the well-known Industrial Organization and Management Series of books. If this sounds like a plug for my old friend Jack Morrow, that is exactly what I intended it to be. I only hope that Jack will have the decency not to write *his* autobiography. At least not until the present work is out of print.

After passing through San Francisco, where we were entertained by the local engineers at Leland Stanford University with a performance of their 3-million-volt spark jump (which I caught in my motion picture camera), we sailed on the *President Jackson*, specially chartered for the trip. Some facetious person in the group of passengers remarked that it would be a calamity of the first order if the good ship *President Jackson* should spring a leak and go down with all the best engineering brains in the country on board. Robert Ridgeway, who was then chief engineer of the city of New York and a passenger, happened to overhear the remark.

"If this ship should sink," he declared, "with this great constellation of the finest engineers and scientists in the country, all

I can say is, that there would be a hell of a lot of promotions made back home."

Our first stop was naturally Honolulu. I shall skip the details of our first dinner of *poi*, because everybody and his brother has gone through this experience at least once, including the so-called "native dances," the tourist-inspired folk songs, the distribution of the *leis*, and the ultimate casting off of these wreaths from the departing steamer from which one is supposed to determine whether or not one is to return to Hawaii by the fact that they either float or sink. And after a rather tempestuous voyage across the blue Pacific, during which I was thrown out of bed at least once, we reached Yokohama, and eventually Tokyo.

In Tokyo we were put up at the Imperial Hotel—designed by the internationally famous American architect Frank Lloyd Wright, and said to be largely owned by the imperial family and subsidized by them. Doctor Makoto Saito, whom we had previously met on our return trip from England in 1914, met us in the lobby.

"*Yoroshiku gozaimasu,*" he announced, grinning as only a Japanese can grin.

"*Arigato gozaimasu,*" I replied, remembering in the nick of time what he had taught me about greetings and salutations. Dr. Saito, of course, spoke excellent English, having been an engineering admiral in the Japanese Navy, a special instructor at the University of Tokyo, and, at the time of my visit, director of a machine-tool building firm known as the Ikegai Iron Works, Ltd.

The meetings of the World Engineering Congress extended over a three-week period, but between sessions and over week ends we were able, through the Congress, and liaisons arranged by Dr. Makoto Saito, to make numerous tours and excursions to the show places of the Japan of 1929. (I am afraid there is less to see in Japan at the present time, unless one considers extensive ruins—as in Hiroshima and Nagasaki—a fit subject for the tourist.)

The *Nippon tetsudo kaisha*, or Japanese Railway Company, was not famous for its celerity (the average speed of passenger trains in 1929 was 18 miles per hour), but the cars were scrupulously clean, the trains were almost always on time, and these people had a wonderful system of handling luggage—at least for us delegates. When traveling from one town to another by rail, you merely tagged your luggage and left it behind you in your hotel room. On arrival at your destination, such as Nikko, Mianoshita, or elsewhere, you went to your appointed hotel and discovered your bags waiting for you in your room. Now if I were to leave the Statler Hotel in Detroit and wind up in the William Penn in Pittsburgh, I would learn that my baggage was still at the Statler, and I wouldn't have a clean shirt to put on.

The Japanese railroads were single line for the most part, and employed the narrow-gauge or meter-gauge track (40 inches), with consequent diminution in the size of the cars and engines. This is probably all very good for a people whose average height is some-where around 5 feet 2 inches, but I recall that several members of our party had to sleep with their knees drawn up under their chins when traveling on the Japanese version of the Pullman or sleeper.

Another point of difference, as far as rail travel is concerned, was brought forcibly to my attention on a trip from Tokyo to Osaka. It was my first overnight journey, and as I went through the cars on my way to the dining car, I was a bit taken aback by what I saw. There were two women in the aisles naked to the waist, a man running around in shorts, an elderly female wearing what appeared to be a flannel union suit, seated on her valise, and two or three children with no drawers on. I learned afterward that this state of dishabille was but temporary, for it was the custom on sleepers for the pas-sengers to dress in the aisle after the beds had been folded up out of the way. Speaking as one who has been required on countless occasions to struggle from a business suit into a pair of pajamas and back again into the business suit—all of this behind the drawn curtains of a upper berth, mind you—I am inclined to think that in this, at least, the Japanese have the right idea.

I visited a fair number of Japanese machine-tool shops, and while I found that nothing approaching the high standards of American design and practice was ever encountered, the average shop seemed to be fairly satisfactory, and I found that the Japanese had overcome tremendous obstacles in building up a machine-tool industry. American methods had been adopted as closely as local working conditions would allow, but apparently the stockholders could not understand why their plants should be equipped with expensive imported machines when Japanese-built equipment (which looked very similar from a distance) could be purchased for half the price. The Japanese, as everyone knows, are imitative rather than creative, clever rather than inventive. Saito Man, a then-prominent Japanese writer, was quoted as saying that "For energy or practical talents the average Japanese cannot hold a candle to the average American."

In a large railway shop at Omiya I found the workmen stretching boiler tubes to required length after cutting them out of a loco-motive boiler, instead of welding on safe ends as is the practice in the United States. The stretching of the tube, it was claimed, helped to remove the scale accumulated from impure water, but it also made the tube thinner and weakened it considerably. They followed a practice, moreover, of building up worn car-wheel treads with welding rods while the wheels and axles turned under the torch—a method that had long before been abandoned in this country.

I got around to the shops at Osaka, where machine tools were being built as well as engines for airplanes, trucks, and other moving equipment. Bicycle parts were being made in small shops with a very simple die for punching out sprocket wheels. Production seemed to be very limited in quantity, and everything looked second-rate when judged by occidental standards. Lathes were run backward for the most part—with the tool upside down in the tool post! Honing of cylinders was coming into vogue at Osaka, but I observed that the Japanese operators were allowing twenty-thou-sandths of an inch for the hone to remove—about ten times the then-current American practice. There were many American machine tools in evidence—Bradford, Pratt and Whitney, Lodge and Shipley, Gisholt, and others, but in the railroad shops the English machines prevailed—Herbert, Asquith, Milton, Bath, etc.—for the railroads had been built by an English company and planned by English engineers with the meter gauge as standard.

I am certain that most of the delegates to the World Engineering Congress went to Japan laboring under the delusion that the ricksha was a native institution that dated away back into the dark ages. We were apprised of the true situation by a number of well-informed natives and by an excellent guidebook. The ricksha, or more properly *jinrikisha* (from the Japanese *jin*, man, *riki*, strength, and *sha*, carriage) was at first a makeshift vehicle that an American missionary threw together for the purpose of taking his invalid wife out for an airing. Originally made from the wheels of a baby carriage brought over by the missionary, its usefulness and portability became readily apparent, and its widespread adoption in Japan and China speaks volumes for the adaptability of the Oriental.

Contrasts in methods of transportation, in clothing, and in building construction seemed to me an outstanding feature of Japanese life. Reinforced concrete, for example, was seen side-by-side with wooden construction and tile or even thatched roofs. Western dress, which is called American or European according to the nationality of the wearer, seemed to be coming into wider use, but while the children, with few exceptions, were clothed in Western garb, the ancient Japanese costume was still very much to be seen. This consists, for men, of the well-known kimono, sometimes worn with a lower divided skirt known as the "hakama." The ladies also wear the kimono, and their dress for social occasions comprised an underskirt, two or three outer garments, and the *haori*, which is an interlined silk coat worn over the upper part of the dress, held together by the *obi*, or belt wound about the figure two or three times, and tied together in the back with a large ornamental bow.

Young men, with of course an exception here and there, go about in western styles, but it is not uncommon for a man to be seen in full Japanese costume wearing an incongruous felt hat or derby. Or one may observe the full Western dress together with the *tabi* (socks with divided toe), *zori* (sandals), or *geta* (wooden clogs). Socks are less likely to be seen, but when worn they are apt to be pulled up over the long underdrawers and held in place by prominently displayed "Paris" garters below knee-length pants. Loose jackets of the coolie type, usually of blue, are very common. With these the pants may be missing entirely, and nothing but long underdrawers used to ward off the wintry blasts of January. Some of the more advanced Japanese we met and spoke with agreed with us that the native costume is a great handicap and that it must eventually give way to Western dress, as has been the case in Holland, Czechoslovakia, Albania, and other parts of the world. As Japan becomes more and more "westernized"—particularly under General MacArthur's highly efficient direction—there seems to be little doubt that the kimono, the *obi*, the *haori*, the *tabi*, and the *zori* are destined to remain only as a pleasant memory, to be revived on occasions as are the *Nō* dramas and other ceremonial affairs.

When it came to entertaining, the Japanese were second to none. The government-owned railroad gave all the delegates free passes permitting us to ride anywhere on their lines, and the Japanese officials invited all of us quite liberally into their homes for dinners and formal gatherings. I will not soon forget the reception held at the home of the then Prime Minister, or our presentation at the palace of Prince Chicibu, who was the brother of the renowned Emperor Hirohito, the gentleman who recently declared he was no longer divine. The Japanese, we had been warned, were very, very formal on such occasions, and laid great emphasis on proper attire. Cutaway coats, striped trousers, and a high hat were always in order for morning affairs, and in the evening, tails were rigorously pre-scribed. I hated above everything to wear a high hat, and although my wife had arranged to take one along for me, I was anxious to avoid wearing it. Leaving the hotel on the way to the reception, I tried to substitute a grey fedora, but my Japanese cicerone nailed me at the door.

"*Ara hai hato o wasurimasen, deshita ka?*" he hissed, grinning pleasantly.

I caught the familiar words "high-hato," but feigned ignorance. "Can't you see I'm in a hurry, Toshio? I have an engagement."

"Has not Colvin-*sama* neglected the *hai hato, gomen-kudasai?* It is most necessary to be worn, *gozaimasu*. I have brought it, Colvin-*hakase*." And sure enough, he produced it from behind his back, and I was trapped. But I left the hat in Tokyo rather than carry it home with me.

My wife and I were entertained at the home of a Mr. Wada, who was then high in the management of one of the many Mitsui organizations. Mr. Wada, who had invited a number of Japanese engineers and industrialists to the gathering, was very flattering, and told me in broken English that the "American Machinists' Hand-book" was very widely used as a reference work by Japanese engi-neers, and that it was being sold in many Japanese bookstores. His home was half-Oriental, half-Occidental in design, the living room and guest quarters being perfectly plain and devoid of furniture, with fine matting laid on the floor, while the family bedrooms were typically Western, with chairs, bureaus, tables, and even radiators.

"*Yoroshiku gozaimasu,*" said Mr. Wada on our entrance. He then introduced us to all of his company, and we had a lot of fun trying to understand each other and reciprocate the almost excessive politeness of our hosts and fellow guests. "Colvin-*san* is the great American writer of the hand volume for machinists," Mr. Wada announced. Cries of *are! dore! So desuka!* and *nani!* greeted the statement, which are about the equivalent of "yeah?" "well, well," "you don't say," and "so what?" After a half-hour or so of well-meant persiflage, we sat down on our heels and Mr. Wada said, "*Dozo o agarinasai mase?*" which is Japanese, I am told, for "Let's put on the feed bag!" The banquet seemed to me to consist largely of *sashimi*—raw fish—eaten with *hashi*, or chopsticks. We had to kneel on the floor on cushions around a horseshoe table about a foot high, and there was much tea flowing, together with a kind of *saki* that I was afraid to drink. But everyone was very cordial and I am sure we had a nice time.

My wife and I spent another evening at a typical Japanese teahouse, in the company of a Mr. and Mrs. Burlingame and the Brown and Sharpe representative of the Ataka Company in Osaka, a man named Chadini. Here again we were supposed to sit on our heels in true Japanese fashion before foot-high tables that were more properly stools. Then the geisha girls filed in carrying the food, which was known as "sukiyaki," or meat, vegetables, and bean curd cooked in a charcoal brazier and served with soy sauce. The girls also acted as hostesses, singers, dancers, conversationalists, and all-round entertainers. Naturally I do not know how far they might go in the field of entertainment, since I was not very responsive to their beguilement, but I have heard that they will supply every conceivable requirement of the tired Japanese businessman, which is a pretty big order.

Before as well as after the meal, one or more of the geisha girls would bring in a dish of steaming hot washcloths, with which the visitor is supposed to remove the dust and grime of travel and to wipe off his chin and hands after the meal is over. The diner may also rinse his mouth between courses by making use of a special dish that seems to be a cross between a large shaving mug and a small cuspidor, and toothpicks, served as a regular part of the meal, are openly used in the best society. Several hundred thousand G.I.'s have by now become accustomed to these facets of Japanese living, and some of them seem to like it well enough to get married and settle down for the duration of the occupation.

We eventually took leave of Tokyo, having said our *sayonoras* all around, and set out for Korea and Mukden, with a stopover at the island of Miyajima in the Inland Sea. On the train to Shiminasaki, where we were to take the steamer for Fusan, Korea, we met Francisco Tavero, a Brazilian whom we had seen at the Congress in Tokyo. He was an interesting young engineer who had spoken no English previously, although he had "read" our engineering journals and books, but he managed to pick up enough of the language to speak at one of the Congress meetings. In Seoul, or Keijo, the capital of Korea, we did a little sight-seeing by hiring a car and a guide to take us out into the interior. The natives were extremely skittish in front of a camera, and would shy away from a still or motion picture camera as though it were a 30-caliber machine gun.

They would stand by quietly enough if you didn't point the camera directly at them. As soon as they saw the lens head on they would scamper out of range, so that all one got was a blur on the film. I happened, quite fortunately, to have a 90-degree prism along with me, and I was able to attach it to my camera so that by pointing it due north I could take an excellent portrait of an unsuspecting Korean standing due west, who thought I was merely aiming at the landscape.

The roads in Korea were thronged with bullock teams and donkeys, most of them carrying huge loads of faggots into town to be used as fuel. The drivers, as well as the numerous pedestrians, were always dressed in white, wearing the peculiar hat that resembles a small stovepipe, and striding along with a vigor that was indeed refreshing. The stovepipe hat protects their topknot of hair, which is done up on the top of their heads to denote that they have achieved manhood. Korean women, I found, were easy to look at, having very good features and well-proportioned bodies. They walked as vigorously as the men, wore much the same costume except for the shoes and hat, but I am told they do not have as yet a very high status in the social scale.

From here we went to Mukden, the capital of Fengtien province and the capital of Manchuria, where I looked in on two railroad shops—or more correctly, one railroad shop and the university, which had a machine shop in which many railway repairs were made. The head of this university (the equivalent of a vocational school by our standards) was a Chinese general who had married a German wife, and she had evidently influenced him in the selection of machine tools—all of them, with but one exception, had been manufactured in Germany.

And from Mukden, Manchuria, we headed toward China.

We entered China at Tientsin, one of the treaty ports where extraterritoriality was much in evidence. Owing to the shallowness of the river only small boats can get up to Tientsin, and these dock by running up beside the bank and using rather long gangplanks. It was midwinter, with the river full of ice and the thermometer hovering around zero. We had just come from Dairen, the Japanese port in south Manchuria (not to be confused with Darien, Panama, or Darien, Connecticut), on a 1,000-ton Japanese steamer after a trip of two days and three nights, spent in the company of eight Japanese, two Germans, and one White Russian.

Nearly all the larger nations are represented by districts in Tientsin. The buildings, street names, and other landmarks proclaim the nation that controls the section of the city one happens to be in. Most of the police are Chinese, although they are in the employ of the different governments in whose territory they serve. And I heard it said that these police did not hesitate to graft upon the poor coolies who staggered under their heavy burdens from one territorial section to another; for, while no tariff existed between the various sections, it was no great difficulty to convince the unlearned coolie that it cost a copper or two to get from one concession to the next.

After we had finally landed at the Astor House in the British zone of Tientsin, I began to scout around among the small machine shops in search of material for the *American Machinist*. As was to be expected, I found much that was primitive. In common with all general repair shops in all countries where the demand is both small and varied, the work ran the scale from small repairs on a fractional-horsepower motor to the building of steam-hoisting engines for mine operation. Moreover, the parts for heavy machinery of the latter type could not exceed a certain gross weight determined by the amount that a mule or camel could haul over the pathways that were humorously referred to as roads.

On the labor-handling end of the Chinese machine-tool industry, the situation is pretty much in the hands of a small group of individuals known as "headmen" or "boys," who hire all the labor, draught animals, and conveyances used in carrying machinery about the countryside. They are paid a fee that is stipulated in advance by the "boy," and he usually has his own way about the price—at the time of my visit it was averaging about one American dollar a month for every man in the organization.

According to the general manager of one shop, such items as new belts, drive gears, chucks, and other machine supplies that can be removed without too much difficulty, had an annoying habit of disappearing at regular intervals. The missing parts were usually located in the nearest pawnshop, where the headboy had a running account to tide him over the middle of the month. By threatening and cajoling, the headboy could usually be prevailed upon to redeem the required parts, but often he had to be fired and the loss written off against depreciation.

At another Tientsin shop I came across my first Chinese "hot-dog" forge, which was the modern American "Buffalo" forge except that its rotary blowers had been removed, and an air pump or Chinese blower had been substituted. These Chinese pumps were in evidence all over town, and got their nickname because they were widely used on sidewalk eating stands to keep food warm. In the shops, however, they do a real honest-to-goodness job of blowing. They are actually pumps made of a rectangular box and fitted piston, operated by two piston rods, with a cross handle between the two rods providing an excellent grip for the blower boy. The edges of the pistons are usually packed by tacking chicken feathers around the side. I was assured by the Englishman in charge of the shop that such a forge was used to melt iron for small castings.

From Tientsin we traveled to Peking, where we met Thomas Sze on the train—the brother of Alfred Sze who later became Chinese Ambassador to the United States. Thomas Sze, a graduate of Cornell University and a learned engineer, was kidnapped and held for ransom by the Japanese in Shanghai during the Second World War, but managed to escape and has recently come to New York. It was he who recommended that we stop over at the Hôtel de Pékin in that city.

I wasn't feeling very well when we arrived. I figured I had caught a cold during my recent wanderings, and therefore I called the local Chinese doctor. He was a well-trained physician and spoke English with no difficulty.

"I guess I've got a slight touch of grippe, Doctor," I said. "I've been running around in the rain and snow for a couple of weeks now, and it's no wonder."

The doctor took my temperature and pulse rate, looked at my tongue, and studied the whites of my eyes. Shortly he said:

"Mr. Colvin, sir, the symptoms indicate that it is something more than a cold which you have. Permit me to suggest that a specialist be consulted. I would recommend Dr. Paul Krieg."

"What the heck have I got, anyway?" I asked, getting excited. "And who is this Doctor Krieg? All I've got is a cold, so just give me a box of aspirins and a hot lemonade—I'll be all right."

"I beg to state that the honorable gentleman's symptoms indicate something more serious—to be exact, a form of typhoid fever."

"Typhoid fever! How did that happen?" I exclaimed. "Get Doctor Krieg over here right away!"

I had calmed down a bit when Dr. Krieg arrived. "Listen, Doc, I was inoculated three times against typhoid fever before I came over here—the health authorities insisted on it. It can't be true that I've caught it now. There must be some mistake."

Dr. Krieg laughed, which I thought was unkind at that particular moment.

"There are more kinds of typhoid fever in this country, Mr. Colvin," he replied, "than the medical profession is aware of. From what you and Dr. Tao have told me regarding the symptoms— headache, nosebleed, pain in the back, shivering, vomiting and diarrhea, you seem to have come down with a case of paratyphoid fever—a mild form of typhoid fever but differing only in degree from the disease caused by *Bacillus typhosus*. It is not often fatal"—here I shivered a bit more—"but it can have annoying consequences. At any rate I am going to bundle you off to the German Hospital here in Peking so that we will be better able to look after you."

I spent Christmas day on the flat of my back in the hospital, and stayed horizontal for nearly a month more in the same place. My wife was permitted to move into the hospital as a guest, and since typhoid fever is communicable but not contagious, she was able to live in the same room with me. Her days were made as pleasant as possible under the circumstances through the good offices of a missionary teacher of her acquaintance, who took her around Peking to see the sights while her spouse lay writhing in delirium—or so it seemed. But I came through the siege with little serious aftereffect, unless you count my tendency towards prolixity, and the fact that I have really never got over the experience of having a Chinese boy nurse, complete with pigtail, instead of the beautiful female kind you see in the movies.

A little shaky on my feet, I left Peking with my wife on the Chinese New Year, from whence we traveled to Tsingtau and boarded a steamer for Shanghai. And from there to Manila in the Philippines, where we spent a few very enjoyable days sight-seeing and visiting the shops. We noted the walls of the old fort at Corregidor, surrounded by a new hotel and a very attractive club, and could not know, of course, that in a dozen years the Japanese army and navy would be in complete control, driving out or slaughtering the hardy band of American soldiers and civilians trapped there in the early days of the Second World War.

At our last luncheon in Manila the native engineers entertained us in great style, some of them bringing their wives along in full native costume, which was a sight to behold. And finally we set our faces eastward for Honolulu and home in the United States. It was nice getting back.

CHAPTER ELEVEN

Machine Tools and Global Warfare

> *Our country is going to be what our people have proclaimed it must be—the Arsenal of Democracy.*
>
> FRANKLIN D. ROOSEVELT,
>   address following the passage of the Lend-
>   Lease Act, March, 1941

Because of my absence in China at the time, I missed a very important celebration on February 16, 1930, held in the auditorium of the new McGraw-Hill Building in New York City. This was the fiftieth anniversary of the founding of the American Society of Mechanical Engineers, which in a half century had grown from the little band of twenty-six men who had met in the office of the *American Machinist* in 1880 to a membership of over 10,000 professional engineers and students by 1930.

The *American Machinist* had grown, too. It now occupied part of the twenty-ninth floor of a brand-new skyscraper building and its circulation had increased some 500 per cent in fifty-three years, with a proportional increase in scope, coverage, and editorial staff. And I had moved along with it, from associate editor in 1907 through the successive positions of managing editor, acting editor, principal associate editor, and, beginning in 1921, coeditor. In that year Kenneth H. Condit, who had joined the *A.M.* staff soon after the close of the First World War as associate editor, became coeditor of the paper with me, following the departure of Ethan Viall. Ken had had experience with Henry Crane in the old Simplex Automobile Plant, and had been in aviation during the war; he later left to become dean of engineering at Princeton.

In 1937 two anniversaries occurred—the first, and more important, being the sixtieth anniversary of the *American Machinist*. The second was my own thirtieth anniversary as a member of the editorial staff. With as much modesty as I am capable of summoning, I should like to reprint an announcement that appeared in the McGraw-Hill Publishing Company's house organ for November, 1937:

> On his seventieth birthday, which occurred Thursday, October 5, Fred H. Colvin became Editor Emeritus of the *American Machinist*. For nearly thirty-one years Mr. Colvin has been on the staff of the publication, and since 1931 he has been co-editor with Kenneth H. Condit. The change just announced by Mason Britton, vice-chairman, is in title only, because Mr. Colvin will continue his active work on the editorial staff and in the field—work that has made him the most widely known business paper editor in the metal working industry.

The word "emeritus" has interesting connotations. The dictionary defines it as follows:

> e-mer'i-tus, *a*. L. Retired from active service (as on account of age or infirmity), but retained in an honorary position; honorably relieved from duty after serving one's time or rendering sufficient service; as a pastor or professor *emeritus*.

On account of age or infirmity. I admit I was retired from "active service," if this means I no longer had to worry about contributors, page make-up, and deadlines; I will even admit that this was due to my threescore and ten years (although I was only a youngster in 1937 in spite of what the Social Security Board had to say), but I'll be doggoned if I will admit to that "infirmity" part of the definition.

Retained in an honorary position. I have no complaint about that one whatever. They are still carrying my name on the masthead and everyone has been very kind and considerate of the old gentleman.

After serving one's time or rendering sufficient service. This has all the earmarks of a dirty crack, as though I had been doing a stretch in Leavenworth for thirty years, or had just completed my tenth enlistment as a master sergeant. I only hope, however, that the service I rendered *was* sufficient.

As a pastor or professor emeritus. This connotation is very flattering indeed, for I like to think I am in such good company as pastors and professors. But I am certain I could never have qualified for either profession.

Interpret the word how you will, I had practically retired from active connection with the *American Machinist* in 1937. I still maintained frequent contacts with the staff, visiting the offices on the average of about once a week, except during the winter months, and contributing an occasional article now and then. Ever since the Great Blizzard of '88 Mrs. Colvin and I had cultivated a decided aversion to snow and cold weather, and now that we both had the opportunity to avoid it, we began to spend our winters in Florida, looking very much like the couple in the advertisements that tell how one can retire on an income of $200 a month.

We spent three such delightful winters among the palm trees and tropic breezes, enjoying our retirement to the hilt. And then in 1940 a little man with a little black mustache, who wore his hair in his eyes and shook his fists, changed not only my plans for the future but the plans of nearly everyone else in the entire world.

After the fall of France on June 14, 1940, it was plain that the "phony war" was at an end and that Hitler had not—as the trusting Neville Chamberlain so wrongly believed—missed the bus. Dunkerque had been a defeat of tremendous proportions for the British, and while the Nazi soldiers sang "wir Fahren gegen England," the Battle of Britain was about to begin. The U-boats were making devastating inroads on the Atlantic life line, and the *Luftwaffe* was stepping up its air raids on English industrial centers.

As an apparently minor but very significant sequel to the fall of France, Great Britain had taken over all the French machine-tool contracts. My friend of long standing, Arthur Baker, then head of the Machine Tool Division of the British Purchasing Commission in New York, called me up one day via long-distance telephone.

"I know you're supposed to be retired, Fred," he began. "But I'll bet you'll be rarin' to go on a new project of ours connected with the war effort." He explained the setup and then added, "We want you on the staff as consultant."

"I'm as good as there now, Arthur," I replied.

I had known Arthur Baker for nearly forty years, having become acquainted with him shortly after his arrival in this country from England in the early 1900's. He was even then an excellent designer of tools, and soon afterwards became connected with the Cincinnati Milling Machine Company, contributing numerous articles to the *American Machinist* in his spare time. Working with Baker on the British Purchasing Commission's Machine Tool Division, I found a few more of my old friends from former days—Charles E. Carpenter, J. R. MacArthur, and Nelson Caldwell.

When it came time for our usual winter vacation in 1940, the international situation was such that it seemed more proper for me to forego it and keep working right through for the British Purchasing Commission. The Battle of Britain was reaching its crescendo in October and November of that year, and the RAF, outnumbered four to one, was fighting a tremendous battle against heroic odds. That the British pilots might have fighter planes and the antiaircraft gunners might have guns and shells to fire, machine tools were perhaps the most important single item of matériel that the British government could obtain through lend-lease. Churchill had said, "Give us the tools and we will finish the job." Roosevelt had replied, through Congress, "The British people need ships. They need planes. From America they will get ships, from America they will get planes. Yes, from America they need food and from America they will get food. They need tanks and guns and ammunition and supplies of all kinds. . . . Our country is going to be what our people have proclaimed it must be—the arsenal of democracy."

Instead of going south for the winter then, we moved to a small apartment in London Terrace in New York City and spent the winter there. After each day's work at the British Purchasing Commission's office, where I helped to specify the types and quantities of machine tools and parts to be sent to Great Britain, I would return to the London Terrace apartment and work on the fifth edition of the "Aircraft Handbook"—a reference work I had originally written in 1918 but which had been rendered hopelessly out of date by the spectacular developments in fighter and bomber aircraft following the outbreak of the war. I was seventy-three at the time, you will remember, and putting in about sixteen hours of work a day. I finished the "Handbook" revision early in 1941, and promptly was carried off to the French hospital in New York with an acute gall-bladder attack, which the doctor, surprisingly enough, said had been brought on by overwork. Overwork, indeed! Didn't he know I had retired with the title of *emeritus?* Fortunately I got better without undergoing an operation, and was up and around working again in a month or so.

The war moved on with increasing speed. Field Marshall Erwin Rommel was rapidly pushing the British back in North Africa as far as Tobruk—which he finally took after fifteen months of siege—and Mussolini was already dreaming of parading on a white horse in Cairo. Yugoslavia and Greece had been overrun by the Nazi war machine. Russia had been invaded as far west as the outskirts of Moscow. But American supplies were reaching the British in increasing amounts, and it seemed as though the Battle of Britain had been won by the RAF and that Hitler had abandoned all plans for an immediate invasion of England. And everyone knew the British were rallying for an all-out attack on Rommel's forces in Africa.

When the late fall of of 1941 arrived, I felt that it was about time I took that deferred vacation to a sunny climate, for I feared the effects of the coming winter on my already weakened gall bladder and other associated parts of my biliary system. I made up my mind.

"I am never going to spend another winter up north," I announced one morning over the breakfast table to my wife. "I mean, the remaining winters of my life shall be spent in the sunny climes of Florida or California—preferably California—and I am not going to be a dope and stick around New York here when the snow is flying and the thermometer reads eight below. I want sunshine and warmth during the declining years of my life."

"I think you are really serious about it this time, Fred," said my wife. "I think you really mean it."

"I'll show you how much I mean it," I said. "You know that new alpaca overcoat I bought only last February? Well, yesterday afternoon I gave it to the elevator operator as a kind of advance Christmas gift—and that's not all! I had Sam over at the garage give the Mercury a complete overhauling from top to bottom the other day. 'Goin' on a long trip, Mr. Colvin?' he says. 'Yes, Sammy me boy,' I said, 'We're going to California!'"

And off to California we started, on Tuesday, December 2, 1941.

On Sunday, December 7, 1941, we reached Arkansas.

About four o'clock in the afternoon we heard the news on the radio.

We forgot all about California and our winter vacation, and turned south to Houston, Texas, after getting in touch with a number of people back east to apprise them of our whereabouts. At the Ben Milan Hotel in Houston the desk clerk handed me a sheaf of telegrams and air-mail letters as soon as we arrived. They were mostly from officials of defense agencies in Washington, and the gist of them was that I should turn around and come back to Washington as fast as the Mercury would carry me.

I did as suggested. We covered the 1,600 miles between Houston and Washington in 5½ days—a record I know I will never again equal or even approach—and landed breathless in our nation's capital on December 16. The first thing I did was to buy another overcoat. It would be a long, cold winter in spite of the feverish activity already apparent everywhere.

The telegrams had directed me to report to the Office of Production Management, of which Floyd Odlum was chief. I was assigned as Consultant to the Contract Distribution Division. My specific task was to help locate and organize all the small and medium-size plants that could be tooled to make parts or subassembles for the guns, planes, tanks, and ships that the larger manufacturers were scheduled to produce. To come back again to the theme of the first chapter, machine tools were again proving that they were the heart of any production problem and were indispensable to mechanized warfare.

The Office of Production Management, which had taken over the functions of the prewar National Defense Advisory Council, was in turn superseded by the War Production Board on January 16, 1942, and the Contract Distribution Division gradually disintegrated. Before this occurred, however, we had made a start in getting production organized. Naturally there was the inevitable confusion resulting from lack of sufficient preparation—there was a good deal of isolationist feeling before Pearl Harbor that hampered all-out production efforts until we had been actually attacked—but co-operation was immediate from every industrial plant in the country. Perhaps the greatest contribution that I made in my own small way was the knowledge I had accumulated in fifty-odd years of the kind of equipment in various plants throughout the United States, the capacities of machine shops that could cut gears, grind shafting, or machine parts of various shapes and sizes, and how all these plants could be given the necessary data and blueprints to get their quota of parts and subassemblies produced in a hurry. It was something like the story of the Springfield rifle and munitions in the First World War, only on a vastly enlarged scale. A good part of my time I spent making long-distance telephone calls all over the country, talking with plant owners and superintendents and getting a quick picture of their equipment and facilities. There was no time for leisurely travel and inspection as in the old days. And we had to know where the most modern machine tools for high-speed, quantity production could be procured, even if it meant moving them by the dozen from one shop to another a hundred miles away.

The reader will remember the troublesome relation between specifications and practical production that was encountered in the making of rifles and other pieces of ordnance in the First World War. The same sort of trouble threatened to arise in the early days of the OPM and WPB. Designs at first were unnecessarily compli-cated, and peacetime specifications, drawn up when speed was not the essential factor, were still being followed after Pearl Harbor. Some plants with relatively old equipment were obliged to improvise methods by which their out-of-date machines could be utilized until new and better ones were available. Continental Motors Corpo-ration of Muskegon, Michigan, for example, rejuvenated their 1930 machines so expertly that they were able to turn out a sur-prising number of radial engines for use in tanks long before they obtained their quota of 1942 equipment. Another example of this kind of adaptability was shown by the Hi-Standard Company of New Haven, Connecticut, guided by a genius named Swibilius, who scoured the country for several carloads of used machines and had his plant delivering machine guns in quantity long before the larger and better equipped shops were ready to produce. Another plant revamped its old lathes and drill presses, largely through the use of welded structures and babbit bearings, using automobile transmissions for power drives—and began to deliver propeller shafts to the Joshua Hendy Iron Works for Liberty ships, promptly on schedule.

A large number of other shops, however, were still waiting for new machines to be built and delivered, and consequently produced little or no war material in the beginning. In too many cases the contractors demanded machine tools of a type they would never have any use for, simply in order to augment the equipment of their shops with an admitted eye on postwar expansion. Horizontal boring machines were ordered for work that could readily be performed on a heavy drilling machine, and since the former were hard to get, the work wasn't done.

Toward the middle of February, 1942, the functions of the Contract Distribution Division began to be distributed among other departments, and it was apparent that I would soon be released from my consultantship.

At this point a former staff member of the *American Machinist*, one James D. Mooney, turned up as a lieutenant commander in the Naval Bureau of Aeronautics, and since he had worked with me on the paper about thirty years before, we were old friends. Commander Mooney, hearing about the incipient breakup of the OPM, said to me, "Why don't you come over to the Navy Department with us, Fred? We have a lot of questions I'm sure you know the answers to."

"Jim," I replied, "my only knowledge of naval problems stems from the time I used to navigate a rowboat on Lake Wachusett about 3 miles out of Sterling, Massachusetts. I remember I had trouble with the oarlocks."

"I'm talking about the Naval Bureau of Aeronautics, Fred. That's where I'm working now—and you're supposed to know something about airplane construction, unless somebody ghosted your 'Aircraft Handbook.' We'd even take on an old man like you—provided you kept regular hours and didn't drink on the job."

"Why you old imitation shellback, you're almost as old as I am. I'll take the job so long as I don't have to take orders from you. But make sure it's connected with airplanes and not submarines."

I soon found myself working for the Navy. This was only fair, of course, for in the last war I had worked for the Army. (On second thought, *with* might be the better preposition.) In the Navy's employ I was delighted to find yet another old acquaintance—Karl Herrmann, whom I had first met in the old Studebaker Plant on Piquette Avenue in Detroit back about 1912, when he was developing a simplified gear-hobbing machine for transmission gears. Karl, somewhat younger than myself but not exactly underage, had ideas as to production procedures that coincided with my own. Commissioned a lieutenant commander, Karl found that the new rank gave him the necessary authority to cut red tape to a certain extent, but for myself I preferred to retain my civilian status. I was afraid that if I wore a uniform with three gold stripes on my sleeve I might suddenly be sent out to sea in command of a PT boat, and I have a great tendency to become seasick, even on the Hudson River Day Line.

One of my first assignments on the new job was to design, with the assistance of Karl Herrmann, a new method of manufacturing the air frames for a certain type of carrier-based plane. The specifications called for the use of a very heavy aluminum forging, weighing in the neighborhood of 100 pounds. For those who know their forgings, it will be readily understood that this was very difficult to make—it required the use of very expensive dies and a 35,000-pound hammer. The dies we could have purchased, of course, but there were only two or three 35,000-pound hammers in the entire country—and these were in constant use turning out airplane propellers.

Herrmann and I accordingly insisted that the original specifications be modified so that the unit might be built in sections rather than forged in one piece. After the usual arguments and discussions we won our point. But we also got ourselves in for a lot of careful study involving the possibility of substituting pressed steel parts for the aluminum forgings, and this meant a few exercises in higher algebra together with a series of conferences with several well-known makers of pressed-steel parts. The net result of our plans, imagination, studies, and propositions was that we deemed it wisest to compromise by using several smaller forgings and bolting them together.

Another important item of production that needed investigation and survey was the landing-gear apparatus—particularly the "oleo" or hydraulic shock-absorber part. Originally designed by the Cleveland Pneumatic Tool Company (which began by making the Gauss shock absorber for busses long before Pearl Harbor), this vital adjunct to the carrier-based plane was naturally developed according to the specifications written by the parent company, and just as naturally accepted by both Army and Navy.

The Cleveland Pneumatic Tool Company, however, happened to own the Champion Drop-Forge Company *in toto*. This made it almost a prerequisite for the use of solid forgings in both cylinders and pistons, inasmuch as welding was still in a rather embryonic stage in terms of permanence and reliability.

The use of solid forgings meant boring the cylinders, much as had been done with cylinders of air-cooled engines prior to 1916. The Cleveland Pneumatic Tool Company, being pioneers in the manufacture of these oleos, had little difficulty in selling the idea to both the Army and the Navy that nothing but forgings should be used, and the specifications were written accordingly. But this of course meant that greatly increased facilities would be needed for both forging and machining—and the development of these facilities naturally delayed the production of landing gears.

Another cause of delay was the lack of standardization—again—based on the work to be done by the oleo. It was generally conceded that the requirements of the oleo part of the landing gear depended primarily on the weight of the plane and the speed at which it landed, a possible third factor being the type of surface on which it was to land—whether a smooth concrete runway, an asphalt, or hard dirt landing strip, or the heaving, unsteady flight deck of an aircraft carrier in the middle of the ocean. But given the same landing conditions, all planes that are of approximately the same weight and speed can use the same type and style of oleo.

It was something of a surprise, then, when I discovered that one shop alone was making over sixty different types of oleos, many intended for use in the same class of plane.

Karl Herrmann and I immediately urged that tubing be used instead of forgings. We were gratified to find out that the A. C. Smith Company of Milwaukee was making landing-gear apparatus by this method, and had also made them with welded tubing as well

Scroll presented by a group of engineers at the Navy Club in Tokyo, November 25, 1929

Letter of introduction to the shops of the South Manchuria Railway at Dairen, Manchuria

Luncheon given to the author and his wife by the Tokyo Keiki Seisakusho (Tokyo Precision Instrument Company), 1929

The evolution of machine tools (opposite page)—showing the developments in design from 1855 to 1912. 1855—the first turret machine having mechanism for automatically turning the turret. 1858—the present form of high turret with substantially the turret-turning mechanism now in use. 1870—one of the links in the chain of evolution showing an automatic clutch. 1882—the first clutch back-geared machine. 1886—the same scheme in more symmetrical form. 1890—the first revolving roller feed. 1891—the first flat-turret lathe and the first quick-opening turner. 1896—lathe equipped with lead-controlling screw-cutting die. 1904—the first flat-turret lathe with cross sliding head. 1906—lathe equipped with turret-chasing tool. 1912—double-spindle Hartness flat-turret lathe

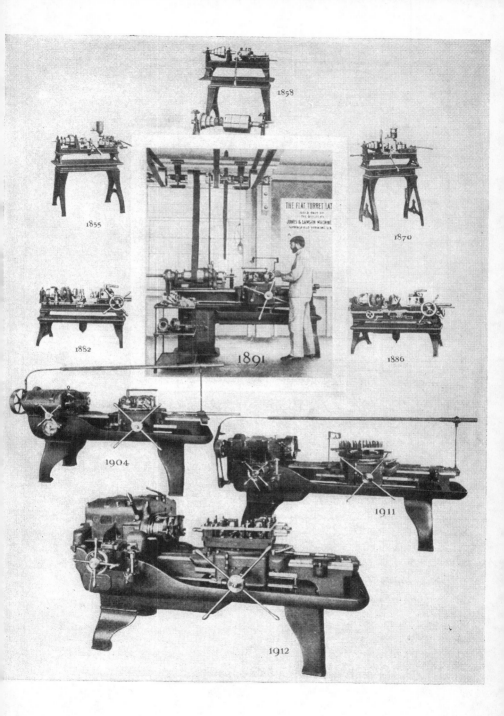

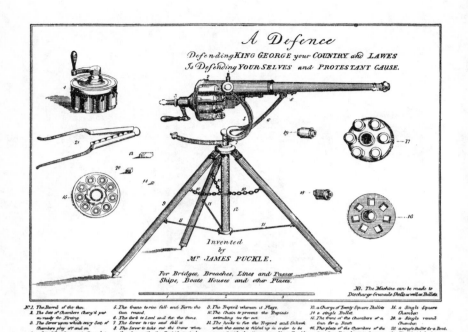

British patent drawing dated July 25, 1718, for a "portable gun or machine called a defense, that discharges soe often and soe many bullets, and can be quickly loaden as renders it next to impossible to carry any ship by boarding"

as the seamless variety, turning out an excellent job in both cases. This company later developed a steel propeller blade made entirely of welded parts. Tubing made with welded lugs had also proved quite satisfactory. One day in Norfolk I went aboard an aircraft carrier of the *Essex* class and was told by the deck signalman that they had never known of a failure of a welded part in any landing on their deck. And landing a plane on a carrier can be one of the roughest jobs, next to actual combat, that a navy pilot has to do.

Investigation of the manufacture of steel-bladed propellers became my next assignment, and it took me all over the country on visits to every shop making blades of this type. The design of these blades involved the application of welding in one form or another, but many of the designs were based upon a very rudimentary knowledge of mechanics. There were, to be sure, a few exceptions where the design had been carefully worked out, but for the most part it was unbelievable that some of the methods I saw had been approved by reputable production engineers.

And all the time the war was going on. The Japanese had spread all over Malaya, the Dutch East Indies, and Burma; Singapore had been lost and the *Prince of Wales* and *Repulse* sunk. But then came the historic battle of Midway of June 3 to 6, 1942, fought with submarines, Flying Fortresses, Navy flying boats, Marine bombers and fighters, in addition to the full complement of Navy fighters and bombers from such carriers as the *Hornet*, the *Enterprise*, and the old *Yorktown*. At least twenty Japanese ships were sunk or damaged, including four Japanese aircraft carriers and three battleships, and at least 275 Japanese planes were destroyed or lost at sea. The battle of Midway ended the retreat in the Pacific and marked a turning point of the war.

Towards the end of October General Montgomery launched his great attack at El Alamein and started a sweeping march across northern Africa to meet the American and British forces under Gen. "Ike" Eisenhower, which had landed in Morocco and Algiers. This led, as everyone should remember, to the invasion of Italy and the eventual defection of the least notable of the Axis partners.

In all these engagements the airplane played a vitally important part, and this fact by extension and inference, takes us back once more to the machine tools that are the underlying theme of the present story. I dislike elaborating a point, but not too many people realized at the time that whenever a Jap carrier was sunk or a battleship put out of action, the machine-tool operator at home on the production line was deserving of credit as well as the American pilot who flew over the target. For the unsung heroes of the machine shop and assembly line made possible not only the fighter plane or bomber, but the precision instruments that directed them in their flight, the bombs and other ammunition they fired on the enemy, and the complicated machinery of the aircraft carriers and warships that assisted in the attack.

Soon after the work on steel-bladed propeller manufacture had been completed, I was assigned to the problem of machining a very involved type of impeller used for turbosuperchargers. The impeller was made from an aluminum forging—or rather several forgings, as it was found necessary to divide the impeller into three parts due to the excessive vibration at the high test speeds at which it was run. It was discovered that at these high speeds—over 35,000 rpm—the body of the impeller stretched, the hole enlarging several thousandths of an inch, and other changes taking place in the structure of the blades. Before finish-boring of the hole, the practical thing to do, we decided, was to spin the impeller blanks at this speed, or close to it. The milling of the impeller vanes or blades was also a very tricky job, for they had been designed with unusual mathematical curves (something on the order of Praxiteles's Aphrodite) that required expensive and fragile milling cutters. So what with the designers and their ever-changing curves—they went from the cissoid of Diocles to the conchoid of Bernoulli and back again, not omitting the spiral of Fermat, wherein $r^2 = a^2\theta$, its inverse with respect to its pole being a *lituus*, and all the other logistic, logarithmic, and catenary curves derived from the formula $r^m = a^m\theta$ (of which I know nothing whatsoever)—and the operators and owners of the machine shops themselves, who were notorious for their fixed ideas on the subject of machining, we never got very far into large-scale production. To sum it all up, it was a costly investment for the Navy without much to show for it in the way of superchargers. But the mathematics of the problem was interesting. Perhaps a new Galois got his rise to fame out of such intensified research.

Gas turbines and jet-propelled units also came to the forefront under a heavy cover of secrecy, and presented an old-timer like me with thoughts beyond the reaches of his soul. It seemed as though I had to be a combination of Buck Rogers and H. G. Wells, and everything was supposed to be done in a great hurry. One design for a jet-propelled plane was finally adopted and assigned to a well-known engine manufacturer to produce, but it was so terribly complicated that I made every effort to have the primary contract split up so that several auxiliary builders might go to work on a sample lot and simplify the procedure as much as possible, but the idea ran into a stone wall and no units of this type were built while the war lasted.

While General MacArthur was launching his attack on New Guinea in keeping with his famous promise, "I shall return," and while the Australian and American paratroopers were landing in the swamps around Port Moresby with jeeps, mortars, and artillery dropped out of gliders, ready to chase the invading Jap back across the Owen-Stanley range, eventually overrunning the coastal strong point, a new type of assignment was given me—one in which I had had quite a bit of experience. Because of my knowledge of machine shops generally and of the layout of Japanese shops in particular, gleaned from my 1929 visit to that country, I was called in to work on plans for demolishing the war plants of the Rising Sun via the medium of our B-29 bombers. The Japs were under the handicap of having had most of their modern shops built by American firms, and consequently we had a complete file of blueprints of nearly all of them, together with their surrounding topographical features. With these drawings and numerous accompanying photographs, we built miniature models of each important plant, with papier-mâché scale buildings of the various shapes and sizes located in the correct position with relation to neighboring rivers, railroads, and other landmarks. These models were then photographed from various angles as they might appear to a bombardier flying over them, and each photograph was carefully labeled, including the angle from which it was taken, and eventually passed on to the pilot and bombardier of the B-29's, so that they could easily pick out the portions of the plant that were supposed to be the most vulnerable. From the reports we have had from Japan since the war ended, it is clearly evident that these "map-photographs" were of tremendous help in destroying the warmaking capacity of the Nipponese.

Although I was passing seventy-five, I really enjoyed the considerable amount of travel, both by train and airplane, which my war work involved. I had to make four trips to California to visit airplane and other types of plants in that vicinity, and on the way I stopped off in Dallas both going and coming, taking side trips also to Houston and Oklahoma City to look at small shops, which might be capable of making oleos and other parts for prime contractors. The air trip, by the way, involved the use of eight different planes. Taking off at Knoxville, Tennessee, the pilot discovered that one tire of his landing gear was soft, so he immediately put the big ship down again and taxied back up the runway. It took two hours to change the huge tire, which time the passengers spent in eating lunch, but all of us reflected that it was indeed most fortunate that the soft tire was discovered at take-off rather than at the next landing, for it would have undoubtedly have caused a ground loop that would have knocked us about quite a bit.

Two developments found at the Alameda (California) Air Base are deserving of mention. Both have to do with Plexiglas, the plastic material developed for airplane windshields and navigator's domes in the Second World War. One of the workmen at the Alameda Base discovered that by inserting a very fine nichrome or other high-resistance wire in a crack that required mending and then applying a weak current, the Plexiglas would weld itself behind the heated wire as it followed the crack. The method was discovered in an almost unbelievably simple manner.

His first idea was to cement the cracks, but he found that he must widen them enough to admit the cement. So he sandblasted a fine wire to roughen it and thus act as a file, and then started to file the crack with this wire. To his surprise, he found the crack closing behind the wire, and thus realized that the low heat of filing was all he needed—that all he had to do was to substitute the weak electric current to provide the necessary heat instead of the friction heat of the filing action.

The other development was in the making of the navigator's dome, or cover, which is, for all practical mathematical purposes, a hemispherical surface. After trying various methods of forming with dies and by forcing the sheet into a hemispherical form by air pressure, a much simpler method was found. A sheet of Plexiglas was clamped to a steel plate by a steel ring that determined the outside diameter of the dome. The plate had a connection for an air hose to the lower plate. The air pressure then forced the Plexiglas into a perfect hemisphere, its height being determined by means of a preset gauge.

Before I leave the subject of landing gears, I must recount a brief anecdote involving John Cautley, the manager of the Bendix Corporation's landing-gear department at South Bend, Indiana. While engaged on the oleo problem referred to in the preceding pages, I naturally had to call on the Bendix Plant, and was looking forward to seeing John again after a lapse of several years. When I arrived early one morning while the plant was already humming with activity, I stuck my head in the doorway of John's office and said, "Hello, John—how are the landing gears coming?"

John looked up from his desk, saw me, and turned a ghastly white. He stared wide-eyed at me for several seconds.

"My God—my God!" he finally gasped. "Ain't you dead yet, Fred Colvin?"

In a way, it was a flattering kind of greeting, and after all he must have been kidding, for he knew I was only seventy-five.

Along about the time the Allies entered Rome and the famed Gothic Line was being pounded by the Eighth Army, while the Navy was destroying 700 Jap planes and 30 ships in the first battle of the Philippines, my employer the U.S. Navy Department had got wind of my long editorial experience, and I was assigned—temporarily, they said—to the Production Aids Division under Lt. Comdr. Harry Anderson.

The purpose of the assignment was to assist members of the International Correspondence School editorial staff to prepare a series of instruction books designed to aid workers in plane factories to increase production. Paralleling these books was a series of animated cartoons made by the Walt Disney Studios (home of

Snow White and Donald Duck), which showed how the various operations were to be performed.

It so happened that the I.C.S. group had their offices in the Disney Studios, and I accordingly had the rather unique experience of working in Hollywood for nearly a month. Not that I was screen-tested or asked to act as stand-in for Lionel Barrymore; but I did get to stand on the corner of Hollywood and Vine and watch the smoked glasses go by and to see some of the hectic life that the press agents in this glamorous movie colony never tire of telling us about. And just for the record, I most emphatically did not have cocktails at the Brown Derby.

I worked with Richard B. Smith, who headed the I.C.S. group, and with his assistants, Charles Hubbell and Harry Wharen. Over one million copies of these instruction books were distributed among the workers in plane plants and the plants of subcontractors, and there is no question that they played a vital part in increasing production during the war. Out of this contact arose a friendship with Dick Smith that was to grow closer than either of us had anticipated. For instead of going directly back to the International Correspondence Schools after the termination of the assignment, Dick came to Washington to prepare more special instruction booklets for another branch of the Navy, and during the ensuing months he and the Colvins lived in the same apartment house—indeed, for a short time, in the very same apartment.

Shortly after Dick Smith had finished his assignments for the Navy, the Mechanical Engineering Committee of the American Society of Mechanical Engineers began to seek out a new executive secretary to replace our original secretary, Herbert B. Lewis. It was fortunate for the committee that Dick Smith was available, as he fitted into the work very nicely, having had experience which peculiarly qualified him for the task.

The record of the Ordnance Department in the Second World War was far more heartening than the story we have told of it in the

First World War in Chapter Nine of the present work. I say this more as an observer than as an actual participant, for during this second holocaust I acted merely in an advisory, or *emeritus*, capacity. In fact, if the truth must be told, I was trying to get away from it all—witness my futile attempt to flee to California—but I was only too happy to render whatever service I could to the armed forces.

I have been reading through "The Industry-Ordnance Team,"[1] an absorbing chronicle of American industry's phenomenal joint achievement with the Army Ordnance Department in producing and delivering fighting equipment to our armed forces and allies during the late war, and I am very much impressed with the spectacular record there set forth. With General Campbell's permission, I should like to quote here and there from the chapter that interests me most, entitled "Machine-tool Panels."

Practically every Ordnance item involves the use of metals and the use of metals necessitates machine tools to form and finish them. Before armament and ammunition can be manufactured, tools are required for making tools with which to manufacture them. Lack of a machine-tool industry of sufficient size to meet an abnormal wartime load was one of the most serious bottlenecks in the early period of the armament program. Following Pearl Harbor, the normal sources of machine-tool production were choked with orders from our allies, from our own aircraft and ship-building industries, and from the various procurement branches of the Army and Navy.

The machine-tool industry performed magnificent service in this war. The demand for machine tools was tremendous in comparison to peacetime requirements. In order to meet this heavy demand the industry inaugurated a large expansion program and financed approximately half of it with private funds. This expansion was expedited so efficiently that the production of vitally important machine tools increased from considerably less than half a billion dollars in 1940 to considerably more than 1 billion dollars in 1942. A highly conservative estimate of the value of machine tools located in the United States and owned by the War Department is 749 million dollars.

In January, 1942, I asked one of my friends, Mr. N. P. Lloyd, a machine-tool distributor of Philadelphia, to come down to Washington to discuss with me the general subject of machine-tool production as applied to the Ordnance effort. After several nightlong conversations we evolved the thought that the best way to obtain machine tools was not to go on ordering new

---

[1] "The Industry-Ordnance Team," by Lt. Gen. Levin H. Campbell, Chief of Ordnance, United States Army, Whittlesey House, The McGraw-Hill Book Company, Inc., New York, 1946.

equipment but rather to make use of existing machine tools wherever they might be located. Here again we could utilize the help of small business. Over a long period of years the Ordnance District offices had made, with their very limited funds and personnel, surveys of industrial plants within their respective territories. These surveys, while large in number, did not get down to include, in detail, numberless small shops. Lloyd and I were certain that many of these shops contained fine equipment and, most certainly, fine mechanics and operators. It was these shops we had to contact if we were to take full advantage of existing machine tools and equipment and if we were to help a larger number of small plants to get into war production.

General Campbell goes on to describe how the idea of Machine-tool Panels was evolved.

A leading machine-tool distributor accepted the position as chairman of the Chicago Ordnance District Tool Panel in February, 1942, and he, in turn, appointed to his staff some 25 practical men who were making their daily bread in the distribution and servicing of machine tools throughout the Chicago Ordnance District. It was decided that these men, upon the call of the District Chief, would meet with Ordnance officers to consider the requirements as to machine tools and equipment to accomplish a given Ordnance schedule of production in any particular plant. They would study the drawings and specifications and would then go with Ordnance officers to the plant of the contractor and survey his equipment as to its adequacy for the job at hand. They would go over his list of machine tools and equipment which he would submit as, in his opinion, necessary to augment his own facilities. Then would come into play their intimate knowledge of the machine-tool equipment to be found in the District which might well be used for the purposes of the contractor rather than to resort to the only possible alternative—that of waiting weeks and months for deliveries on new machine tools.

The Chicago panel, General Campbell tells us, functioned well on one of their first assignments. Seven million metal components of artillery shells known as "adaptor-boosters" were required in a great hurry. Early advice indicated that this job required a multiple-spindle automatic screw machine, and an intensive search was accordingly begun for capacity of this type. A month's search indicated that only one-fourteenth of the required capacity could be obtained—a mere 500,000 units. The Machine-tool Panel was consulted, and it suggested several alternate methods of production that employed turret lathes, chuckers, engine lathes, and drill presses instead of the virtually unobtainable automatic screw machines. Although this procedure was the more expensive, immediate production was the first consideration, and the required capacity was obtained in short order.

General Campbell cites a number of other accomplishments of Machine-tool Panels, all of them leading to increased production and savings not only in time but in actual cost.

The members of the various panels some time ago proposed a perpetuation of their association with Ordnance. Today there is a club of Ordnance Machine-tool Panels, the members of which are known in industry as "Campbell's Cowboys." The officers of this unique club have such fitting titles as Lasso Boss and Chief Wrangler. It is my good fortune to be a life member. I am hopeful that, for the good of the country, similar groups will be organized and fostered to maintain the friendly and mutually helpful contacts that have developed during the war years between Industry and Ordnance.

Thus Lt. Gen. Levin H. Campbell, recently retired Chief of Ordnance, U.S. Army, now vice-president of the International Harvester Company—one of the most competent men to hold the job of Chief of Ordnance, and who has reason to be very proud of his record in that capacity.

Well, the war was coming to a close in 1945, as everyone who followed the communiqués could see. A long succession of victories from January to December of 1944 had paved the way for final triumph in 1945. Anzio, the Marshall Islands, Normandy, the liberation of Paris, the invasion of Germany, the invasion of Leyte, the defeat of the Ardennes pocket, the taking of Luzon, the liberation of Manila—all these landmarks of the Second World War had already taken place when Captain Louis Marshall asked me one day to go to France with a small group of officer engineers in order to study the conditions and methods of the Germans in the French shops which they had made free use of during the occupation.

I was full of enthusiasm for the project. We were to follow the armies of Bradley and Patton into Germany and get as much first-hand information as possible, both as to tools and methods, and possible plans for new weapons for the prosecution of the war.

I was in high spirits. I selected a young man named Jack Wills, and made all of the necessary preparations for him to go as my aide. Then, as an added precaution, I paid a quick visit to my family physician, much as soldiers have to do before departure for overseas.

"You tell me you want to go to France," said my doctor.

"Yes sir, on the first available plane. There's a lot of interesting work to be done there, and I think I can help."

"Let's see—you're seventy-six years old, aren't you?"

"Seventy-seven, to be exact—I'll be seventy-eight in October of this year. But what has that got to do with it? I've never felt better in my life—and you yourself told me only recently that my heart is in good shape, and my blood pressure O.K. If I take it easy, why can't I go?"

"For one thing, the war isn't over yet—you're liable to be a little slow dodging artillery shells and machine-gun bullets, to say nothing of getting into an air-raid shelter in ten seconds flat. And then there's something else—at your age there is a slight predisposition to pulmonary infection if there is prolonged exposure to low temperatures combined with dampness and other conditions."

"You mean I shouldn't go?"

"I mean you shouldn't go unless you want to run the risk of a fairly certain attack of pneumonia, arthritis, rheumatism, and related disorders that will keep you in a base hospital most of the time, weaken your heart, and render you practically useless to the war effort. I'm speaking frankly, but you must know that you are getting on in years. In fact, as an old man, you ought to have sense enough to stay at home. Take my advice and give up this overseas tour. As a pleasure trip—yes, you're certainly healthy and strong enough—I daresay you'll live to be 100 if only you'll cut out the late hours and the prolific writing—but under the present circumstances, why not give your insurance company a break for a few more years?"

Of course I was disappointed. No one had ever spoken to me quite so frankly about my age before, and I was just beginning to realize I wasn't the man I used to be. I am by no means admitting to senility, but there was the doctor's advice that I was expected to follow, and the net result of it all was—*no European trip*. This was very definite, and my family were employed to coerce me.

So John Meader went in my stead, replacing me most effectively, taking the aforementioned Jack Wills with him. Don Randolph also went over at the same time.

Talking with them later and seeing the photographs they took did not increase my regrets over not being with them at the time. They got close enough to the front line on one occasion for Jack Wills to collect some shrapnel in one arm while on a tour of inspection of the shops I was scheduled to look at.

Everyone knows what followed in quick succession. On March 8, the United States forces under General Hodges found the Ludendorff bridge at Remagen still intact, crossed the Rhine, and established a bridgehead. The Allied forces pressed on to make a junction with the Russian Army sweeping through Berlin, and General Patton wheeled from Czechoslovakia into Austria soon after the death of President Franklin Delano Roosevelt. On May 7 came the unconditional surrender of Germany; April 1 saw the invasion of Okinawa, and the final *coup de grâce* of the whole global war came on August 6, 1945, when the first atomic bomb was dropped on Hiroshima. Eight days later Japan surrendered unconditionally, and the second great Armageddon in history had come to an end. Or was it only a truce? Being an old man who will leave this mortal coil before the next dozen years or so, I am inclined to believe that there is hope for civilization in spite of the atomic bomb and our present state of international politics.

To explain why I think so would take a volume twice the size of this one.

And this leads me to a final summing up in the next chapter.

CHAPTER TWELVE

Past, Present, and Future

So there ain't nothing more to write about,
and I am rotten glad of it, because if I'd 'a'
knowed what a trouble it was to make a book I
wouldn't 'a' tackled it, and ain't a-going to no
more.
MARK TWAIN
"The Adventures of Huckleberry Finn,"
1884

Unless I turn quickly to the comic-strip page and take up where I left off in the adventures of Blondie and Dagwood, the first thing that greets my eye these days when I lift a newspaper is a notice of a new strike taking place somewhere and tying another knot in the production system. Everybody feels strongly about these things and agrees that something ought to be done about it, but of course nobody actually does anything. There was some talk in Congressional circles a while back about putting through strike-control legislation, but then there was the matter of coming elections, and no senator or representative wanted to have union leaders going around saying he was no good.

So the result is that every once in a while the railroad men, the meat packers, the elevator operators, the truck drivers, the coal miners, the automobile workers, the dairymen, the stevedores, the shipfitters, the cargomen, the bus drivers, the transit workers, the longshoremen, the steelworkers, the tugboat operators, the telephone operators, the lockmakers, the electrical-appliance workers, and the electric utility men—and damn near every other type of wage earner, including the machine-tool operators—get together and decide to go out on strike for a 30 per cent increase. Billions of dollars are lost, the workers' yearly income is substantially reduced, and production is set back anywhere from one month to two years. And yet the strikes continue, with a new one reported almost daily. The situation is slightly cockeyed.

I do not pretend to know more about these things than Secretary Schwellenbach and his advisors, nor the informed general reader, but in the past sixty-five years I have not been concentrating entirely on mechanical details alone. I had one eye on the problems of management-labor relations for a good part of the time, and felt keenly about all the factors that make up the background. Over a considerable period of time I put these observations into the form of articles in the *American Machinist* and other magazines, generally over the pseudonym of "John R. Godfrey," in which I let off steam about many things that were bothering me at the moment. In this final chapter I am going to make a kind of general reexamination of the whole situation in the light of what I have seen of these things to date.

The first topic I think of in this connection is that of Management. The term itself is difficult to define in precise language.

The owners of a plant, shop, or office make up a set of rules for running the place, and this process alone is sometimes considered to be "management." If this were all there were to it, the owner or general manager could close up his desk once the rules were made and go fishing or golfing, leaving his subordinates to enforce the rules.

Needless to say, a business run in this manner is most certainly headed for the well-known rocks. A good manager will stay on the job, not in order to enforce a set of rules and play the role of the Big Boss, but rather to meet contingencies as they arise, seeking to modify and adjust practices in order to meet the new situation. The good manager or executive is the one who, having once formulated a set of rules or principles of operation, knows how and when to break them when required. A further definition might be: "The good manager is the one who guesses right in the majority of cases."

And the most important single job the manager or executive has to perform is this—to deal successfully with the employees. The day has long since gone when this could be done by means of arbitrary rulings, pronouncements, bulletin-board directives, mimeographed memorandums, and other forms of ukases. That sort of thing worked well enough in the "master-and-man" era or the days of apprenticeships, when the employee was considered little more than a chattel owned outright by the employer. Anyone who might be inclined to cry down the principle of unionism should remember this simple fact—without, of course, having to condone in the least some of the current tendencies on the part of organized labor.

In recent years there has been a great deal of serious thought devoted to the general subject of industrial organization and management, and a number of highly significant books have been written by experts in the field of personnel and labor relations. The attitude of industry toward labor has changed greatly since the days of Samuel Gompers and the Knights of Labor. Successful managers today realize that *personnel* is one of the main factors in the operation of any business, and that the proper handling of personnel requires an almost scientific approach on the part of the personnel manager.

Even in industries that make use of a large amount of specialized machinery, successful managers insist that they would rather lose their machine equipment than lose their operators—this in spite of the fact that machines are popularly supposed to reduce the number of jobs available to workmen.

I have found, then, that in recent years, at least, the tendency has been toward an increased interest on the part of management in the numerous problems relating to the employee and his part in the production picture. A proof of this increased interest is the fact that there is in this country today a really impressive number of management-consultant firms, job-evaluation-and-employee-rating engineers, time-and-motion-study experts, labor-relations authorities, collective-bargaining counselors, suggestion-plan advocates, house-organ planners, management-humanizing preceptors, executive-control programmers, foreman-and-steward-relationship analysts, and many other really serious and competent developers of a better understanding between management and labor. The literature on the subject is extensive, and I am told by my erstwhile associates in the publishing world that a rather large number of people read it.

Well, if everything is so scientific, how does one explain the strikes and the postwar industrial situation?

I would, of course, prefer to leave that explanation to the experts.

But I should love to get off a few extemporaneous remarks on the subject, feeling confident that nobody will consider me an authority and that I can therefore speak quite freely.

"More money," the man in the street would reply, if asked what the rank-and-file worker was striking for these days. "They want more dough, like everybody else, because the cost of living is getting higher."

Wages these days seem indeed to be the most important problem of the entire management-labor struggle, and the subject has been written up so frequently in magazines, newspaper editorials, and Sunday supplements that even the tabloid reader is familiar with such terms as the spiral of inflation, take-home pay, a look at the books, swollen profits, and all the rest. The editorial cartoonists put all these ideas into graphic form as well.

Conferences are being held with increasing frequency whereby representatives of both labor and management discuss their respective sides of the case, and while many wise and well-intentioned generalities are got off by the speakers, it is doubtful if any lasting good is obtained; and the audience, as well as the principal speakers, go away from the conference with their minds very much in the same *status quo*. Legislation to control strikes and to make union leaders at least as responsible as management has been proposed, but with the exception of the rather ineffectual anti-Petrillo bill and the vetoed Case bill, nothing very tangible has been produced.

Annual wage payments, to take a specific instance, are being widely discussed pro and con at the moment, not only by businessmen and their employees but also in the pages of the public press. To some, the principle of a guaranteed annual wage is the solution of all our labor troubles, while to others it is just another kind of headache in labor-management relations. For myself, I think it may be a step in the right direction, but I always keep in mind the fact that anything that is held to be a panacea usually has a habit of turning out to be somewhat less than a cure-all, and, especially if a number of correlative factors are disregarded, it may do far more harm than good.

But the idea of annual wage payments is not entirely theoretical or idealistic. It has been proved to be a workable arrangement by the experience of both the Hormel Company and the Nunn-Bush

Company. Neither of these two firms claims it to be perfect, but they are still advocating and practicing it at this writing.

It is perhaps fortunate that neither management nor labor is too optimistic or too enthusiastic for the plan. Labor that is accustomed to a high hourly rate balks at the idea of a reduction of this rate— witness the reaction of the high-hourly-rate workers in the building trades when President Franklin D. Roosevelt proposed a guaranteed yearly income in his housing program. On the other hand, employers see great difficulties in arriving at a yearly rate that can be guaranteed in the face of unpredictable changes in business income and profits.

The necessity for better business management cannot be questioned, and this fact, by itself, may be reason enough to urge the adoption of a guaranteed annual wage. It will be remembered that the Hoover report in 1921 credited 50 per cent of business troubles to poor management. (Rumor had it, indeed, that the original report actually quoted 75 per cent as the true figure, but that it was reduced to 50 per cent out of deference to the uncertain and even jittery state of management at the time.)

An interesting side light, which might even be termed unprecedented, is the case of accident compensation. Up to about thirty years ago, workmen injured in industry depended upon the good nature of the employer—or, if necessary, upon machinations of a wily lawyer—to get any compensation for injuries sustained in the line of duty. As a matter of fact, not much earlier than thirty years ago a workman who was injured on the job through no fault of his own stood a very good chance of being fired in addition to receiving no compensation whatever and of having to pay all the hospital and doctor's bills himself. If it could be shown that another workman was in any way responsible for the accident—for example, if he failed to say, "Look out, Joe, the belt's coming off!"—the boss was immediately cleared of any liability in the case by the so-called "fellow-workman" law. Management was actually insured against damage suits brought by employees injured while on the job, and the idea of insuring the employees against accidents with the costs to be paid by management was considered fantastic and visionary.

With the coming of accident-compensation legislation, however, when accidents began to be a costly item for industry, the concept of safety became an important consideration, and as a consequence safety programs and campaigns were established, with a resulting decrease in the frequency and severity of accidents. I might state here, with pardonable pride, that the *American Machinist* had a leading part in selling the idea of accident prevention and accident compensation to industry.

Reasoning by analogy, there are those who contend that unemployment insurance or compensation, since it is also a costly item for business and industry, will bring about a serious effort on the part of management to keep unemployment at a minimum. If this turns out to be true, unemployment insurance should have a fate similar to that of the famous snake in American folklore that caught its tail in its mouth, began eating, and ultimately vanished entirely. In other words, unemployment itself should vanish.

There is another angle to the problems of a guaranteed annual wage and unemployment compensation. Admitting the claim of industry that all wealth comes from production, it follows that industry is already paying the bill for the unemployed. Not by direct payments, of course, but through the medium of taxes, dividends on which the stockholders pay taxes, and through income taxes on salaries and other means. Industry (which includes employees, executives, and stockholders) pays the entire bill.

Annual wages, or whatever method is used to guarantee some kind of subsistence to both workers and unemployed, might be distributed at much less expense if it were done directly instead of circuitously through taxation and the various bureaus of distribution. If, as is often claimed and demonstrated, government administration is not the last word in efficiency, here, I should say, is industry's great chance to do the job itself, avoiding the circuitous route and thus saving itself a considerable piece of change. This saving would be accomplished not by individual firms, of course, but through the large trade associations such as the National Association of Manufacturers—N.A.M. for short, which has, at the moment, a kind of undefined stigma because of its not too tactful approach—and other groups or organizations.

If anyone were to ask me, I should say that unemployment relief is here to stay—a permanent feature of our industrial civilization, so to speak. As I have already indicated above, it is the better part of valor for industry to make every effort to keep unemployment at a minimum, for the very good reason that industry itself pays the bill, or a large part of it at least, when any workman is unemployed.

Leaving the subject of labor relations for the moment—I shall return to it later in the chapter—let us go back to a theme on which I lay claim to broader knowledge—the problem of specifications. I have talked about it before in this rambling chronicle, and by this time the average reader will realize that I am somewhat hipped on the subject. It came very violently to the fore in my dealings with the Ordnance Department in the First World War, but I have thrown out hints all along in this account that I consider it a very vital topic. In the present section, therefore, I shall have my last fling at the subject of specifications. I would not be too angry if the word "specifications" were given prominence in my epitaph, or cenotaph, or whatever it is that they erect over a fellow's last resting place.

The purchaser of any piece of equipment—and this includes not only machines and machine tools, but also such domestic devices as the lawn mower, washing machine, automobile, oil burner, and others—is interested in only one thing: the equipment must perform the work for which it was purchased. This includes such items as speed (where necessary), accuracy, dependability, and reasonably long life. When we get to machine tools, these requirements still hold. Why should the buyer, then, demand that details of design or the choice of materials conform to his own specifications? If the builder of the machine has the reputation of making a piece of equipment that fills the requirements, why should the purchaser insist on having his own ideas as to materials and design?

These may seem like purely rhetorical questions, a kind of dialectic wherein arguments are raised merely for the sake of demolishing them. But I find them necessary for a full exposition of the subject. Specifications were, strangely enough, an outgrowth of cheating, deception, and out-and-out hornswoggling on the part of unscrupulous manufacturers in the days when *caveat emptor* was held to be the guiding principle of business. One has only to think of the monstrous deals that were perpetrated against the United States government during the Civil War, when, for example, thousands of glue-factory horses were sold over and over again to the cavalry, and shoddy material of the worst sort was sold at fancy prices to clothe the Union and Confederate troops. There was a fairly sincere feeling on the part of manufacturers in those days that it was perfectly honest and aboveboard to cheat the government at every turn, and this feeling extended, of course, into the entire field of marketing. To paraphrase the slogan of a leading department store—without any implications whatever—it was smart to be tricky.

Detailed specifications, then, became necessary in order to protect from blame and censure those persons responsible for buying material and machines. This was a worthy purpose, and everyone, particularly the purchaser, was protected in theory at least. But because of the simple fact that the buyer necessarily knew less about the product than the manufacturer, there was little chance of coordination between them, and the result was a strong tendency in the direction of *overspecification*, a term which I lay claim to having invented.

What, exactly, does overspecification mean?

It means that those who make the specifications know too little about the machine and its uses and are basing their specifications upon a single machine that has proved satisfactory in a general way, concluding by inference and inductive reasoning that all machines in this class must be built along identical lines.

It is the same as though a plant owner were to say, "John Jones, here, is a good engineer and has proved that he knows how to design and lay out a plant. He has black hair and is 6 feet tall. Go out and get me two more men who have black hair and are 6 feet tall—mind you, they must be exactly 6 feet tall, not 5 feet 11½ inches or 6 feet 1¼ inches—and they must have *really* black hair, no implication of brunette or dark brown, and should have the same general manner, bearing, background, breeding, heredity, chromosomes, environment, education, social contacts, hobbies, literary interests, complexion, moral character, intestinal fortitude, skin coloration, cranial index, intelligence quotient, Wassermann-test reaction, political affiliations, Crossley and Hooper ratings, Rorschach-test response, religious affinities, Rotary Club standing, preference in literature, taste in cigarettes, discrimination in music, business acumen, practical ability, and all-around knowledge as has John Jones here.

"Find me two men who have exactly the same qualifications as John Jones and I will hire them on the spot."

The above is, of course, an oversimplification of the problem, but it is surprising how many purchasers of equipment operate on similar lines of thought.

But in my sixty-odd years of observation—even if you discount 10 per cent for faulty interpretation—I have found that in too many instances the people in charge of purchasing machines or equipment know next to nothing about their function or application. So they purchase a type of machine, as I have intimated, that has proved satisfactory for a specific type of job, and then, regardless of what potentialities it may have for future developments, they set up a strict compilation of rules and regulations concerning its manufacture that actually limits its application to a very narrow field. The effect of this program is detrimental in at least two ways: it may prevent the maker of an equally good machine from offering his device because it does not comply with the previously laid-down specifications; or, secondly, it may compel the manufacturer to supply a machine that has become obsolete since the original machine was bought. And this is the catch—if the old machine is still available, the purchaser gets an inferior product, whereas if he knows enough to demand the latest model, he must necessarily wait for three months or even twelve months until new specifications can be written. And it is not amiss to point out that a good number of specifications have been drawn up with the avowed purpose of making certain that the "order" is given to a court favorite. Ah, yes, we have politics even in the recondite field of machine tools, something not even Richelieu counted upon. If he had, perhaps the Industrial Revolution would have occurred somewhat earlier, but this is neither an affirmation nor a denial of the present trend in industry and manufactory.

It has long been my contention that the degree of specifications should be largely confined to the degree of results required in the finished product. The results required should include accuracy, improved rate of production, extended life of machine, increased capacity, and general over-all economic improvement.

Detailed specifications of any kind add greatly to the expense of purchasing a machine, and the unequivocal reason for the added expense is that many perfectly usable parts are rejected simply because they do not conform with some specification which should never have been made in the first place. If performance alone were made the criterion of acceptance—with severe penalties for attempting to deliver machines not suitable for the work—all reputable builders would be much better off, the government would get better materials, and much useless labor in the field of inspection would most certainly be dispensed with.

The same criticism applies to some extent to the purchasing departments of large corporations where too much system creeps into management. When it comes to specifications for special equipment or for parts designed by the purchaser—the Army or Navy, for example—a great deal depends upon the article itself and also upon the amount of practical experience possessed by the designer. This was true of Ordnance and other divisions of both Army and Navy. It delayed production in the First World War, as I have been at pains to point out—*vide* Chapter Nine—and delayed it on the same relative scale in the Second World War.

Many munition elements, for example, were designed by men who had no idea of the problems involved. The to-be-expected result was the usual waste of time and money—with *time* being the most serious waste, for the enemy was not inclined to wait, as in duels, upon his opponent, but was usually a step or two ahead of us, since by nature we are a pacific people.

My only complaint is this—before any part, particularly those parts needed in large quantities, is sent to the shop for mass production, it should be studied by first-class production engineers and simplified as much as possible from the shop point of view. I realize that this was actually done in the First World War on a somewhat limited scale, and more so in the Second World War, but every once in a while the Ordnance Department was wont to promulgate the opinion that nobody could possibly improve on its ideas or methods, and inevitably much time, money, and material were wasted.

Good judgment by competent inspectors must be the last resort

whenever the function of a part of machinery and its possible variation from the limits and tolerances specified may be questioned.
Because a good deal of this type of inspection must necessarily be
done by persons of limited experience, their "rejects" should be
sent to top-notch inspectors who can then decide whether or not
the variation is serious enough to prevent proper functioning of the
part in the machine. Once permissible variations have been established, those who thoroughly know the working of the particular
part can salvage a considerable number of units that would otherwise have been relegated to the scrap heap.

As an example of what I mean by "specifications that should
never have been written," I present an extract from a literary gem
promulgated by the War Department, entitled, *Instructions for the
Construction and Receiving of Three-inch Field Shrapnel Forming Part
of the Specifications to the Foregoing Agreement*. It is a First World War
document that should get into the archives. It follows:

> If, during the verification of the shrapnel, there shall be found such which
> [*sic*—and this sort of grammar was never taught in *my* high school], though
> not complying with all the rules of the Instruction, are, however, considered
> by the receiver suitable for service, the receiver sets apart such projectiles from
> those unconditionally accepted according to the Instructions, and, according
> to the importance of the deviations in these projectiles reports them on to
> his superiors, or else solves the doubt for himself, and finally receives them.

The latitude allowed in this classic directive is on the order of
several hundred parsecs, or a few thousand light-years; it is every
man for himself, and no holds barred.

This section is admittedly for the technicians, but I do hope the
general reader will not pass it by. What I have to say about traditions
in machine-tool building should apply, I think, to many other
modes of enterprise and design.

It is difficult for any of us to know to what extent we are affected
by tradition. Some of the first "horseless carriages," as I may have

already pointed out, had whipsockets on the dashboard, in which a nonexistent whip was placed so that the driver could lash a nonexistent horse. Thomas Edison's first electric locomotive had a smokestack, from which the smoke of a nonexistent furnace did not issue at intervals. These early designers were merely trying to carry on the tradition of preceding models, fearing that the general public was averse to radical change, and that if anything looked too futuristic it would turn out to be what we call a lemon.

This same aversion to change is clearly evident in connection with machine-tool design and machining methods. It is quite true that we have changed the outer appearance of many machines by what we are pleased to call "streamlining," so that the lathe, for example, may look like a modernistic television and radio-phonograph combination, suitable for installation in the living room. Streamlining, we know, was originally an aeronautical term, applied to the design of fast-moving objects whereby the wind resistance was substantially cut down at velocities above 100 miles per hour. How this fits in with a stationary object like a machine tool, or even with modern automobile, is beyond me, but it does lead to attractive-looking surfaces, judged from an artistic standpoint.

But while we change the outward contour of a machine to please a passing fancy, some machine builders still cling to the practice of handscraping the ways—an admission that the machine work is not quite so accurate as it should be. In these days of precision machine tools, it is indeed surprising to find tool engineers who believe that a man with a scraper can produce a surface more nearly flat than can be planed with a single-point tool on a modern planer.

For years we have had machine-tool builders who did not agree with the foregoing theory. The old Sigourney Tool Company in Hartford, Connecticut, was noted long years ago for its excellent planing on the paper-handling machines it built. The Gray planer has not scraped its ways to a bearing for many years, nor has the Cincinnati Planer Company. Both of these companies remove the "fuzz" that is roughed up by the planer tools, but there is no attempt to scrape to a bearing. The ways are sometimes "spotted" with a scraper to please customers who have the scraped-way complex, but the real bearing surface is made by the planing tool. Sometimes an abrasive "brick" is used to remove the fuzz.

"Machine Shop Terms Illustrated"—from a program prepared by the Hill Publishing Company about 1915 for a theater party in honor of the National Machine-Tool Builders Association.

The head of one of the best-known firms building high-grade machine tools told me not long ago of a recent experience regarding the eye appeal of a spotted surface. It is much like serving oleomargarine without adding the yellow color—it tastes better when the color is added, we seem to think.

This concern had not scraped a slide or other bearing for years; but it does spot the bearing to cater to the old idea. Just as an experiment, they had shipped to men in their acquaintance two machines with slides just as they came from the grinder without spotting. In both cases the men replied somewhat as follows:

"We know you are very busy with war work, but we are sorry you did not have time to scrape the ways on the machines you sent us."

In reply, the builders explained that they had not scraped bearings for years, and that the bearings on the machines in question were as true as any they had ever turned out, but that if the user were not satisfied, the machine would be replaced in each case by one with "spotted" ways. Neither machine was returned.

Scraping, incidentally, was once considered necessary in all good shaft or spindle bearings. In the early days, all automobile engine bearings were scraped—yet as early as 1920, when Rolls-Royce were operating their American plant at Springfield, Massachusetts, they had found that they could bore a bearing more nearly round than they could scrape it. As Maurice Ollie, the Rolls-Royce superintendent, told me at the time, "After we bore a bearing surface round we don't want anyone scraping it full of holes."

Today no one scrapes a round bearing that is bored on a modern machine with a single-point tool. When modern boring and grinding machines are used, there should be no need of touching the surface with a scraper.

But the scraping idea dies hard. On my last visit to a large machine-tool building plant, I saw more metal removed by scraping then I had seen for many years. A husky scraper hand was removing several thousandths of an inch from the whole surface—more than should have been taken as a finishing cut by the machine. Knowing that accurate surfaces can be produced by planing, milling, broaching, and grinding—particularly the latter—it is hard to understand why so many shop superintendents persist in scraping the surfaces of bearings. And I do hope the foregoing has not been to abstruse for the patient general reader. I had to get it off my chest.

Robert Wolf, the industrial engineer who was extremely successful in increasing output by means of nonfinancial incentives, spurred his men to increased effort by appealing to their pride in their work and by making them realize that each was playing an important part in industry. In the same way, my own particular field of editorial work has its compensations above and beyond the monetary stipend that goes with it. As in all branches of business and industry, management feels, and perhaps naturally, that salesmen who bring in the actual contracts deserve first consideration when it comes to paying off. On the other side is the argument that unless the workers in the shop (or editorial room) produce a salable article, the salesman cannot in the very nature of things produce customers.

But aside from this there are many compensations in connection with editorial work that cannot be counted in mere dollars, although everyone seems to like having a collection of mere dollars around in time of need.

The extramonetary compensations I am talking about may be more clearly pointed up by reference to an experience I had in visiting a small shop in New Orleans about twenty-five years ago. I entered the shop as a total stranger, and presented my calling card that read "F. H. Colvin, Editor, *American Machinist*, McGraw-Hill Publishing Company, Inc.," with a rather timid and deferential approach as I handed it to the boss.

The boss looked at it a second or two and responded most favorably.

"Hell, Colvin," he said, "I've never met you, but I've known you for twenty years!"

There was no necessity for getting acquainted; he knew me from my interminable writings in the *American Machinist* and from my list of books, including the current edition of the "Handbook," and was most anxious to show me the work he was doing at the moment—some of it quite out of the ordinary.

It so happened that this little shop was building coining presses for a mint in—of all places—China. I've forgotten just how he obtained the contract—normally it should have gone to one of the larger companies involved in this work, such as Ferracute, but obtain it he did, and a lot of Chinese currency was turned out by this little New Orleans shop, in the Crescent City of Louisiana, U.S.A.

As the years went by, similar receptions occurred, and there were comparatively few shops in which the name on the card was not immediately identified with the perpetrator of a spate of articles, not all of them intelligible, in the oft-mentioned *American Machinist*. Acquaintance of this kind proved to be of great value to me in keeping posted as to progress in shops and in mechanical work of all kinds. Such contemporaneity is vital to the editor, because this gent must perforce maintain contact with new developments, new methods, new techniques, new designs of machines, new procedures, new tactics of management, new repercussions of organized labor, new ideas from inventors and tool engineers, new applications, and every other new fact that will keep the editor abreast of the changing situation. This, one can readily see, is quite a project. It entails responsibilities on the part of the fellow who goes out and writes about such things.

To most old-timers, mass production means repetitive work, and consequent monotony. Few of us whose work varied from day to day—now making a tap, now a reamer, or repairing a countershaft—would have been content with running a machine day after day on the identical operation. It gets to be tedious after a while, and nobody with any sense of imagination is satisfied with a job that apparently has no future in it, no room for expansion.

But all of us must recognize the very obvious fact that low production costs are obtained mainly through the application of repetitive methods, utilizing, of course, rather specialized machines.

I have been asked at various times what could be done to get more apprentices for regular trade training. The difficulty is largely a financial one. While it is a great advantage to any young man to have had an all-round training in various kinds of work, in far too many instances his value as a full-fledged mechanic is not entirely recognized. He spends three or four years at comparatively low wages (although a lot more than the 5-cent-an-hour rate, which prevailed when I started) and gets to be a journeyman at the regular rate of pay. But during training he frequently sees boys come in from farming or other occupations and learn to be operators of turret lathes and other equally complicated machines. Inside of six months or so, the new operator will be paid more on piecework than the young man who has served four years' apprenticeship receives.

Too often management sees nothing but the number of pieces produced per day. It completely ignores the fact that if it were not for the all-round mechanic, who keeps the turret lathes in condition, there would be no production from them. Wise management puts the thorough mechanic in a class by himself, more as a necessary part of the shop equipment than as a direct producer of parts at so much per piece. In a great many cases these men who are well trained in general machine practice play as great a part in economical production as the designer of the machine equipment.

Well, we are getting near the end of our present tether.

Before I go I want to say a word or two more, believing that I still have a reader left. I want to talk about the Knights of Labor and certain other unions.

It was during my apprenticeship that I first heard of labor unions as such. My father had belonged to the Brotherhood of Locomotive Engineers for many years—had actually participated in one of their strikes on the Delaware, Lackawanna, and Western (famous in the American folk song, "Where-a You Push-a Da Truck-a, John?") before I was born, and had been chief of the Providence Division—Division 57, as I recall—before we moved to Philadelphia in 1878. But he never considered the B. L. E. as a labor union, probably because they called themselves a "brotherhood," and were looked up to as being in the upper strata of workingmen. At any rate, when the Knights of Labor began to be heard of they were not at all popular around our dinner table or in the shop itself.

I recall strikes in St. Louis, with Martin Irons leading the movement, and several others in Milwaukee, but we in our shop looked upon such things with aloofness and even disdain. This leads me to believe that there would probably never have been any unions at all if all of the shops and plants had remained as small as ours, with the boss and his men knowing each other as intimately as we did in the Rue Manufacturing Company. No doubt piecework and its concomitant abuses had more to do with the growth of unions than any other single factor, unless we take into account the utter disregard for the comfort and feelings of the men which too many managements displayed during the 'eighties, 'nineties, and 1900's. Although time-and-motion study as we know it today was then virtually unheard-of, much repetitive work was put on a piecework basis and rated on what the best man could be counted on to produce over an average period. Good men could frequently earn 25 per cent over the basic rate, but the man who went much above this was immediately a subject for gossip of an unfriendly sort among his fellow workmen. This was not because they wanted to delay production, but because they knew that a rise in the "best man's" productivity rate meant a slash in the piece rate for all hands, and it naturally led to certain countermeasures.

The "fast" man was "encouraged" not to let his output exceed that of the average worker by too big a margin. When things went swimmingly, as they sometimes do, the "extra work" was very apt to be tucked away under the bench as a backlog against the day when everything went wrong. On the inevitable day when belts would break, tools get dull, and castings be full of sand and blowholes, with the day's work accordingly below par, the "backlog" would come out and get added to the day's work in order to bring it up to "average."

Another custom of the early days, which did not tend to promote good feelings and proper harmony among the employees, was the method of punishing men for being late. Habitual tardiness is of course inexcusable—we all know of the fellow who simply can't get to work before 9:30 A.M., and who has a variety of excellent excuses, none of which is at all plausible—but I am talking about the occasional late arrival caused by defections in the transportation system.

In the early days, the gate of the average shop closed promptly at 7:00:00 Eastern Standard Time, established with hair's breadth accuracy by one of those annoyingly efficient railroad watches that couldn't get out of order unless you hammered it or soaked it in gasoline. The workman who arrived breathless at the gate at 7:00:01 had to make his entry through the main office, in a very dramatic

"Our Engine Room"—drawing from a humorous catalog of Sterling Elliott, about 1888.

fashion, somewhat in the same manner as Joseph Jefferson in the second act of "Rip Van Winkle," and with a very attentive audience. After this preamble had been accomplished, he was then prohibited from starting work until 7:15:00, and the extra fourteen minutes and fifty-nine seconds were promptly and accurately deducted from his pay.

If this tardiness should happen twice in any one week, the late arrival was indeed a marked man, for then, no matter what time he arrived on the second occurrence, he was not allowed to begin work until twelve noon, with the half-day's pay efficiently subtracted from his weekly earnings. With the average journeyman's wage stabilized at about 25 cents an hour, this half-day's adjustment left a sizable hole in the weekly pay envelope. But management actually lost more than the individual workman—aside from losing the employee's good will and cooperation, it lost production man-hours on its machine equipment, and this added directly to management's overhead and increased its production costs.

Another builder-upper of ill will was the custom of making the men collect their weekly or biweekly pay by passing in line in front of the paymaster's window located inconveniently on the sidewalk and exposed to rain, wind, snow, and other forms of inclement weather. Now this may sound like a trivial objection to some people, but I will guarantee that the returned G.I. will appreciate the situation. An actuary interested in such things might have worked up a chart showing how this waiting on line in fair weather and foul contributed to absenteeism from colds, rheumatism, arthritis, pulmonary congestion, coronary thrombosis, and a few other systemic disorders. But the fact is that this waiting-on-line situation was one of the annoyances and needless hardships that led men to join up with unions that promised them relief from such things.

And then we have the matter of wages and costs. I have been impressed mainly with the lack of appreciation on the part of both management and labor of the effect of wages and other expenses incident to the total cost of whatever is being made. Many managers assume quite blithely that a 20-per cent increase in wages adds 20 per cent to the cost of their product. Yet, in some lines of work, *wages in the plant* may be only 10 per cent of the total cost. In such cases, a 20-per cent boost in wages adds only 2 per cent to the total cost.

Labor, on the other hand, often assumes that the difference between the labor cost and the selling price is all gravy—profit, in the vernacular—and labor is often wrong in this assumption. Both sides need a lot more knowledge of fundamentals. A vast number of employees have not the slightest idea of how much profit their company makes, and management makes little or no attempt to inform them—although it would generally be to management's advantage to so inform them—for there is a lot less profit earned by the large corporations than the general public seems to think.

All wealth comes from labor that is expended on materials. Miners dig coal and ore; oilmen bore wells; lumbermen work in forests; steelworkers work with coal and iron, and so on. All labor expended on raw materials adds to the cost of these materials.

Management, which is or should be the efficient direction of manual labor, the selection of proper machinery and the disposal of the product, is sometimes considered as a function of capital. It is really a form of labor—surprisingly enough—and adds to the total value of the product.

Capital, I should say, is that part of the product of labor which is not distributed as wages, salaries, or dividends. It is the financial reserve that is used to build new plants, to buy new machines, and to carry over in periods of subnormal activity. Both labor and management accumulate capital by paying out less than the amount received. Capital earns money only when it is used by labor and management. Capital of itself never earns anything at all—it is like the billions of dollars in gold deposited in Fort Knox, a superb collection of jewelry that is of no earthly use to anyone.

Labor, management, and capital all desire the greatest possible return. Each of these three components is necessary for the production of everything from the crude ore to the finished product. Labor does the actual work of production. But management must direct purchases of materials, selection of machines, design of machine tools, and the securing of markets for the products. This involves, necessarily, the matter of plant overhead and sales costs, together with the scale of wages that can be paid consistent with a margin of profit. High wages give labor greater buying power, and increase consumer buying power—unless, as everyone these days seems to be finding out for himself, the wage increases boost prices to the point

Master and apprentice of the 'eighties

The oldest dated drawing of a turret lathe, made in 1856 by Henry D. Stone

Rules & Regulations

TO BE OBSERVED BY ALL PERSONS
EMPLOYED IN THE FACTORY OF
AMASA WHITNEY

RULE 1. The Mill will be put in operation 10 minutes before sun-rise at all seasons of the year. The gate will be shut 10 minutes past sun-set, from the 20th of March to the 20th of September; at 30 minutes past 8, from the 20th of Sept. to the 20th of March Saturdays, at sun-set.

2d. It will be required of every person employed, that they be in the room in which they are employed, at the time mentioned above for the mill to be in operation.

3d. Hands are not allowed to leave the factory in working hours, without the consent of their Overseer: if they do, they will be liable to have their time set off.

4th. Any one who by negligence or misconduct causes damage to the machinery, or impedes the progress of the work, will be liable to make good the damage for the same.

5th. Any one employed for a certain length of time, will be expected to make up their lost time, if required before they will be entitled to their pay.

6th. Any person employed for no certain length of time, will be required to give at least 4 weeks notice of their intention to leave (sickness excepted) or forfeit 4 weeks' pay, unless by particular agreement.

7th. Any one wishing to be absent any length of time, must get permission of the Overseer.

8th. All who have leave of absence for any length of time, will be expected to return in that time; and in case they do not return that time, and do not give satisfactory reason, they will be liable to forfeit one week's work or less if they commence work again. If they do not, they will be considered as one who leaves without giving any notice.

9th. Any thing tending to impede the progress of manufacturing in working hours, such as unnecessary conversation, reading, eating fruit, &c. &c., must be avoided.

10th. While I shall endeavor to employ a judicious overseer, the help will follow his directions in all cases.

11th. No smoking will be allowed in the Factory, as it is considered very unsafe, and particularly specified in the Insurance.

12th. In order to forward the work, job hands will follow the above regulations as well as those otherwise employed.

13th. It is intended that the bell be rung 5 minutes before the gate is hoisted, so that all persons may be ready to start their machinery precisely at the time mentioned.

14th. All persons who cause damage to the machinery, break glass out of the windows, &c., will immediately inform the overseer of the same.

15th. The hands will take breakfast, from the 1st of November till the 1st of March, before going to work—they will take supper from the 1st of May till the last of August, 30 minutes past 5 o'clock, P. M.—from the 20th of September till the 20th of March between sun-down and dark—25 minutes will be allowed for breakfast, 30 minutes for dinner, and 25 minutes for supper, and more, from the time the gate is shut till started again.

16th. The hands will leave the Factory so that the doors may be fastened within 10 minutes from the time of leaving off work.

Winchendon, July 5, 1830.   **AMASA WHITNEY.**

Amasa Whitney's pronunciamento to the hired help

that nobody can afford to buy anything. This is the old "vicious spiral of inflation" that is so frequently talked about these days.

Management has the great responsibility for the welfare of the country. It is frequently unfair to productive labor because it seems to expect that all economies must be achieved by keeping wages at a respectable minimum. Management often condones inefficiency and waste in departments that are only indirectly productive. Salesmen, for example, seem to be the fair-haired boys who are entitled to that most wonderful of all features of our present civilization—the unlimited expense account, which is the delight of bellboys, taxicab drivers, Pullman porters, and hotel managers. Because salesmen bring in money directly, their expense accounts are tolerated, but unless the shop makes a good, salable product, the salesmen would of course be out on a limb.

We must, I think, learn that shop wages in a plant are only a comparatively small part of the total cost of doing business, and that other costs must be scrutinized as carefully as we scrutinize labor costs. Demands for increased wages or shorter hours can only be granted when the amount produced makes labor's share in production—increased production, I mean, with increased profits all around—sufficient to warrant the increase in wages.

Work stoppages, regardless of the cause, reduce production and consequently reduce the level of the nation's economy. This would seem to be a very simple fact, as demonstrable as $(a^2 + 2ab + b^2)$ equals $(a + b)^2$, or the proposition that Lee lost the Battle of Richmond, but somehow nobody seems to realize it. The tremendously costly strikes against General Motors, General Electric, Westinghouse, Yale and Towne, Western Electric, U.S. Steel, and the New York elevator strike, the New York truckmen's strike, the strike of the Longshoremen's Union, the dairymen's strike, the railroad strike, the musician's strike, and every other type and kind of strike that is at this moment disrupting the national economy represent breakdowns in our democratic system that seriously affect the lives of our inhabitants. They also reduce the wealth-producing capacity of our country. Every intelligent person knows this.

Unless such work stoppages can be prevented by cooperative action on the part of labor and management—and I frankly doubt it, unless legislation is brought to bear on the problem—it is quite possible that industry as a whole will be placed in a special category wherein work stoppage will be classed as desertion, in the military sense, and subject to such punishments as desertion from the army now entails. This would be a rather drastic solution, for everyone knows that desertion from the army is punishable by death, but I am speaking in terms of analogies. And it must work both ways.

I also realize that what I seem to be advocating is a form of regimentation—Fascism, if you will, although I have enough good sense to understand that regimentation or Fascism is the last, hopeless, resort of a people who do not have the intelligence to live under democracy.

But as society grows more complex, codification of existing laws and their enforcement—regimentation, in fact—becomes more and more necessary. The more we depend on others for such services as light, heat, power, transportation, shipment and deliveries, sewage disposal, snow removal, entertainment, and all the etceteras, the more we must try to control work stoppages in all of these fields. I hope to high heaven that no one will conclude that I am advocating any form of dictatorship. I am against it. I know that reasoning men and women can solve their problems by mutual cooperation and the application of their intelligence. No so-called "superman" is required to direct their destinies. There is no such thing as a superman, anyway. The leaders of thought, opinion, and even politics must always proceed by a process of trial and error. Only a fool thinks he has all the answers.

And yet we must not forget that our rights as individuals in a democratic system—which, with all its imperfections is the only sensible system—entail *responsibilities*. I italicize the word because I think it is the most important word to be considered these days. How many workmen, do you think, give a thought to their responsibilities as workmen when they go out on a strike that they know will tie up production, distribution, and their own income for weeks or months? We all realize that many of these decisions are made by labor leaders rather than by the so-called "rank and file." But a little more intelligence in these affairs would be appreciated. Only the sole inhabitant of a desert island can afford to be completely independent.

And so we come to the end of the story. As I bring this book to a close, however, I am gratified to receive notice of my appointment as a consultant at the Clinton Laboratories at Oak Ridge, Tennessee, where I shall work on one of the many mechanical phases of the atomic power pile project. It is good to learn in this way that the passing years have not rendered me entirely incapable of further service on engineering problems. It is particularly interesting, also, that in my eightieth year, I shall be privileged to assist in the development of the most advanced type of power technology—a field that will occupy much of the attention of future generations of engineers and scientists.

It is a far cry from the old shop at 211 Race Street in Philadelphia to the vast atomic energy plant at Oak Ridge, and I have greatly enjoyed writing down the experiences and the observations of that hectic interval of industrial progress. I hope the reader has enjoyed it as much as I have.

Index

H

G